NINE MUSES

MODERN PLAYS FROM CLASSIC MYTHS

WIM COLEMAN

PERFECTION LEARNING®

Logan, Iowa 51546-0500

Editorial Director	Julie A. Schumacher
Senior Editor	Rebecca Christian
Assistant Editor	Suzanne Foggia
Design	Kay Ewald
Illustration	Nicholas Wilton

A Martha y Monserrat,
con cariño.

Acknowledgments

The playwright would like to thank his father,
William S. E. Coleman; his brother and sister-in-law,
Eric and Julie Coleman; and his wife, Pat Perrin,
for all the help they gave him in writing this book.

Note: The plays in this volume are royalty-free.

Art Credits: Archivo Iconografico, S.A./CORBIS pp. 240, 249; ArtToday (www.arttoday.com) pp. 12, 13, 244, 246, 247; Christie's Images/CORBIS p. 236; Corel pp. 5, 6, 8, 10, 239; Historical Picture Archive/CORBIS p. 245; David Lees/CORBIS p. 9

Printed in the United States of America

2 3 4 5 6 7 8 9 10 VH 08 07 06 05 04

#31423 ISBN 0-7891-5356-4

TABLE OF CONTENTS

CREATING CONTEXT

Playwright's Foreword 4
What Is Mythology? 5
From Chaos to Olympus: How It All Began 7
The World of Classical Mythology 11
The Gods and Goddesses at a Glance 12

THE PLAYS

Pandora 14
Phaeton and the Sun Chariot 38
Demeter and Persephone 62
Orpheus and Eurydice 92
Eros and Psyche 116
The Apple of Discord 146
Odysseus and the Sirens 168
Proteus 188
Prometheus Unbound 214

EXTENSIONS

Thumbnail Myths: Selected Summaries of
    Greek and Roman Stories 236
Glossary 251
For Further Reading 262

PLAYWRIGHT'S FOREWORD

Myth and drama were made for each other. In fact, they have been together for a very long time. No one can say for sure when the first myth was performed on a stage by actors, but the world's oldest plays tell mythic stories. Aeschylus, Sophocles, and Euripides—Athenian playwrights who wrote during the 5th century B.C.—based most of their plays on mythology.

Playwrights have followed their example up to the present day. Many 20th-century dramatists found exciting stories in Greek and Roman mythology. For example, the American playwright Eugene O'Neill based his trilogy *Mourning Becomes Electra* on the *Oresteia* by Aeschylus. Indeed, even as you read these words, some playwright is probably finding inspiration in a classical myth.

What explains the long, happy marriage between mythology and drama? Perhaps it has something to do with the theatre's power to breathe life into the world's oldest stories. On the stage, the gods of Olympus live again. So do mortal heroes and heroines like Odysseus and Psyche.

So this collection continues a truly ancient tradition. Here you will find nine plays based on stories from classical mythology. When you read these plays aloud—or better yet, perform them on stage—I hope you will feel the magic of their stories come alive. Even if you only read the plays silently, you still can conjure up some of that magic in the theatre of your imagination.

Of course, a mere nine stories barely scratch the surface of classical mythology. There are hundreds more, and I hope you will get to know many of them. In the back of this book, you will find an assortment of "Thumbnail Myths"—very short summaries of other stories to be found in classical mythology.

The stories of these plays have been told many times in the past, and never in quite the same way. Like all other playwrights and storytellers, I have approached them with my own ideas, feelings, and questions. The "Playwright's Postscript" following each play will tell you something about choices I have made and liberties I have taken. The bibliography at the end of this book will help you find other retellings of the stories you read here.

But don't stop there. You can also retell the myths in this book in stories, poems, and plays of your own—or simply by repeating them aloud to some other person. For myths live on by being told again and again.

WHAT IS MYTHOLOGY?

Myths explain things. Long ago, when life was full of mysteries, myths helped people make sense of a perplexing world. For example, winter comes when the grain goddess grieves for her daughter's death. Spring comes when the goddess rejoices over her daughter's rebirth. And lightning bolts are magical spears hurled by the king of the gods.

Myths also explain deeper questions. For example, how did the world itself come to be? How did life begin? How were human beings created—and why? And why is there suffering and death in the world?

People of ancient cultures all over the world puzzled over such

questions, and they all created stories to answer them. Myths from different parts of the world often seem eerily similar. For example, many cultures tell of a god or goddess who dies and is reborn again and again, producing the cycles of nature. They also tell of a great trickster who gave fire to humankind and who was then punished for his deed.

So in attempting to explain the same great mysteries, many people in different places and cultures have wound up telling very similar stories. No one knows exactly how.

But if myths do nothing more than explain, why do they still inspire our imaginations? We have science to explain things now. We know that seasons are caused by the angle of the earth's axis, which exposes different parts of the globe to different levels of sunlight

Eros Punished by Venus, fresco from Pompeii, now at the National Museum, Naples

5

during the year. We know that lightning is a discharge of electricity through the atmosphere. We don't need gods or goddesses to explain these things.

So why do we still seem to need myths?

For one thing, the world is still more mysterious than we often admit. And mythology still addresses that mystery. A goddess who grieves and rejoices for her lost and regained daughter may not tell us much about the seasons. But she *does* tell us something about the cycle of human joy and sorrow, of good and bad fortune. A god-king who hurls a magical spear may not tell us much about lightning. But he *does* tell us something about how power is wielded—and about the unpredictability of rage.

The Graces (detail), 1482, Sandro Botticelli

And perhaps, in addition to explaining things, myths renew our sense of mystery and wonder. They stir our curiosity, our questing spirit. And they touch us in ways we can't always explain. Upon hearing a myth, we are likely to nod and murmur—without quite knowing why—"Yes, that's true."

As long as mysteries remain, myths will be with us—always true in their way and always stirring up ancient questions in our hearts.

FROM CHAOS TO OLYMPUS:
HOW IT ALL BEGAN

To begin with, the universe was a huge, shapeless mass called Chaos. Land, sea, and sky were all mixed and tangled together in a dark and infinite expanse. Who can say how long the universe went on this way? Perhaps time itself had no meaning back in the age of Chaos.

Then, most mysteriously, Chaos gave birth to two children. These were Night, a fearsome, bird-shaped shadow with black wings, and Erebus, a bottomless deep filled to the brim with Death. Night laid an egg in Erebus' bosom, and from that egg hatched Love.

Now, it might be said that Love is the opposite of Chaos. And so Love immediately set about putting the universe in some sort of order. Since this was hard to do in total darkness, Love created Light and Day.

When Light and Day poured through the universe, Gaia—also known as Earth—was born. Presently, Gaia gave birth to Uranus, also known as Heaven.

Together, Mother Gaia and Father Uranus had numerous children. The first were three enormous monsters with many heads and hands. Uranus loathed these frightful creatures, and he buried them one by one. Mother Gaia was heartsick to see her children so cruelly imprisoned.

Then she gave birth to three Cyclopes, one-eyed giants that were somewhat more human in shape than the monsters. Finally, she gave birth to the Titans—the first true gods. There were twelve of them, and their names were Tethys, Oceanus, Thia, Hyperion, Mnemosyne, Crius, Phoebe, Coeus, Themis, Iapetus, Rhea, and Cronus.

Mother Gaia begged the Cyclopes and the Titans to take revenge on their cruel father. Only one Titan dared to do so—the youngest, Cronus. Cronus took up a sickle and wounded Uranus horribly and mortally.

From Uranus' blood sprang up weird new creatures—a race called Giants and three female creatures called Furies with snaky hair and bat-like wings. These weird sisters stalked the earth for untold ages, punishing wrongdoers with pangs of conscience and despair. Some say that they are among us even today.

As Uranus died, he bitterly cursed his son, Cronus. "If you have children, beware!" he exclaimed with his last breath. "For like me, you will be slain by a child of your own."

So when Cronus' sister-wife, Rhea, began giving birth to baby gods, Cronus was understandably horrified. The moment each god was born,

Cronus swallowed it whole. He swallowed five baby gods in all—Hestia, Demeter, Hera, Hades, and Poseidon.

When Rhea's last baby was about to be born, she hurried away to where her murderous brother-husband couldn't find her. She gave birth to her son Zeus and turned him over to the care of shepherds. Then she found a small boulder, wrapped it in swaddling clothes, and took it home and held it to her breast, singing lullabies to it.

Upon seeing Rhea, Cronus naturally assumed the rock to be another newborn god. So he snatched it away from her and swallowed it whole.

Zeus, from Pompeii, now at the Museum of Olympia, Greece

Rhea had no more children, so Cronus believed he had escaped his father's curse. As the chief Titan, he ruled all the universe as king and saw no reason why he shouldn't do so forever. Little did he know that his only uneaten child was growing up to be a strong, cunning young god.

Eventually, the day came when Zeus returned home. Rhea introduced Zeus to Cronus as a new cupbearer. Not knowing that the handsome lad was his own son, Cronus eagerly accepted him into his royal court.

Rhea mixed a potion in a golden cup, and Zeus served the potion to Cronus. Cronus drank it and immediately began vomiting up his children. They came out of his gorge one by one, somewhat the worse for the wear, but nevertheless whole, alive, and strong. When at last Cronus vomited up the boulder he had swallowed in Zeus' place, he realized how he had been tricked.

Zeus and his brothers and sisters were determined to seize power from Cronus. Cronus called the other Titans to his side, and a great war broke out between the Titans and the younger gods, who were led by Zeus.

The Titan Iapetus had three sons—Atlas, Prometheus, and Epimetheus. Atlas, the strongest Titan of all, led the fight against the younger gods. But Prometheus, perhaps the cleverest being who ever lived, foresaw that the future belonged to Zeus and his siblings, so he fought on their side. The rather dull-witted Epimetheus stayed loyal to his brother Prometheus.

The war, which lasted for ten years, was so violent and terrible that some feared that the universe itself would return to Chaos. But at long last, the younger gods won. Zeus took bitter revenge on the Titans by burying them in Tartarus, a realm as far below the surface of the earth as the sky is above it.

Among the Titans who fought against the young gods, only Atlas escaped this fate. But, if anything, his punishment proved even worse. For he was forced to stand forever in a desolate wasteland, holding the world and the sky upon his back.

The younger gods built a palace upon Mt. Olympus from which they would rule the universe. From then on, they were known as the Olympians. The time had come for Zeus and his brothers, Poseidon and Hades, to divide the universe among themselves, so they drew lots. Poseidon became the ruler of the sea, and Hades the ruler of the Underworld and the dead. Zeus took control of the sky, which made him the supreme ruler of all.

Over time, new Olympians were born. Zeus and his sister-wife Hera had two sons—the war god Ares and the forge god Hephaestus. Leto, a daughter of Titans, bore Zeus a pair of twins—Apollo, the god of light and wisdom, and Artemis, the goddess of the moon and the hunt. Maia, daughter of the Titan Atlas, bore Zeus the messenger god Hermes.

Zeus also had nine daughters by the Titan Mnemosyne. These were the nine Muses—Clio, Urania, Melpomene, Thalia, Terpsichore, Calliope, Erato, Polyhymnia, and Euterpe. The Muses were wonderful singers

Poseidon, Athena, Apollo, and Artemis depicted on a 5th-century-B.C. relief sculpture in Bauron, Greece

and came to inspire both gods and mortals to great acts of thought and creativity.

Two more goddesses were born in rather peculiar ways. The wise but sometimes warlike goddess Athena emerged from Zeus' head, fully grown and dressed in armor. And Aphrodite, the goddess of love, was miraculously born upon the crest of an ocean wave.

Zeus had two other important children. The wine god Dionysus was his son by Semele, a mortal woman. The great hero Heracles was Zeus' son by Alcmena, another mortal. Always bitter over Zeus' many infidelities, Hera made life extremely difficult for Dionysus and Heracles. However, they both were eventually accepted among the Olympian gods.

Even after the defeat of the Titans, the Olympians' rule was rocky for a time. To avenge the defeat of her children the Titans, Gaia provoked her children the Giants to fight the Olympians. The Olympians slew the Giants in terrible war. Gaia also gave birth to a hundred-headed monster named Typhon. Zeus defeated Typhon with his thunderbolt, then buried him beneath Mt. Etna, the tallest volcano in Europe.

Once Zeus and his fellow gods reigned securely, it came time to create living things upon the earth. Zeus assigned this task to Prometheus and Epimetheus, who had fought on the gods' side against the Titans.

But Prometheus made humankind a bit too perfect for Zeus' taste. Worse, the Titan stole fire from the sun and gave it to mortal humans, making them extremely powerful. Zeus came to hate both Prometheus and his mortal creations. He began seeking a way to punish Prometheus, and also a way to destroy humankind . . .

And that is where our stories begin.

Prometheus, 1934, Paul Manship, Rockefeller Center, New York, New York

THE WORLD OF CLASSICAL MYTHOLOGY

River Eridanus

Siren Land

Italy

Adriatic
Sea

Thrace

Greece

Aegean
Sea

● Troy

Sicily

Mt. ▲
Etna

Mediterranean Sea

Mt. Ida
▲

Crete

Pharos

Mt. ▲
Olympus

Aegean
Sea

Greece

Ithaca ●

Delphi
●

Mt.
▲Helicon

Eleusis ●

● Athens

● Sparta

THE GODS AND GODDESSES AT A GLANCE

Greek name: ZEUS
Roman name: JUPITER, JOVE

Job description: king of all gods; god of heavens and earth; ruler of weather and giver of justice
Symbols & emblems: thunderbolt; eagle; woodpecker; oak tree

ZEUS

Greek name: HADES/PLUTO
Roman name: PLUTO

Job description: god of the Underworld; ruler of the dead
Symbols & emblems: gems and coins; invisibility helmet; golden chariot with black horses

HADES

Greek name: HERA
Roman name: JUNO

Job description: queen of the gods; goddess of marriage and childbirth
Symbols & emblems: cow; peacock; lion

HERA

Greek name: DEMETER
Roman name: CERES

Job description: goddess of earth, agriculture, and fertility
Symbols & emblems: sheaf of wheat; cornucopia; poppy flower

DEMETER

Greek name: POSEIDON
Roman name: NEPTUNE

Job description: god of the sea and earthquakes
Symbols & emblems: trident; dolphin; horse; bull

POSEIDON

Greek name: HEPHAESTUS
Roman name: VULCAN

Job description: god of fire, artisans, and metalworkers
Symbols & emblems: quail

HEPHAESTUS

Greek name: ATHENA/ATHENE
Roman name: MINERVA

Job description: goddess of wisdom, courage, and war
Symbols & emblems: owl; olive tree; Medusa-head shield

ATHENA

HESTIA

Greek name: HESTIA
Roman name: VESTA

Job description: goddess of the hearth; protector of beggars; inventor of house-building
Symbols & emblems: fireplace

ARTEMIS

Greek name: ARTEMIS
Roman name: DIANA

Job description: goddess of moon, hunting, and unmarried women
Symbols and emblems: she-bear; deer; silver chariot; silver bow and arrows; crescent-moon crown

APHRODITE

Greek name: APHRODITE
Roman name: VENUS

Job description: goddess of love and beauty
Symbols & Emblems: dove; sparrow; seagull; rose; myrtle shrub

HERMES

Greek name: HERMES
Roman name: MERCURY

Job description: god of trade, travel, and theft; messenger of the gods; conductor of souls to the Underworld
Symbols and emblems: winged headband and winged sandals; staff with two snakes wound around it; crane

ARES

Greek name: ARES
Roman name: MARS

Job description: god of war, hatred, and violence
Symbols & emblems: dog; vulture; wild boar; bloodstained spear

DIONYSUS

Greek name: DIONYSUS
Roman name: BACCHUS

Job description: god of wine, parties, and drama
Symbols and emblems: ivy; vine; grape bunches; wine cup; leopard

APOLLO

Greek name: APOLLO
Roman name: APOLLO

Job description: god of sunlight, prophecy, medicine, archery, poetry, music, and unmarried men
Symbols and emblems: laurel wreath; mouse; golden chariot; golden lyre; golden bow and arrows

PANDORA

SETTING THE STAGE

A character in James Joyce's novel *Ulysses* called history "a nightmare from which I am trying to awake." And when one looks back over history, it is all too easy to think of awful events, including famines, plagues, and wars. Why has human history been so troubled? Is there any waking up from its nightmare? Clio, the Muse of history, is surely interested in such questions. So it is she who introduces this play, which deals with how the sorrows of humankind began.

She shares the stage with Hesiod, a poet-farmer of the 8th century B.C. He lived near Mt. Helicon, the home of the Muses, and claimed that they often visited him to help him with his poetry. "We know how to speak many false things as though they were true," they told him; "but we know, when we will, to utter true things."

In his epic poem *Theogony*, Hesiod describes the creation of the universe, the gods, and humankind. In another long poem, *Works and Days*, he tells of the first woman, Pandora. In Hesiod's view, Pandora and all the women who came after her have caused humankind great suffering. But this was part of a divine plan. For as Hesiod wrote in *Works and Days*, "Zeus who thunders on high made women to be an evil to mortal men, with a nature to do evil."

Could Hesiod really have been told this by the Muses—who are, after all, women themselves? That's one of the questions this play explores.

MUSING ABOUT THE MYTH

Most early cultures around the world told origin stories to explain how things in our world came to be. As you read, list the things in the myth whose origins are explained.

14

PANDORA

CHARACTERS:

CLIO (klī' ō), the Muse of history

HESIOD (hē' si od), a Greek poet

PROMETHEUS (prō mē' thē us), a Titan

EPIMETHEUS (ep i mē' thē us), brother of Prometheus

MIGHT

VIOLENCE

ZEUS (züs), the king of the Olympian gods

HEPHAESTUS (he fes' tus), the celestial artist and god of the forge

PANDORA (pan dō' ra), the first woman ever created

APHRODITE (af ro dī' tē), the goddess of love and beauty

ATHENA (a thē' na), the goddess of war and wisdom

HERA (hir' a), the queen of the Olympian gods

EVILS:

DISEASE

FAMINE

WAR

PAIN

ENVY

GREED

CRUELTY

VOICE OF HOPE

OTHER NAMES MENTIONED IN THE PLAY:

CALLIOPE (ka lī' o pē), the Muse of epic poetry

GOETHE (gehr' ta), German author (1729–1832)

HIPPOCRENE (hip' ō krēn), a fountain on Mt. Helicon

MT. HELICON (hel' i kon), the mountain of the Muses

PEGASUS (peg' a sus), a winged horse

SETTING: *A meadow near Mt. Helicon, Mt. Olympus, other mythic places*

TIME: *Partly in the 8th century B.C., otherwise, no time in particular*

(Upstage right is a raised area from which CLIO *and* HESIOD *will watch most of the play's action. A small pool of light in this area represents an open campfire. Upstage left is a small area masked by a curtain.* PANDORA *will be revealed there, and so will the jar.* HESIOD *enters down by the fire. He closes his eyes meditatively. After a long pause,* CLIO *enters downstage and speaks to the audience.)*

CLIO. Ah, the clear, sweet air of the meadow! All the sweeter now that night has fallen and dew is starting to gather. A moist, cool softness lingers wherever you turn. Go on, breathe deep, take it in. There's nothing like it in the whole wide world.

I'm partial, of course. This country belongs to my sisters and me. Over there at the edge of the meadow rises the slope of Mount Helicon, where we Muses live. And just a short hike up the slope, you'll find the magical fountain Hippocrene with its waters of inspiration. That fountain burst forth when the great winged horse, Pegasus, kicked the mountainside with his mighty hooves. It really happened. I saw it with my own eyes.

(His eyes still closed, HESIOD stretches out his arms and speaks.)

HESIOD.
Sing to me, Muse, a sighing song.

CLIO. But here's the man I came looking for, warming his hands and his wits by a pleasant little fire. His name is Hesiod—a farmer and shepherd who lives nearby. He's also a poet, and he's calling for a Muse's inspiration.

HESIOD.
Sing—oh sing, hushed and sweetly—
A song among roses ready for rest,
Among drowsy daisies forgetful of day,
Among lazy lilies laden with night.
Sing while they doze, dancing in dreams,
Sing while they sleep, unknowing, serene,
While I wake alone, watching for words.
Sing to me, Muse, a sighing song.

CLIO (to HESIOD, stepping up onto the platform). Here I am, ready to sing.

HESIOD (opening his eyes, surprised). Who are you?

CLIO. A Muse, of course.

HESIOD. Not *my* Muse.

CLIO. No, not your usual Muse—not Calliope, the epic Muse. I'm her sister Clio, the Muse of history. Calliope asked me to take her place tonight.

HESIOD. What's history?

CLIO. Never heard of it? Well, it hasn't quite caught on yet. It's the art of finding out what really happened in the past.

HESIOD. Newfangled nonsense.

CLIO. If you say so.

HESIOD. Where's Calliope?

CLIO. Helping another poet. There *are* other poets, you know.

HESIOD. I'll wait for her to come back.

CLIO. Oh, but why waste such a perfect night for poetic inspiration? Calliope should be back tomorrow, but the weather might take a bad turn by then. What if it's hot and muggy? Or rainy and stormy? Or what if it hails? You won't be in any mood to make beautiful poetry. Come on, now—give me a try. *Invoke* me some more.

(Pause. HESIOD closes his eyes again.)

HESIOD.
Of women, Muse, sing words to me—
Of women vile, venomous as vipers,
So deadly to all in doom and deed.
Not one, not one is worthy of trust.
So of the first of those frightful furies
Now tell me, Muse; tell the whole truth
Of meddling Pandora, mother of mothers.

(Pause)

CLIO. Excuse me, but . . . I'm not exactly comfortable with this.

HESIOD. Why not?

CLIO. Well, you're making rather sweeping assumptions about women—*unfounded* assumptions, I think. We Muses are women, after all. And aren't you rather fond of us? Or of Calliope anyway?

HESIOD. You're immortal.

CLIO. Ah, so it's only *mortal* women who are—how did you put it?—"venomous as vipers."

HESIOD. I'll wait for Calliope.

CLIO. Oh, no, no, no, let's continue this fascinating conversation. I want to get to the bottom of why you think this way. And what *about* Pandora, that "mother of mothers"? What makes you so sure that she was wholly evil?

HESIOD. So it is said in story.

CLIO. But stories don't always tell the truth.

HESIOD. Don't they?

CLIO. History teaches us never to take mere stories at face value.

HESIOD. Then I haven't much use for history.

CLIO. Is there any reason to think that Pandora wasn't a sublime *gift* to humankind—and not an evil at all?

(HESIOD *laughs*.)

CLIO. What's so funny?

HESIOD (*pointing to the campfire*). This fire is a gift, isn't it? A great blessing to humankind?

CLIO. Of course.

HESIOD. Given to us by that master thief, the Titan Prometheus?

CLIO. Yes.

HESIOD. Well, then—I believe I'll scoop up its coals and embers in my hands. I'll seize a great armful of this precious fire, hold it in a loving embrace, give it a kiss of thanks. (*He reaches toward the fire.*)

CLIO. Stop.

HESIOD. Why?

CLIO. You'll burn yourself.

HESIOD. What? The fire will hurt me?

CLIO. You know it will.

HESIOD. But how? Didn't we just agree that fire is a blessing—the greatest gift of all? How can it possibly cause me pain?

CLIO (*turning to go*). Perhaps you *should* wait for Calliope.

HESIOD. Oh, no, no, no, let's continue this fascinating conversation. I really must learn something about this "history" business. Let me invoke you a little more . . .

Together, we two, let's tangle our voices—
Sing of gifts that once gladdened and were good,
Gifts turned to trouble by a woman's touch.
Together, let's sing—though our song be sad.

CLIO.
Well, then, we shall—we'll share and not shirk,

Link our two minds, be like in our
  labor.
But, bard, tell me boldly—where to
  begin?

HESIOD.
  Ah, with two tricksters, twins and
    Titans,
  Marvelous makers, amazing givers.

CLIO. Wise Prometheus and foolish
  Epimetheus.

HESIOD. Those very two.

(PROMETHEUS *and* EPIMETHEUS *enter the
main acting area as* CLIO *and* HESIOD *watch
from the raised area.*)

PROMETHEUS. Epimetheus, dear
  brother, you seem deep in thought.

EPIMETHEUS. I suppose so.

PROMETHEUS. It's very unusual.

EPIMETHEUS. True. You usually do the
  thinking.

PROMETHEUS. What's troubling you?

EPIMETHEUS. I've been thinking about
  how you snatched a spark from the
  axle of the Sun Chariot—how you
  took that spark to Earth and gave fire
  to humankind. I remember it as if it
  were only yesterday.

PROMETHEUS. It *was* only yesterday.

EPIMETHEUS. Oh.

PROMETHEUS. What about it?

EPIMETHEUS. I'm wondering if it was
  such a good idea.

PROMETHEUS. Do you, now? It's a little
  late to tell me so. But then, you're not
  called Epimetheus for nothing.

HESIOD. For, you see, Epimetheus means
  afterthought.

CLIO. I know.

EPIMETHEUS. Lord Zeus didn't want
  humankind to have fire.

PROMETHEUS. No, he didn't.

EPIMETHEUS. And you gave it to them
  against his will.

PROMETHEUS. So I did.

EPIMETHEUS. He's likely to be angry.

PROMETHEUS. I don't doubt it.

EPIMETHEUS. And he's liable to punish
  you.

PROMETHEUS. Almost certainly.

EPIMETHEUS. Dear brother, I don't
  understand. You're so wise. Why, it's
  said everywhere that no one is wiser
  than you—not even Lord Zeus
  himself. So how could you do
  something so—

PROMETHEUS. Foolish?

EPIMETHEUS. Well—yes.

PROMETHEUS. I suppose the act of
  creation brings out the fool in anyone.
  Do you remember how I reached into
  the earth, seized a handful of damp
  clay, and molded it into the first living
  man? Then how I repeated my deed
  again and again and again, populating
  the earth with thousands of his kind?
  What an experience that was! I can
  still feel it in my fingers—the warm,
  moist pulse of life.
    Oh, how I love those makings of
  my hands! And out of love, I suppose I
  did throw all my wisdom to the winds.
  I wanted my creatures to have the
  greatest gift of all—a gift by which
  they could forge bronze and steel,
  cook their food, keep themselves

warm when nights are cold. And such a gift it is—a hot, golden wind! The most powerful force there is, and yet the most gentle! It has made men just a little lower than the gods!

EPIMETHEUS. So is it any wonder that Zeus might be angry?

PROMETHEUS. None at all. In fact, I expect my punishers to arrive at any moment.

EPIMETHEUS. How do you know?

PROMETHEUS. Come now, dear brother. I'm not called Prometheus for nothing.

HESIOD. For, you see, Prometheus means—

CLIO. —*forethought*. Yes, I know. He knows almost everything about the future, to say nothing of the present and the past.

(MIGHT *and* VIOLENCE *enter.* VIOLENCE *is carrying chains.*)

MIGHT. The Titan Prometheus, I presume.

PROMETHEUS. At your service.

MIGHT. I'm Might, and this is Violence. We're agents from Lord Zeus. He sent us for you. Come along quietly, please. We'd rather not use these chains until we have to.

PROMETHEUS (*approaching* MIGHT *and* VIOLENCE). I won't give you any trouble.

EPIMETHEUS (*to* MIGHT *and* VIOLENCE). But where are you taking him? What are you going to do to him?

MIGHT. We're not at liberty to say.

PROMETHEUS (*to* EPIMETHEUS). I have a fair idea. But it's best for you not to know. I can bear the torments that lie ahead. But you, poor brother! Even to hear of them would be too much for you.

EPIMETHEUS. But will you—ever—?

PROMETHEUS. Come back? Yes, I'll be freed someday.

EPIMETHEUS. But when?

PROMETHEUS. If I told you, it would only bewilder you. You're no good at thinking about the future—or even about the present and the past. But while I'm gone, it's up to you to watch out for humankind. Zeus still means ill to men, and you'll have to protect them.

EPIMETHEUS. But I'm not like you. Everybody knows how foolish I am. I won't know what to do.

PROMETHEUS. You must do your best. Humankind depends on it. *I* depend on it.

EPIMETHEUS. I'll feel so lost. I *already* feel lost. Please, give me some advice. Tell me something, anything.

PROMETHEUS. Never accept gifts from the gods.

(PROMETHEUS *exits between* MIGHT *and* VIOLENCE. EPIMETHEUS *stands staring after them for a moment. He exits soon after* CLIO *and* HESIOD *begin to speak.*)

CLIO. Poor Epimetheus!

HESIOD.
But poorer Prometheus! Save pity for him!

Violence and Might, marshals of the
    almighty,
Drag him away in daunted
    disgrace—
High in the mountains, where
    hardship hangs
Like an angry cloud. A cliff side they
    clamber
With him in hand, and there they
    hang him
By chains that chafe—hang up our
    champion,
Our giver of gifts, the great
    Prometheus.
A beast from the sky will bite at his
    belly,
Dine on his liver day after day,
But his guts will grow back. And so
    it will go
For years upon years, unyielding and
    long.
Yes, pity Prometheus—poor, poor
    Titan.

CLIO. Poor Prometheus, indeed. But we
    stray from our story. For didn't you
    want a song of the first woman—that
    mother of mothers?

HESIOD. Pandora, yes.

CLIO. Now, let's not forget, there were
    no women in the world before
    Pandora came along—no *mortal*
    women. Only men.

HESIOD. It was the Golden Age.

CLIO. So they say. I'm skeptical.

HESIOD. The song, the song.

CLIO.
    Well, then—we must hurry to the
    heights of heaven,

To great Olympus, where the gods all
    gather.
For while the Titan is tormented and
    tied,
A pair of gods are pondering
    Pandora,
Tending to her creation, talking of
    this task.

(ZEUS *and* HEPHAESTUS *have entered the
main acting area.* HEPHAESTUS *walks with a
pronounced limp.*)

ZEUS. Is she finished, Hephaestus?

HEPHAESTUS. See for yourself, Lord
    Zeus.

(HEPHAESTUS *opens the curtain to reveal*
PANDORA, *plainly dressed and motionless.*)

HEPHAESTUS. What do you think of
    her?

ZEUS. She's got possibilities.

HEPHAESTUS. I could have done better, I
    think. But your instructions put me at
    a bit of a handicap. I'm used to
    working in bronze, steel, gold, silver,
    and suchlike. But clay? Well, that's new
    to me. Can't say I much like it.

ZEUS. I wanted her made of the same
    material that Prometheus used to
    make men.

HEPHAESTUS. She won't last forever.

ZEUS. I don't want her to. I want her to
    be like men—a creature of a day.

HEPHAESTUS. That she is, without a
    doubt.

ZEUS. You've done your work well, god
    of the forge.

HEPHAESTUS. I'm glad you think so.
    But if you don't mind my asking,

O Ruler of the Heavens, just what is she for?

ZEUS. A gift for humankind.

HEPHAESTUS. A peace offering, eh? It's no secret that you've never been too fond of men. Well, this should make things better—I hope. Say, I'm not going to get in trouble for my part in this, am I?

ZEUS. How so?

HEPHAESTUS. Well, you never know. I seem to have a knack for making gods angry without meaning to. Why, you yourself once threw me off this mountain in a fit of rage, remember? Still don't know quite what I did to provoke that. I fell for a whole day, smashed this leg up when I finally hit the ground. Don't guess I'll ever be rid of this limp. ·

ZEUS. You'll be a hero for your part in this—a true hero.

HEPHAESTUS. Happy to hear it. Still, it's a shame she's only a statue, and a clay one at that.

ZEUS. Oh, she's much more than a statue.

HEPHAESTUS. But, Sire, she's—

ZEUS. She's what?

HEPHAESTUS. Dead.

ZEUS. Not dead. This creature has never lived.

HEPHAESTUS. It amounts to the same thing, doesn't it? She's got no working parts. I don't see how you're going to bring her to life.

ZEUS. You'll anger me yet, Hephaestus.

Do you suppose my powers are less than those of Prometheus?

HEPHAESTUS. Bringing clay to life *is* rather a feat.

ZEUS. I am the god of the thunderbolt. Just one tiny breath of lightning— that's all that's needed . . .

(ZEUS *approaches* PANDORA *and breathes into her ear. There is a flash of lightning, followed by a loud thunderclap.* PANDORA*'s eyes snap open. She sways back and forth, extending her arms to keep her balance.*)

HEPHAESTUS. She's alive! She's alive! She's alive!

ZEUS (*to* HEPHAESTUS). Quiet, you fool! Do you want to frighten her to death the moment she's born? (*To* PANDORA, *taking her by the hand*) Welcome to the world, my dear. Step right this way.

(*Guided by* ZEUS, PANDORA *moves forward. Her expression is startled, her movements bizarre and jerky. After a few steps, she almost topples, but* ZEUS *catches her by the arm and helps her upright. Then she almost topples in the opposite direction, but* HEPHAESTUS *catches her by the other arm and helps her upright again. When* PANDORA *regains her balance, she stands with more confidence, although her expression is still wild and frightened.* ZEUS *and* HEPHAESTUS *step away from her to gaze at their handiwork.*)

HEPHAESTUS. She's astonishing!

ZEUS. Yes—but not yet complete. She needs some finishing touches.

(ZEUS, HEPHAESTUS, *and* PANDORA *freeze.*)

PANDORA

CLIO.

> Some *women's* touches are what he
> wants.
> He and his helper are somewhat
> hampered
> In making this model—for they are
> mere men.
> Now goddesses come to give their
> gifts.
> And, lo! Leading them is the goddess
> of love.

(APHRODITE *enters, and* ZEUS, HEPHAESTUS, *and* PANDORA *come to life.*)

ZEUS. Greetings, Aphrodite. Here she is—the first mortal woman, a gift to men.

APHRODITE. What's her name?

ZEUS. She doesn't have one yet.

APHRODITE. A gift to men, you say. Who would have thought it, O Lord of the Heavens? I thought you *hated* humankind. Really, so did everybody. We were all quite sure that you meant to destroy the whole race of them.

ZEUS (*indicating* PANDORA). Does she look like an instrument of destruction?

APHRODITE. To be truthful, she doesn't look like much of anything yet.

HEPHAESTUS. You don't like her?

APHRODITE. Oh, I didn't say that. She's got possibilities. But she needs work. May I?

ZEUS. I was hoping you would.

(APHRODITE *approaches* PANDORA *and studies her more closely.*)

APHRODITE. Her figure is good. Count on you men to get *that* part right. But her face ... Let me see ...

(APHRODITE *reaches toward* PANDORA*'s face. Frightened,* PANDORA *draws back with a slight hiss.*)

APHRODITE. Don't be frightened. It won't hurt a bit. I promise.

(PANDORA *holds still, uneasily.* APHRODITE *touches her face, as if molding clay.*)

APHRODITE. Oh, you poor thing! How can you even *live* with your eyes so close together? Let's spread them apart a little. And make them wider and larger. And your cheekbones—a good bit higher and sharper. And a bit more color there, too. With the right natural tones, you'll never need makeup. And a more prominent nose. Yes, we mustn't be afraid to make your features bold and strong. We don't want you to fade into the woodwork, do we?

(APHRODITE *steps back to look at her work.*)

APHRODITE (*to* ZEUS *and* HEPHAESTUS). There. What do you think?

ZEUS. Oh, much better.

HEPHAESTUS. Yes—much, much better.

(APHRODITE, PANDORA, ZEUS, *and* HEPHAESTUS *freeze.*)

CLIO.

> Next comes a goddess, grand and
> good,
> Of weaving and sewing as well as of
> wisdom,
> Of elegant wardrobes as well as of war

(ATHENA *enters, carrying a folded robe with a tiara upon it.* APHRODITE, PANDORA, ZEUS, *and* HEPHAESTUS *come to life again.*)

ZEUS. Greetings, daughter Athena.

ATHENA *(to* ZEUS*).* I came as soon as I heard, Father. Such extraordinary news! A gift for men! This must mean you don't intend to destroy them, after all. The next thing we know, you'll free Prometheus.

ZEUS. That remains to be seen.

ATHENA. Oh, please let him go. I know the two of you have had your differences, but he's a fine fellow— the very best of Titans. *(Seeing* PANDORA*)* And this must be her. What's her name?

HEPHAESTUS. She still hasn't got one.

ATHENA. We must do something about that. Her face is extremely pretty. Do I detect Aphrodite's work there?

ZEUS. You do.

ATHENA *(to* APHRODITE*).* Quite beautiful.

APHRODITE. Thank you.

ATHENA. But her clothes—oh, what were you men thinking? It's beyond dowdy! I expected as much—which is why I brought a little something for her to wear. Aphrodite, help me for a moment, please.

(*As* CLIO *speaks,* APHRODITE *and* ATHENA *help* PANDORA *into the elegant robe, then put the tiara on her head.*)

CLIO.
    Improved? Partly. And yet, hardly perfect;

For still, there's an essence that's missing, I think.
She's fierce and frightened, even feral—
Hardly human, yet hardly beast.
What *is* she, really? An idiot imp—
Or less than that, a lump of live clay.
But she can be fixed, let's not fret or fear.
The queen of Olympus, that lovely lady,
Now comes to complete this promising creature.

(HERA *enters.*)

ZEUS. Hera, dear wife! I'm glad you could come!

HERA. I wouldn't have missed it. And this is her? Let me have a look. She's really quite extraordinarily lovely.

(HERA *steps toward* PANDORA*, who draws back fearfully.*)

HERA. Poor dear! You're terrified, aren't you? There's no need. You're among friends here with us. And among men, you'll be treasured and adored. Come, take my hand.

(HERA *extends her hand to* PANDORA*, who takes it cautiously.*)

HERA. Now tell me, dear—how do you feel?

HEPHAESTUS. She can't speak.

HERA. Of course she can. She just hasn't had anything to say so far. But she does now. Come on, child, speak.

(*Pause*)

PANDORA. I belong dead.

HERA. Nonsense! You're just not used to life, that's all. You'll learn to enjoy it—and the sooner you start, the better. You're just a creature of a day—so you must learn to *seize* the day. *(In a soothing and somewhat hypnotic voice)* Trust me, child. Fear nothing. Look deep into my eyes. Lose yourself in their clear, still pools. Delve into their uttermost depths. Search and seek. Find your humanity, your womanhood there. Become who you were destined to be. And then—tell me how you feel.

(Long silence as PANDORA stares into HERA's eyes. At last, PANDORA lets go of HERA's hand and backs slowly away from her. Then, with startling grace, she curtseys deeply.)

PANDORA. I feel deeply honored to share the company of you immortal gods and goddesses.

(All the GODS except HERA gasp with delight, then applaud.)

HERA. The honor is ours, child. It's such a joy to witness the birth of a splendid new creature. But what is your name?

PANDORA. I have no name.

HERA. Then you must give yourself one.

PANDORA. Very well, then. I shall be—Pandora.

(Delighted, the GODS applaud again.)

ZEUS. Yes—Pandora, the bride of man!

(The GODS all exit as HESIOD begins to speak. PANDORA pulls the curtain shut, then freezes.)

HESIOD.
The bride of a *Titan*, to make truer our tale.
For as soon as she lives, she's swept away swiftly
And brought to the fool, the bungling brother.
She's meant for *his* bride—and more is the menace
To mortal souls. Just see, just see!

(EPIMETHEUS enters, and PANDORA comes to life.)

EPIMETHEUS. Who are you?

PANDORA. Your wife.

EPIMETHEUS. I—do I have a wife? I don't remember having a wife.

PANDORA. You do now.

EPIMETHEUS. You're a goddess?

PANDORA. No, a mortal.

EPIMETHEUS. There's no such thing as a mortal woman.

PANDORA. There is now.

EPIMETHEUS. I'm asleep. I'm dreaming.

PANDORA. No. You're very much awake.

EPIMETHEUS. What's your name?

PANDORA. Pandora.

EPIMETHEUS. That name—it must mean something. I can't think what.

PANDORA. *All-Giving.* For I, myself, am a gift.

EPIMETHEUS. Who from?

PANDORA. The gods.

EPIMETHEUS. Oh, no!

PANDORA. What's the matter?

EPIMETHEUS. You must go away! I can't have anything to do with you!

PANDORA. Why not?

EPIMETHEUS. My brother told me never to accept gifts from the gods.

PANDORA. Your brother Prometheus.

EPIMETHEUS. That's right.

PANDORA. I'm sure he couldn't have meant me. Let's ask him.

EPIMETHEUS. He's gone.

PANDORA. Where?

EPIMETHEUS. I don't know. Somewhere being punished.

PANDORA. Oh, yes—for stealing fire from the sun and giving it to man. Foolish Titan.

EPIMETHEUS. No, *I'm* foolish. He's very wise.

PANDORA. Wise? For committing a crime for which he was sure to be caught? A crime that did neither him nor you any good? He sounds foolish to me. I think you are much wiser—wise enough to accept me as your wife.

EPIMETHEUS. I can't.

PANDORA. Now don't *you* be foolish, Epimetheus. For is it wise to spurn the gods when they wish us well—to turn away their gifts?

EPIMETHEUS. I—I—

PANDORA. Of course, if you don't *like* me—

EPIMETHEUS. Oh, it's not that. I like you very much. You're the most beautiful creature I've ever seen.

PANDORA. Thank you.

EPIMETHEUS. It's just that—you simply can't be here. Please leave.

PANDORA. Well. I can't very well stay if you don't want me to.

EPIMETHEUS. I'm glad we agree.

(Pause)

PANDORA. Tell me, husband—

EPIMETHEUS. I'm not your husband.

PANDORA. Tell me, Epimetheus—do you remember what it was like being nothing?

EPIMETHEUS. I don't understand.

PANDORA. It's very simple. We were all nothing once, weren't we? Before we were born or even conceived, before we existed? What else could we have been—but nothing?

EPIMETHEUS. Well, *nothing*, I suppose.

PANDORA. Exactly. And do you remember being nothing?

EPIMETHEUS. I—well—It was a long time ago.

PANDORA. As it happens, I *do* remember. For you see, I wasn't born yesterday. I was born *today*. I vividly remember what it was like to be mute, unthinking, lifeless clay. There I was, resting in a riverbank, neither happy nor unhappy, without so much as a head to have a thought in, waiting patiently for absolutely nothing to happen. And then the forge god came and scooped me up, carried me to Olympus, and molded me into my present shape. Yes, I remember it all vividly—and also the moment when

Zeus breathed life into me. And before I knew it—I *was*. You see my predicament, don't you? I have more experience at being *nothing* than at being *something*. So where can I go if you turn me away? What can I do?

EPIMETHEUS. I—I don't know.

PANDORA. Don't be cruel. Don't make me live with no purpose. If you don't want me, destroy me.

EPIMETHEUS. I couldn't do that.

PANDORA. Why not? You're a great trickster, aren't you? A maker and unmaker, just like your brother. So *unmake* me. Go on. Return me to clay. I liked being clay. I was whole and complete in that river bank. I'm broken and divided now. I feel lost.

EPIMETHEUS. I won't destroy you.

PANDORA. Then we've reached an impasse, haven't we? I can't stay, but I've got nowhere to go. You don't want me, but I can't leave. We'll just stand here staring at each other till the crack of doom—or until I die. That won't be too awfully long. I *am* just a creature of a day.

I really don't understand. Why don't you want me to be your wife?

EPIMETHEUS. I've already told you. Prometheus said—

PANDORA. —"never to accept gifts from the gods." Nonsense. That's not the reason. I know it's not. You're keeping something from me. You've got a secret.

Oh, of course! How stupid of me not to see it before. You've already *got* a wife—some beautiful goddess, no mere mortal.

EPIMETHEUS. No.

PANDORA. Oh, yes. It's the only thing that makes sense. Where is she? The least you can do is introduce us.

EPIMETHEUS. She's not here—I mean, I don't *have* a wife!

(PANDORA *walks toward the curtain.*)

PANDORA. Yes, you do. Where's she hidden? Here, I expect. (*She sweeps the curtain open, revealing a huge, covered jar.*)

PANDORA. What have we here? A beautiful piece of pottery! Made from the same sort of clay as myself, I believe. Ah, happy jar! How lucky you are, to have this shape and not mine! How blessed you are, to know nothing of the breath of life! And what do you contain? The wife of a Titan, I'm sure. Let's open you and see. (*She reaches to open the lid.*)

EPIMETHEUS. Wait! Stop! Don't touch that lid!

PANDORA. What's wrong with my meeting her?

EPIMETHEUS. There's no "her."

PANDORA. Then it's empty?

EPIMETHEUS. No.

PANDORA. What's in it, then?

EPIMETHEUS. Terrible things.

PANDORA. I'm intrigued. What are you doing with a jar full of terrible things?

EPIMETHEUS. It's a long story.

PANDORA. I love stories. Tell it.

EPIMETHEUS. Well—once upon a time, long, long ago . . . uh, *not* so long ago, actually—pretty recently in fact . . . my brother made all the creatures that live upon the earth. And when he was done, the gods gave me that jar. It was stuffed to the brim with wonderful gifts. And it was my job to give those gifts away to all living things. Warm fur to protect against weather. Keen smell for the hunt. Sharp eyes to see even by night. Ears that could catch the slightest sound miles away. Mighty paws and hooves for swift running. Scales and fins for swimming. Feathers and wings for flight. Because of gifts like those, man is the wonderful creature he is today.

PANDORA. Warm fur, keen smell, sharp eyes and ears, paws and hooves, scales and fins, feathers and wings?

EPIMETHEUS. Yes.

PANDORA. Men don't have any of those.

EPIMETHEUS. Oh . . . that's right. My fault, I'm afraid. You see, I gave all those things away to the animals, and by the time I got around to men, there were no gifts left.

PANDORA. Nothing at all?

EPIMETHEUS. Nothing except evil things, the dregs of that jar.

PANDORA. What sorts of evil things?

EPIMETHEUS. They're too dangerous to even whisper their names. And they've been festering in there ever since, growing greater and greater and worse and worse. So if anyone ever opens that lid, they'll get loose into the world. They'll cause all kinds of misery and unhappiness.

(Pause)

PANDORA. Did you make all that up?

EPIMETHEUS. No.

PANDORA. And it's really not your wife in that jar?

EPIMETHEUS. It's all true. I swear.

PANDORA. Well. That's quite a story.

EPIMETHEUS. It is, isn't it?

PANDORA. Sad, though—for men, I mean. To have missed out on all those glorious gifts, to be left with absolutely nothing.

EPIMETHEUS. It didn't turn out sadly—not at all. For when my brother saw what had happened, he gave men gifts from his very own soul, gifts not to be found in any jar. He made them stand straight, gave them the posture of gods, so they could look toward the sky instead of the ground. He also gave them minds—godlike minds—and a sense of purpose that no other animal possessed. Then he taught them all the wonderful things they could do with their minds and bodies. He showed them how to work in wood and stone and metal, to make tools and homes for themselves. He gave them the wheel, with its thousands of amazing uses. He taught them numbers and letters so they could count and write. He explained the movements of the sky to them so they could understand the changing of seasons. And—oh, it would take more books than the world could even hold to tell of all the things he did for them. And then, at last . . . *(He stops, on the verge of tears.)*

PANDORA. What? What did he do?

EPIMETHEUS. He gave men fire—the greatest gift of all. A hot, golden wind that does all good things and never harms. He gave it to them, knowing full well that it meant an end to his own happiness, that he would suffer terribly for his deed.

PANDORA. Poor Epimetheus! You're crying! You miss him terribly, don't you?

EPIMETHEUS. If I hadn't blundered—if I hadn't squandered all the gifts—maybe—maybe—

PANDORA. Maybe he wouldn't have stolen fire from the gods?

(EPIMETHEUS nods.)

PANDORA. He made that choice himself, made it out of love. My guess is that he couldn't have been stopped. Even if you had given men *all* the good things in that jar, he would have gone on giving more and more and more until there was no good thing left in the universe to give. He would have given until he himself vanished into thin air. You couldn't have helped that.

EPIMETHEUS. Without him, I feel so—so—

PANDORA. Alone?

EPIMETHEUS. Worse than alone. So awfully afraid. Afraid of the dark and of the light, too. Afraid of everything that moves, even of things that are still. I feel—incomplete.

PANDORA *(taking him by the hand).* Then let me complete you, and you can complete me. Each of us has been torn away from a wholeness—you from your brother, me from my riverbank of clay. But now we are each other's gifts—god-given gifts. Accept me for what I am, just as I accept you for what you are.

EPIMETHEUS. And together, we'll be—

PANDORA. Something whole and new.

EPIMETHEUS. Yes.

(PANDORA and EPIMETHEUS freeze, hand in hand. CLIO sniffs and wipes her eyes.)

CLIO. Oh, it's lovely.

HESIOD. Evil is what it is.

CLIO. How can you say that? What can be more good than two lonely souls finding each other in love?

HESIOD. She's wickedness incarnate.

CLIO. No! She's compassionate, caring!

HESIOD. She's cunning, conniving. She's leading him by the nose.

CLIO. You can't really mean that.

HESIOD. You don't believe it? Consider the turn our story's about to take.

CLIO. Oh—the jar.

(EPIMETHEUS exits. PANDORA comes to life and slowly approaches the jar.)

HESIOD.
    The jar, indeed—with its dregs of death.
    For see this scene! As soon as our Titan

Leaves his lair to do his day's labor,
That child, unchecked, leaps at her
  chance,
Pries loose the lid to have a look.

(PANDORA *begins to pull and twist at the lid
of the jar.*)

CLIO.
But not wickedly—it's not in her
  nature.
An innocent she is, ignorant of evil—
Too unwary to worry, too new to the
  world.
She cannot know, cannot name what
  is near.

HESIOD.
Ah, don't be fooled! Fiendish and
  foul
She was born and is—a bitter bane
Steeped in ill, a disastrous seed.
Innocent, her? Heed me—she's a
  hazard.

(PANDORA *continues to struggle with the lid.*
VOICES *speak in unison, apparently from
inside the jar.*)

VOICES.
A glimmer of light!
A crack in the door!
An end to our night!
A sight to adore!

PANDORA (*pausing in her attempt to pull
  loose the lid*). Who's there? Who
  speaks?

VOICES.
Never mind that!
Why did you stop?
Come on, lazy brat!
Get to it! Hop!

PANDORA (*working again*). There's no
  need to insult me.

(*The* VOICES *speak individually.*)

1ST VOICE.
Twist to the right!

2ND VOICE.
No, to the left!

3RD VOICE.
Move it with might!

4TH VOICE.
Hoist it with heft!

PANDORA. I'm trying, I'm trying! Just a
  little patience, if you don't mind.

3RD VOICE.
I'll push from in here.

2ND VOICE.
Yes, push—push it free!

1ST VOICE.
I'll shove it clear.

4TH VOICE.
No, get back—let me!

PANDORA. Stop quarreling! I've half a
  mind to go away and leave you all
  shut up inside!

VOICES (*in unison again*).
What—walk off and leave?
Do you call that fair?
It's too much to believe!
Don't even dare!

(PANDORA *pulls the lid free.*)

PANDORA. There, it's done! You can
  come out now.

(PANDORA *puts the lid on the floor and steps
aside as the voices continue inside the jar.*)

2ND VOICE.
Get out of my way!

1ST VOICE.
Let me go first!

4TH VOICE.
The devil, you say!

3RD VOICE.
Move—or be
cursed!

PANDORA. A selfish bunch, aren't you? And rude, too. You're not called *evils* for nothing, I suppose. But let's have a look at you.

(DISEASE *climbs out of the jar and steps to the ground.*)

DISEASE.
Ah, the air—the open air!
To breathe it at long
last!
So sweet and fresh, and
healthful, too—
So spacious and so vast!

And yet I'll dare to foul this
air
Infect it near and far,
And make the sky much ranker
than
The depths of any jar.

PANDORA. Don't touch me, frightful, smelly thing! Who *are* you!

DISEASE.
I am Disease; I'll stab the bowels
And raise up boils for sport.

I'll bring old age and make men's
lives
Nasty, brutish, and short.

PANDORA. But men are mere creatures of a day. Their lives are short already.

DISEASE.
> Not short enough; and when they die
> > It's easy—that's an error.
> And so it is my will to fill
> > Their dying hours with terror.

(FAMINE climbs out of the jar and steps to the ground.)

FAMINE *(to* DISEASE*).*
> Since you're inclined to make life
> > misery,
> Kindly accept a little help from me.

DISEASE.
> Ah, welcome, welcome, infamous old
> > friend!
> Tell me, now—what ill do you
> > intend?

PANDORA. Such a sickening creature—
so parched, wan, and scrawny! Oh,
don't come near me!

DISEASE *(to* PANDORA*).*
> Allow me to present a nuisance
> > fervent:
> This grisly shade is Famine.

FAMINE *(bowing to* PANDORA*).*
> > > Your humble servant.
> There's too much bounty in the
> > world, I think—
> Too many wholesome things to eat
> > and drink.
> I'll dry up wells and springs, and salt
> > the earth,
> And where there's bounty, I shall
> > leave a dearth.
> Let grain die in the field—and
> > livestock, too;
> Let harvests offer nothing but
> > troubles new;

> Let bellies bloat with hunger; let eyes
> > protrude;
> Let infants weep and pine for lack of
> > food;
> Let parents grieve—and with each
> > mournful breath,
> Let them pray to heartless gods for
> > death.

(WAR climbs out of the jar and steps to the ground.)

WAR.
> That's right—make scarce, make
> > meager,
> And pave the way for me!
> I'll make men wild and eager
> To start a killing spree.

> They'll fight for just a trifle—
> For just a patch of land.
> Till they invent the rifle,
> They'll grapple hand-to-hand.

> They'll raid each town and village;
> Whole cities they will burn;
> They'll plunder and they'll pillage,
> And mercy they will spurn.

PANDORA. Fiendish thoughts! Your
name must be War.

WAR *(offering a knife to* PANDORA*).*
> Smart girl—and also pretty;
> For soldiering you'll do.
> Come on, now—show no pity;
> Here's a knife for you.

PANDORA. I'll leave bloodshed to men.

(PAIN climbs out of the jar and steps to the ground.)

PAIN.
> Famine, War,

And foul Disease—
Cause all the trouble
That you please.
Go on, have fun.
It's all in vain
Without my help.

DISEASE, FAMINE, and WAR *(together).*

For you are Pain!

PAIN.

The very same—
A *special* bane!
For without me,
Your stings and blows
Won't hurt a bit.
In aching throes
I'll plunge all men.
Why, I'll make bad
Even what's good!
Yes, I will add
The Titan's gifts
To human harms.
For even fire
With all its charms—
That ever-gentle
Golden wind—
Will burn and blister
All humankind.

(PANDORA, DISEASE, FAMINE, WAR, and PAIN freeze as HESIOD speaks.)

HESIOD.

The devils that remain will maim
    heart and mind,
Scourge our souls and scratch out
    what's good.
A ghastly gremlin with green eyes
    comes,
Turning us to mistrust, to sly treachery.

(ENVY has climbed out of the jar.)

ENVY. I am Envy!

(As HESIOD continues speaking, ENVY steps to the ground and freezes among the other evils.)

HESIOD.

Get ready now for this grudging
    grasper.
Dead things we'll yearn for, dazzling
    but dumb—
Gems and jewels, those joyless
    trinkets.

(GREED has climbed out of the jar.)

GREED. I am Greed!

(As HESIOD continues speaking, GREED steps to the ground and freezes among the other evils.)

HESIOD.

Next, a monster of mirthful
    meanness,
Goading to glee over others' grief—
Provoking to malice, to pain beyond
    pardon.

(CRUELTY has climbed out of the jar.)

CRUELTY. I am Cruelty!

(As HESIOD continues speaking, CRUELTY steps to the ground and freezes among the other evils. Seven EVILS now stand around the stage in a tableau.)

HESIOD.

And, oh, a host of things more
    horrible
Comes surging forth, both fell and
    fierce—
Until—just listen! A lone voice is
    left.

(As the VOICE OF HOPE is heard from inside the jar, PANDORA comes to life, but the EVILS remain frozen.)

VOICE OF HOPE.
Here I come—
Last but not least,
And more than ready
To be released!

PANDORA. And who are you?
Something more horrible than all the
rest, I expect.

VOICE OF HOPE.
My name is Hope,
A sister of Pain—
And down in these depths
Too long I have lain.

PANDORA (*rushing toward the jar and seizing the lid*). I'm shutting up the jar.

VOICE OF HOPE.
Not yet, not yet!
Toward the light I am headed!
Don't shut that lid!
I swear, you'll regret it!

PANDORA. You're one evil too many.
You'll not get out.

(PANDORA *slams the lid on the jar, then freezes. As* HESIOD *begins to speak, all the* EVILS *exit in different directions.*)

HESIOD.
The jar is sealed—and so is our story.
Evils roam far, growing as they go,
Flooding the world to fullness
  overflowing.
And so here it ends—my sighing
  song.

CLIO. But you've not proven your point.

HESIOD. Which was?

CLIO. That Pandora was evil—and all women who came after her.

HESIOD. Haven't I? She *did* open the jar full of terrible things.

CLIO. But she didn't know what was inside.

HESIOD. Oh, didn't she? She also slammed the lid on the one good thing in that jar—Hope.

CLIO. How could she know that Hope wasn't just another evil? For that matter, does *anyone* understand what Hope really is? "A sister of Pain," Hope called herself. But a good sister or a wicked sister? Is she a blessing who gives meaning to life? Or is she a lie who keeps us from embracing each living moment? If she's a good thing, what was she doing in a jar full of evils?

HESIOD (*laughing grimly*). Well, we needn't bother ourselves much about Hope, we mortals. Thanks to Pandora, there's precious little of her in the world.

CLIO. Pandora, talk to this man. Explain yourself to him. He won't listen to me.

(PANDORA *comes to life.*)

PANDORA. Tell me, poet—who made me?

HESIOD. Lord Zeus, of course.

PANDORA. For what purpose?

HESIOD. To release the evils from that jar.

PANDORA. And why did he want those evils released?

HESIOD. To destroy humankind.

PANDORA. Then he failed, didn't he?

For here *you* are, untold generations later, the descendent of countless men and women who came before you. Indeed, there are rather a great many human beings upon the earth. Lord Zeus must be dreadfully disappointed in me.

HESIOD. You did harm enough. You ended the Golden Age.

PANDORA. Oh, yes—that strifeless time when men had nothing better to do than twiddle their thumbs and play with painless fire. It doesn't sound like much of a life to me. And I can't imagine that it does to a hardworking farmer like you. Prometheus gave you marvelous minds, bodies, skills, and tools—but nothing to do with them. *I* gave you that gift. My deed spurred your ingenuity—made you strong, creative, and great.

CLIO. Of course! You completed the work of Prometheus! You *were* a sublime gift to humankind—and so were all women who came after you. There'll be a poet named Goethe someday—how will he put it? Oh, yes . . .
    "The Eternal-Feminine
    Lures to perfection."
Zeus intended you for ill, but you defied him. You loved humans—and that's why you did such a wonderful thing for them.

(PANDORA *laughs.*)

CLIO. Why do you laugh?

PANDORA. Who knows why people do the things they do? You want to pluck out the heart of my mystery,

but you can't. And now—I must be gone. I *am* just a creature of a day.

CLIO. Pandora, wait—

(PANDORA *exits.*)

HESIOD. I think I'll go, too.

CLIO. No, not yet. I still don't understand why you feel the way you do about women.

HESIOD. Why not? You heard the story.

CLIO. But it's *only* a story—and a story with more than one meaning.

HESIOD. The way I see it, I'm just a story, too.

CLIO. That won't do. I won't let it go at that. I must know the reason. Has no woman ever loved you? Or was your love unrequited? Or were you loved by a woman who turned unfaithful? Or—(*Pause*) Oh, I think I know. She died, didn't she? Yes, that must be it. There's nothing more cruel than to leave a loved one alone in this life. Is that what she did? Is that what happened?

(HESIOD *stamps out the fire.*)

HESIOD. Ask history.

CLIO. But Hesiod—

HESIOD. I am a man untouched by Hope—and I am happy. Let's leave it at that. (*He exits.*)

CLIO (*to the audience*). Well—the night's certainly gone sour. Even the meadow air suddenly seems stale, somehow. It serves me right, I suppose, for dabbling in myth and poetry. I *am* the Muse of history, and my time hasn't come yet. Why, it'll be more than 300 years before the first real historian comes along— Herodotus will be his name. Till then, I'd better be patient and not try to do other Muses' work.

And as for Pandora—well, who's to say that she ever really lived? She's probably just a fairy tale. Nothing historical about her.

Still, it frustrates me not to know—what really happened to that poor poet to make him despise women so?

What was it he said?
Oh, yes.
"I am a man untouched by Hope—and I am happy."

What on earth could he have meant?

And what *is* Hope, anyway?

(Long pause. CLIO *opens the jar.)*

CLIO. I guess we'll find out.

(She exits.)

PLAYWRIGHT'S POSTSCRIPT

According to Hesiod, Pandora "Took off the great lid of the jar with her hands and . . . caused sorrow and mischief to men." But as the tale was retold again and again, storytellers confused the jar for a box. So today, the story is usually called *Pandora's Box*.

When we are faced with something that might cause unknown problems, we call it a *Pandora's box*. The phrase is often used when talking about new technology. For example, genetic engineering has allowed us to clone animals, create specially designed crops, and fight diseases. But many people wonder if it might also lead to terrible dangers, so they sometimes refer to it as a Pandora's box.

CONNECTING TO OTHER CULTURES

Cultures all over the world have told stories of why there is suffering and evil in the world. Women often get the blame, as in the biblical story of Eve, who ate a piece of forbidden fruit from the Tree of Knowledge, bringing hardship and death into the world.

People everywhere also tell stories about how the world and humankind began, and these stories are often strikingly similar. Like the story of Prometheus, many myths say that living things began from clay. For example, the Hopis of the southwestern United States say that animals and people were molded out of clay by the creator goddess Spider Woman.

PHAETON AND THE SUN CHARIOT

SETTING THE STAGE

The gods of classical mythology can be alarmingly human in their moods and behavior. Like mortals, they quarrel, fall in love, lose their tempers, and have spells of pride and vanity. In much of what they do, it is hard to see how they are any wiser than mortals. They are different from mortals in one important way, however. They are unbelievably powerful.

It's sobering to think that a being with human emotions can wield superhuman powers. For example, according to the Greeks and Romans, the sun is a god who drives a fiery chariot across the sky—a god sometimes known to make unwise decisions. Can we really trust such a god with the most powerful force in the universe? Do we have any choice?

This play tells the story of how the sun god let his inexperienced son drive his chariot for a day. The story is most fully told by the Roman poet Ovid in his epic poem *Metamorphoses*, written in the 1st century A.D. According to Ovid, the driver of the sun chariot was Apollo, the god of light and wisdom. But in earlier Greek versions, the sun god was a lesser deity named Helios. He is Helios in this play.

The story of Phaeton is of natural interest to Urania, the Muse of astronomy, so it is she who introduces this play.

MUSING ABOUT THE MYTH

The story of young Phaeton is a perfect illustration of the old saying "Pride goeth before a fall." As you read, think of other examples where too much pride has led to disaster.

Hubris: overbearing pride.

PHAETON AND THE SUN CHARIOT

<table>
<tr><td>

CHARACTERS:

URANIA (yü rā′ ne ə), the Muse of astronomy

CLYMENE (klī mē′ nē), Phaeton's mother

PHAETON (fā′ a ton), the son of Helios

TIME, Helios' secretary/receptionist

HELIOS (hē′ lē ōs), the sun god

HELIOS' ADVISORS:
WINTER
SPRING
SUMMER
FALL

NEWSCASTER

FOUR REPORTERS

CONSTELLATIONS:
LEO, the lion
TAURUS, the bull
CANCER, the crab
SCORPIO, the scorpion

</td><td>

MOTHER EARTH

ZEUS (züs), the king of the Olympian gods

HERA (hir′ a), the queen of the Olympian gods

CHARON (ker′ an), the ferryman of the river Styx

OTHER NAMES MENTIONED IN THE PLAY:

ERIDANUS (e rid′ a nus), a river in Italy, now called the Po

HERACLES (her′ a klēz), a hero demigod

SEMELE (sem′ e lē), the mother of the god Dionysus

STYX (stiks), the river that surrounds the Underword

TETHYS (tē′ this), a sea goddess

</td></tr>
</table>

SETTING: *Mythical Greece, India, and the sky*

TIME: *No time in particular*

(URANIA *enters onto a bare stage. She looks around briefly, then goes offstage. She comes back with two small stools and sets them center stage.*)

URANIA. Can I have the lights down, please? Just a little bit?

(*The lights dim slightly.*)

URANIA. That's it. Nice dusk effect. Think dusk a minute. Not quite dark. No, not quite night yet. Maybe just a star or two. Soon, very soon, the sky will be filled with monsters. (*Stopping to survey the audience*) Oh, I see you're going to be one of *those* audiences. Not going to swallow this "monsters-in-the-sky" bit. No, you're too smart for that. You know too much. You know that stars are made of flaming gas, all about light years, supernovas, quasars, galaxies, black holes, that kind of thing. You're a regular bunch of astronomers. Well, I'm Urania, the Muse of astronomy, and you'll have to forgive me if I insult your ultra-educated minds for just a little while. In the days of my story, the sky was filled with monsters. People traveling the heavens met a great bull, stomping and snorting and threatening to charge. And also a hungry lion, ready to devour any living thing that came along. They braved the deadly claws of a giant crab, the poisonous tail of a great scorpion. I know it sounds silly, but that's how it was.

(PHAETON *and* CLYMENE *come onto the stage.* PHAETON *sits on a stool.* CLYMENE *stands nearby. They freeze into these positions.*)

URANIA. But it's dusk, remember. The monsters are just starting to show themselves. I take you to a modest little house in Greece. A young man sits on the front porch, watching as the sky begins to fill with stars.

(URANIA *steps aside to watch* PHAETON *and* CLYMENE *come to life.*)

CLYMENE (*looking up from a list she's been making*). Phaeton, why are you sitting out here? It's getting chilly.

PHAETON. I'm just thinking.

CLYMENE. Do you want me to get your jacket?

PHAETON. No.

CLYMENE (*sitting next to him*). Could you pick up some things on the way

home from school tomorrow? We need more milk. And cheese. And lamb, don't forget lamb.

(*But* PHAETON *isn't listening to her.*)

PHAETON (*looking at the sky*). The sky's so clear. You'll be able to see every star tonight. There. They're starting to come out. (*Pointing*) There's Venus. And do you see that dim strip of light? That's the Milky Way. That's his road. That's where the Sun rides across the sky.

CLYMENE. What did I just ask you to do?

PHAETON. I'm sorry. I wasn't listening.

CLYMENE. What makes you think of your father?

PHAETON. I think about him all the time.

CLYMENE. You never ask about him.

PHAETON. You never seem to want to talk about him.

CLYMENE. We can if you want to. What do you want me to tell you?

PHAETON. Why did you leave him?

CLYMENE. I've told you that.

PHAETON. No, you haven't. Not really.

CLYMENE (*a bit evasively*). Well, it wasn't my kind of life, being married to a god. The Sun Palace was rather gaudy for my taste. Everything was very bright. It hurt my eyes. And I never took to gods that well. Oh, the talk was so serious. All about history and destiny and fate all the time. I was bored. And to tell the truth, I bored the gods. I was too simple for them. They were happy to see me go.

PHAETON. I've heard all this before. Those aren't the real reasons.

CLYMENE. What makes you say that?

PHAETON. I just know. *(Pause)* Didn't you love him?

CLYMENE. Oh, Phaeton, really.

PHAETON. Well, didn't you?

CLYMENE. I—I loved him early on, and he loved me, but . . . your father and I, we—*(Touching her forefingers together)*—we just didn't meet here and here. I don't know how else to say it. Why now, Phaeton? Why do you want to talk about him all of a sudden?

PHAETON. Don't you think it's about time? I'm not a kid anymore. All my life, I've tried to tell people who I am, who my father was. Nobody's ever believed me, not once. When I was little, all the other kids teased me. "Phaeton doesn't have a daddy," they'd say.

CLYMENE. You never said anything about it.

PHAETON. But you knew.

CLYMENE. Yes, of course I did. Well, you showed everybody you were a winner, no matter what they thought.

PHAETON. But nobody believes the truth. Doesn't that bother you? Don't you care what people say about—?

(PHAETON stops himself in mid-sentence.)

CLYMENE *(finishing his thought)*. About me? That I'm some crazy woman who claims she was once married to the Sun? No, it doesn't bother me. I don't know why, but it doesn't. Your sisters are his children, too, and it doesn't seem to bother them.

PHAETON. I'm not like them.

CLYMENE. Phaeton, I swear to you it's true. The Sun really is your father. If I'm lying, let Zeus kill me here and now. I'm sure he's got a bolt of lightning handy.

PHAETON. I believe you. I've always believed you. I just want to know why you left him, really. Was he cruel? Did he mistreat you? Was he such a terrible father?

CLYMENE. No. He was—is very good.

PHAETON. Then why?

CLYMENE *(reluctantly)*. Because I wanted you and your sisters to live human lives. I thought it would be hard for you, growing up among immortals. Too much pressure, too many expectations. Your father was against our leaving. So were all the gods. They fought me tooth and nail. I was just a mortal girl, and I couldn't do anything, not even bring up my own children. But I did what I thought I had to do. I left the Sun Palace and brought you here. He sent me money, but I sent it back. I worked in the vineyards and olive groves and made as much time as I could for my children. But . . .

PHAETON. But what?

CLYMENE. I've always wondered if I did the right thing.

PHAETON. You did. We couldn't ask for a better home—or a better family.

CLYMENE. So what do you want?

PHAETON. I want to know—what does it mean to be part god? Do I have powers I don't know about? Or duties? Will I die someday—or will I live forever?

CLYMENE. I don't know.

PHAETON. Then how do I find out?

(Pause)

CLYMENE. Go to see him. Ask him yourself—in person. That's what you want to do, isn't it?

PHAETON. Will you come with me?

CLYMENE. No. *(Pause)* Come on. We'd better get you packed.

(CLYMENE and PHAETON freeze. URANIA steps forward.)

URANIA. I think we can skip the journey. You've seen lots of "journeys-to-the-east" in movies. This one won't be any different.

(PHAETON and CLYMENE exit.)

URANIA. As our hero makes his way, though, I'd better clear up one or two things. You're all used to living on a round little world that hurtles around the sun, a veritable moving target for asteroids and meteors and comets and the like. And the sun itself wobbles chaotically from the weight of nine planets tugging at it from different directions. All this doesn't even seem to worry you. Time was, though, when the earth was much more stable, just a great platform resting squarely on the shoulders of a Titan. And the Sun was a god who rode a fiery chariot. You might be too young to remember. Ask your parents about it.

(TIME enters, wearing sunglasses and carrying a tall stool. She sets the stool in front of one of the small ones, as if it were a desk. She sits behind it and freezes.)

URANIA. The god Helios lives in the Sun Palace—a classy place, all gold and ivory decorated with precious jewels, located in a very cosmopolitan, very posh district of India.

(TIME comes to life. She pantomimes answering a phone.)

TIME. Sun Enterprises, Far East Office, this is Time speaking. Could you hold, please? Thank you. *(Pantomiming again)* Sun Enterprises, Far East Office, this is Time speaking. Could you hold, please? Thank you. *(Again)* Sun Enterprises, Far East Office, this is Time speaking. Could you hold, please? Thank you. *(Throwing up her hands in exasperation)* It'll never stop! *(She freezes again.)*

URANIA. Now the poet Ovid doesn't mention Helios having a secretary/receptionist. In his version of our story, the Sun god is waited on by servants named Hour, Day, Year, and Century. But if you ask me, a celebrity who travels day in and day out can't get by without a receptionist. I hope no one minds my writing one in.

(URANIA steps aside to watch. PHAETON enters cautiously. TIME doesn't see him at first.)

TIME *(picking up the phone again).* Sun Enterprises, Time speaking, thank you for holding, can I help you? No, he's not giving interviews this week. I'm sorry, but that's positively the last word. Good-bye.

PHAETON. Excuse me—

TIME. What are you doing here?

PHAETON. I want to talk to Helios.

TIME. Have you got an appointment?

PHAETON. Well, no, but I—

TIME. How did you get past Security?

PHAETON. I just walked in.

TIME. Those guys are never on the job.

PHAETON. You're Time?

TIME. That's right. I'm in charge of years, months, days, hours, minutes, and seconds. If you want an appointment with Helios, I'm the one to talk to. But I can tell you right now, you'll never get to see him.

PHAETON. But you don't understand—

TIME. No, *you* don't. He's got a flight leaving in five minutes. He's not seeing anyone right now, with or without an appointment. Now if you don't mind, I've got a lot of calls. *(Picking up the phone again)* Sun Enterprises, Time speaking, thank you for holding, can I help you? No, there's no truth to that rumor, and if you print it you'll hear from our lawyers. Look, buddy, if you've got a problem, call Public Relations.

PHAETON. If you'll just let me explain—

TIME. Do you want me to call a guard? *(To the phone)* Sun Enterprises, Time speaking, thank you for holding, can I help you? Oh, Zeus, thank you for returning his call.

PHAETON *(excitedly).* Zeus? You're talking to Zeus?

TIME *(to PHAETON).* Do you mind? This is long distance. *(To the phone)* Yes, Zeus, I'm sorry. The office is a little crazy this morning. Helios just wondered if you could give him a little cloud cover. Nothing overcast, just a few scattered—what did he call them?—cirrus clouds. At about 20,000 feet. You know, just for variety. Weather's been awfully clear lately. Public gets tired of it. Oh, thank you very much. He'll really appreciate it. *(To PHAETON)* Still here, huh?

PHAETON. My name is Phaeton.

TIME. So?

PHAETON. I'm his son.

TIME. Oh, brother.

PHAETON. It's true.

TIME. Do you know how often I hear that one? *(To the phone)* Sun Enterprises, Time speaking, thank you for holding, can I help you? If I've told you once, I've told you a thousand times, he will not endorse your chariots. He doesn't even ride one of yours. No, he doesn't want one for free. He's happy with the one he's got, thank you very much.

PHAETON. I won't leave till I talk to him.

TIME. I'm not a baby-sitter.

PHAETON. Then you'd better let me see him.

TIME. You don't know his temper.

PHAETON. I'll take my chances.

TIME (*to the phone*). Mr. Helios? There's a kid here to see you, making a real pain of himself. What do you want me to do with him?

PHAETON. Tell him who I am.

TIME. He says he's your son.

PHAETON. Phaeton.

TIME. Yes, I know, the third one this week.

PHAETON. Clymene's son.

TIME. He says he's Phaeton, the son of— (*To* PHAETON) Who was that again?

PHAETON. Clymene.

TIME. Clymene's son. (*A bit surprised by what she hears on the phone*) Oh. All right. I'll tell him. (*To* PHAETON) He'll be right out.

PHAETON. Thanks. I'll be sure to tell him how pleasant you've been.

TIME. Don't get cute. Have you got sunglasses?

PHAETON. What?

TIME (*handing him a pair of sunglasses*). You can't look at him without sunglasses. Do you want to go blind?

PHAETON (*putting on the sunglasses*). Oh. I almost forgot.

(HELIOS *enters, wearing his bright solar headdress.*)

HELIOS (*delightedly*). Phaeton!

PHAETON. Hello, Father.

(HELIOS *shakes* PHAETON's *hand warmly.*)

HELIOS. Is it really you, boy?

PHAETON. I could ask you the same.

HELIOS. Time, this is my son Phaeton. Phaeton, this is—

TIME. We've met.

HELIOS. Spitting image of his mother. Gorgeous woman. My, how you've grown. When was the last time I saw you?

PHAETON. I wouldn't remember.

HELIOS (*uncomfortably*). Yes, well, it has been quite some time, hasn't it? Have a seat, son. Make yourself comfortable. Would you like anything at all? Cigar, perhaps? A cup of coffee? Some of our delightful Oriental spiced tea?

TIME. Mr. Helios, you're due for your chariot in a minute and twenty-seven seconds.

HELIOS. I'll be going up late this morning.

TIME. Oh, no, please.

HELIOS. An hour or two, maybe.

TIME. The stars will disappear at their usual time, whether you're in the sky or not. And you know how mortals get when they're plunged into total darkness unexpectedly. Or have you forgotten the hysteria caused by the last solar eclipse?

HELIOS (*firmly*). I said I'll be late.

TIME. Am I taking the flack for this?

HELIOS. Of course not. Pass the buck. Go down the hall and tell Public Relations to take care of it. Oh, and while you're at it, send in my advisors, would you? I want them to meet my son.

TIME. I don't like this.

HELIOS. Relax. I'll give you a hefty raise next week.

TIME. If you're not going up yet, you might want to take off your headgear.

HELIOS (*absently*). Eh?

TIME. That way, the boy can skip the shades.

HELIOS. Oh, yes. Excellent suggestion.

(TIME *exits.* HELIOS *sets his headdress aside, and* PHAETON *removes the sunglasses.*)

HELIOS. Dedicated employee, Time. Been with the firm for an eternity. But she can be overzealous. She greet you well? Make you feel at home?

PHAETON. She's very nice.

HELIOS. My boy, you're about to witness a crisis of international proportions. For the first time in hundreds of years—why, no, in millennia!—the sun is rising late. The world will go completely crazy. In just a little while, every emperor, king, president, prime minister, and dictator-for-life on the planet will call, asking what in the name of Heaven has gone wrong. This phone will ring right off the hook. Oh, it will be fun! Don't know why I've stuck to such a tight schedule all this time. Responsibility gets to be a habit, I guess. So. Tell me everything. How are your sisters?

PHAETON. Fine.

HELIOS. And your mother. Does she speak well of me? No, let me rephrase that. Does she speak of me at all?

PHAETON. Not really.

HELIOS. Hardly any wonder. Our parting wasn't exactly a happy one.

PHAETON. So I'm told.

HELIOS. At least she's come to her senses and sent you here. Yes, I knew she'd finally see the light. That boring little peninsula—which is it, Greece?—is no home for a young demigod. India is the place for you.

PHAETON. But, Father—

HELIOS (*ignoring him*). You're an ambitious boy. I can see it in your eye. Mortal life hasn't quelled your godlike spirit. You want to move up in the world. Well, Sun Enterprises is just the place to do it. I'll get you your own office this afternoon, start you on an executive's salary.

PHAETON. Wait a minute. I don't even know if I want to stay here.

HELIOS (*startled*). Don't be absurd. Of course you'll stay. This is where you belong.

PHAETON. But I just came here to meet you, to get to know you. I just want us to talk.

HELIOS. And so we shall! I'll tell you what, I'll take the whole day off. The world can cope with an extra night this once. And before you know it, you'll forget all this nonsense about going back to Greece. Just wait and see.

PHAETON. But I don't even know you.

HELIOS. How can you say that? I'm your father.

PHAETON. Most boys my age have seen more of their fathers.

HELIOS. You're hitting a little low, son.

PHAETON. I'm sorry.

HELIOS. You've got a right, I suppose. I could blame it all on your mother, tell you she simply didn't want me to come around, but that wouldn't be fair. It was an awkward situation, one of those marriages no one quite approved of, mortals or gods. It seemed best for me to keep my distance. Someday you'll learn that no one's to blame in these matters.

PHAETON. That's supposed to explain everything?

HELIOS. Oh, come now. You surely didn't come all the way to India to whine about your life. If you did, I've got other business to attend to. You're testing my patience, and it's just not done. *(Pause)* I'm sorry. It's easy to forget you're my son.

PHAETON. That's just my point.

(SPRING, SUMMER, FALL, and WINTER enter. SPRING is garrulous and outgoing, a cockeyed optimist. WINTER is fretful, anxious, and officious. The personalities of SUMMER and FALL are somewhere between these two extremes.)

SPRING. Good morning, sir.

SUMMER. You called for us, sir?

FALL. Is there anything we can do, sir?

WINTER. Aren't you running just a little late this morning, sir?

HELIOS *(resuming his usual vigorous manner)*. Come in, come in! I'm not going up today. No, don't argue, you'll soon see it's for a good reason. Phaeton, these are my trusted advisors, Spring, Summer, Fall, and Winter. Seasons, this is my son, Phaeton.

SPRING. The son of the Sun! What an unexpected pleasure!

SUMMER. Unexpected is right.

FALL. I didn't know you had a son.

WINTER. How do you know he *is* your son?

SPRING. Oh, Winter, you're such a killjoy.

WINTER. I think it's a good question, considering how many kids come around claiming to be his children.

FALL. He *is* the third one this week.

SUMMER. Surely the boss knows his own son when he sees him.

HELIOS *(a bit huffily)*. Not that it's necessarily any of your business, Winter, but I once was married to a lovely mortal woman named Clymene.

SPRING. A mortal!

SUMMER. I never knew!

FALL. Don't you think, as your advisors, we might have been, well . . .

WINTER. Advised?

HELIOS. The marriage didn't work out, I'm sorry to say. But before it ended, we produced four splendid children.

PHAETON. Five.

HELIOS. Five splendid children. Well, this

strapping lad says he's one of them, and I believe him. If I'm not flattering myself unduly, I believe I see something of myself in him. A bit of my drive, my ambition, my gusto, my get-up-and-go. Am I right, son?

PHAETON. Well—

HELIOS. Come now, don't be modest. Tell us some of your accomplishments.

PHAETON. I'm just a kid from Greece.

HELIOS. I'll hear none of that. There'll be time for false humility when you've made your mark in the world.

PHAETON. Well, I'm captain of the football team—

HELIOS. An athlete! Excellent!

PHAETON. —student body president—

HELIOS. A natural-born leader!

PHAETON. —top of my class academically—

HELIOS. A mental giant!

PHAETON. —a black belt in Tae Kwan Do, a chess grand master, a theoretical physicist, a contender for the next Olympic decathlon, and the inventor of an all-purpose vaccine against every known disease.

HELIOS. Don't stop there. Continue.

PHAETON. That's pretty much it.

HELIOS (trying to hide his disappointment). Well, you're still young. Stick with us, and we'll add untold glories to your name.

WINTER. I still don't like it.

SPRING. You never like anything.

FALL. I'm not sure I do, either.

WINTER. How do we know whether this boy is telling us the truth?

PHAETON. Winter's got a point, Father. I haven't given you any proof. I brought along my birth certificate, but how do you know I didn't forge it? I need to *do* something to prove I'm really your son.

HELIOS. You've got nothing to prove. I've taken you at your word, and my decision is final. I won't be contradicted. Is that understood by everybody?

(The SEASONS *all murmur their agreement.*)

SUMMER. I guess that leaves us with the question of how to go public with this news.

FALL. *Should* we go public?

SPRING. Of course we should!

WINTER. Of course we shouldn't!

HELIOS. Yes! Absolutely! We'll issue a press release immediately. Announce to the world that Helios and his son have been reunited after fourteen years—

PHAETON. Fifteen.

HELIOS. —fifteen years, and that Phaeton is joining Sun Enterprises as executive vice president.

PHAETON. Father, I haven't even decided—

HELIOS. Don't interrupt, son, we're making big plans here.

SUMMER. If I may make a suggestion, sir, I think we need a publicity angle. It's not enough to just say the two of you are reunited, Phaeton's working for the firm, and blah-blah-blah. It lacks a certain drama, a certain—oomph. It'll leave the public cold.

FALL. Summer's right. We need something to humanize what's happening here. The whole world needs to feel this wonderful new bond between you two.

SUMMER. A gimmick!

FALL. A stunt!

HELIOS. Now you're talking! What have you got in mind?

SPRING. I've got it! Listen! You promise to grant Phaeton any wish he makes! You swear it by the river Styx!

WINTER. But that's the most binding oath there is. No god can go back on it.

SPRING. Exactly! That's what makes it so dramatic!

WINTER. It's a recipe for disaster! Don't you remember what happened when Zeus made the same oath to that mortal girl, what's-her-name?

SPRING. Semele.

WINTER. That's right, Semele. She asked to look Zeus in the face. Zeus knew that the sight of his celestial radiance would kill the poor thing outright. But he couldn't refuse his oath. So Semele looked at him and died.

HELIOS. Semele was a little mortal fool. My son's different. He takes after me. I like this idea!

SUMMER. It's got risk!

FALL. It's got emotion!

WINTER. It's insane!

HELIOS. We'll do it!

(HELIOS *turns toward* PHAETON *with solemnity.*)

HELIOS. Phaeton, my boy, I'm a deity with unimaginable power and influence. I can give you anything your heart desires. So make a wish. Anything. I swear by the river Styx to grant whatever you ask.

PHAETON. I want to drive your chariot across the sky today.

(*A tense silence*)

SUMMER. Oh, no.

FALL. What do we do now?

SPRING. Perhaps this wasn't such a good idea.

WINTER. Didn't I tell you?

PHAETON. What's everybody so upset about?

HELIOS. Son, you don't know what you're asking.

PHAETON. Sure, I do. This is the perfect way to prove to the world who I really am.

HELIOS. No one can drive that chariot except me.

PHAETON. And your son.

HELIOS. No. Even Zeus can't drive it.

PHAETON. If I'm your son, I can do things Zeus can't do. What's the matter with all of you? You wanted drama, you wanted "oomph." Well, here it is! Imagine the headlines! "Sun God Passes the Reins to His Son for a Day."

It's perfect. It's sensational. You can't buy publicity like this.

HELIOS. Phaeton, I can't back out of my oath. But you can change your request.

PHAETON. Why would I want to do that?

HELIOS. Because you can't do this. It's much too dangerous.

PHAETON. It's not like I've never driven a chariot before. Did I happen to mention all the races I've won?

HELIOS. Listen to me. The ascent into the sky is so steep, my horses can barely climb it. And the height! It's frightening! Even I don't dare look down. And what do you think you'll find up there? Cities of gold? Beautiful forests? Angels, maybe? You'll find monsters waiting to kill you, and it sometimes takes more than a crack of a whip to scare them off. Then there's the descent—

PHAETON. You can't change my mind.

HELIOS. Phaeton, I beg you—

PHAETON. Don't beg. The father I've always dreamed of would never beg.

(Pause)

HELIOS *(resignedly).* Very well, then. Let's get on with it.

(The characters onstage freeze. URANIA *steps forward.)*

URANIA. Well, there you have it. A solemn oath and a rash request. I don't suppose I'm giving away too much of my story to say that disaster is about to strike.

(PHAETON, HELIOS, and the SEASONS *exit.)*

URANIA. Human relationships are messy and confusing—especially between parents and children. Imagine that every little problem in your family affected the whole cosmos and every living thing in it. Well, that's how things used to be. The forces of the universe were all-too-human. What's human can go very wrong.

(A NEWSCASTER *comes onto the stage and freezes.)*

URANIA. And when things go wrong, you can always count on the media to swing into action.

(The NEWSCASTER *comes to life.)*

NEWSCASTER. As the whole world knows, there's been no sunrise today. The stars have disappeared, plunging the planet into darkness. Worldwide panic is setting in. The doors to the Sun Palace are shut tight, even to reporters. Unconfirmed rumors are rampant. What is the truth? What's gone wrong? Will the sun ever rise? I'm here in India to find out.

(TIME enters, holding a sheet of paper. She is surrounded by FOUR REPORTERS.*)*

NEWSCASTER. Here's somebody from the palace. Perhaps she can tell us what's going on.

(The REPORTERS *all speak more or less at once.)*

1ST REPORTER. Could you tell us, please—?

2ND REPORTER. Do you have anything to say about—?

3RD REPORTER. What is the meaning of—?

4TH REPORTER. Will the Sun ever—?

TIME *(to the reporters, sternly).* Quiet, please. *(Reading)* "Sunrise has been rescheduled for 7:34 A.M., give or take a few seconds. At the present moment, Sun Enterprises will not divulge the reason for this delay. We will make a full statement at sunset, at which time the entire planet will be satisfied with our explanation. But be assured that the situation is well in hand. The world is in no danger from permanent darkness or any other threat." *(Folding up her paper)* That concludes my statement.

1ST REPORTER. Would you like to quell theories that Helios is too ill to fly?

TIME. No comment.

2ND REPORTER. Is Helios actually on strike for Olympian status among the gods?

TIME. No comment.

3RD REPORTER. Is is true that the gods intend to freeze the human race to death?

TIME. No comment.

4TH REPORTER. What about rumors that Helios' son is going to fly the chariot today?

(Pause. TIME is taken aback.)

TIME. Totally unsubstantiated.

(The REPORTERS speak at once again.)

1ST REPORTER. But surely you can explain—

2ND REPORTER. What is the meaning of—?

3RD REPORTER. Why do you refuse—?

4TH REPORTER. What can we expect—?

TIME *(silencing them again).* I said there would be no questions. That's all for now. Thank you for your attention.

(TIME exits, followed by the four grumbling REPORTERS. The NEWSCASTER remains onstage.)

NEWSCASTER. And there you have it—a statement marked by evasion and half-truth. It all smacks of a cosmic cover-up. Why this delay? Will the sun really go up at 7:34 A.M., or will there be no daylight ever again? If the sun does rise, should we reset our clocks? If it doesn't, is all life on the planet threatened with extinction? We will get back to you with every new development in this breaking story. *(With a flashy, professional smile)* And now, back to our regularly scheduled program.

(The NEWSCASTER exits. URANIA steps forward.)

URANIA. The ancient Greeks had a word for excessive pride. They called it "hubris." When good, moral, well-meaning people are flawed by hubris, it often leads to tragedy.

(PHAETON and HELIOS enter. They place a small stool near the center of the stage, then freeze.)

URANIA. Now, I'm sure we all agree that Phaeton is a fine young man—capable, considerate, and honest. I'm sure we also agree that he's way too full of himself for his own good—that he suffers from a bad case of hubris. Which side of his family do you suppose he got it from?

(PHAETON *and* HELIOS *come to life, both standing to the right of the stool, which they pretend is Helios' chariot.* PHAETON *is upbeat and eager, examining the chariot closely.* HELIOS, *carrying his headgear at his side, is gloomy and depressed.)*

PHAETON. This chariot's a beauty. I've never seen anything like it. What are these jewels along the railing? Real diamonds?

HELIOS. Diamonds and chrysolites.

PHAETON. I had no idea. You can't see this stuff from the ground. And all this gold and silver leaf on the wheels and undercarriage—

HELIOS. It's not leaf. The rims, spokes, and axles are solid gold and silver. They're tempered by the god of the forge to make them as hard as any steel.

PHAETON. Incredible! *(He walks toward the front of the stool.)* And these horses! Magnificent—and huge! Their coats even match the gold on the chariot. What are they, some kind of palominos? *(To one of the horses)* Hey, big fellow, don't be shy.

HELIOS. Stay away from them.

PHAETON. Why? Shouldn't I give them a carrot or some sugar? I'd better make friends with them.

HELIOS. Those creatures are no friends of humankind—or of gods, either. Take a look at their nostrils.

PHAETON. They're breathing smoke!

HELIOS. Yes, and they breathe fire when they break into a gallop. They've got furnaces inside their bellies and lungs.

PHAETON. Like dragons!

HELIOS. Indeed, more like dragons than horses—strong, fast, and bad-tempered. Hold the reins tightly, or they'll turn against you. And whatever you do, don't use the whip on them. Save that for the other monsters in the sky.

PHAETON. How do I control them?

HELIOS. Their names. Say them often, and perhaps they won't run mad on you. *(Pointing to each of the horses)* Quasar, Pulsar, Nova, and Nebula.

PHAETON. Got it.

HELIOS. Repeat them.

PHAETON. I said I've got it.

HELIOS *(insistently).* Repeat them.

PHAETON. Quasar, Pulsar, Nova, and Nebula, all right? When I say I've got something, I've really got it. Have a little confidence in your son.

HELIOS. There's a path of wheel tracks left by the chariot. Stay close to them. Don't swerve to the right or left. Don't go too near the sky, or too near the ground. Otherwise, you'll set heaven and earth on fire.

PHAETON. We've been over this already.

HELIOS. Take it slow; don't rush.

PHAETON. Father, I know what to do.

HELIOS *(rubbing his son's face with his hand).* You'd better use some of this ointment.

PHAETON AND THE SUN CHARIOT

PHAETON. Why?

HELIOS. To keep your flesh from burning to a crisp when you wear my helmet.

(HELIOS *reluctantly hands* PHAETON *his headgear.* PHAETON *puts it on. The two of them gaze at each other in silence for a moment.*)

HELIOS. Son, I can give you any treasure on the planet, any precious thing you can think of, all the wealth you can imagine—

PHAETON. This is what I want.

HELIOS. Remember one thing. It isn't just your own life you're risking. You're taking the safety of the universe in your hands. How does it feel to do that?

PHAETON. It feels right.

HELIOS. You're not frightened?

PHAETON. No.

HELIOS. Then you're not a god. You're a fool.

(HELIOS *and* PHAETON *freeze.* URANIA *steps forward.*)

URANIA. It's time for Dawn to set the scene for sunrise. She goes out into the world and chases away the last shadows of night. Then her paint-drenched fingers splash lovely brindle patterns across the eastern sky. You know the colors—yellow, orange, and flaming rose, all pretty and pastel. A worried world begins to breathe more easily.

(HELIOS *exits.* PHAETON *places one foot on the stool. He holds imaginary reins in one hand, an imaginary whip in the other, posing as if driving a chariot. Then he freezes again.*)

URANIA. Then the sea goddess Tethys opens the doors to the Sun Palace, and our hero takes to the sky-road. The climb is steep and sheer, and Phaeton is impatient. Right away, he disobeys his father's orders. He uses his whip.

(PHAETON *comes to life, cracking his imaginary whip.*)

PHAETON (*to the horses*). Faster, you lead-footed mules! What do you think this is, some small-town parade? No staid old god is driving you today. I'm young, and for the first time in my life, I'm free! You've got bridles on, not me! I want the whole world to know who I am. So let's make the axle-sparks fly!

(PHAETON *freezes.*)

URANIA. Not wise. For you see, the first thing the horses notice is the lightness of their load. Phaeton is thin and gangling and lacks his father's heft. The steep climb into the sky, normally so difficult for the horses, is much too easy. Even without the whip, they'd be likely to run away with Phaeton. With the whip . . . well, now they're positively furious.

(PHAETON *lurches about, tugging desperately at the reins.*)

PHAETON. Whoa, not *that* fast! Hey, the four of you stay together! Quasar, don't rush out ahead! Pulsar, stick to the track! Nova, don't veer to the right! Nebula, keep up with the others!

(PHAETON *freezes again.*)

URANIA. Oh, he remembers the horse's names. Alas, he no longer knows which one is which! He's lost all control. And the world below is starting to take notice.

(*The* NEWSCASTER *comes onto the stage.*)

NEWSCASTER. We interrupt this program to bring you an urgent announcement. Our astronomical bureau reports that the morning sun is seriously off course. While there is not immediate danger to the earth or heavens, the Sun Chariot has strayed into dangerous territory. It is likely to be attacked by sky monsters.

(*The* NEWSCASTER *exits.* LEO *and* TAURUS *enter and freeze at opposite sides of the stage.*)

URANIA. Look up into the daytime sky and you won't see a single star, at least not from the ground. But that doesn't mean they're not there. Up where our hero is, he can see the starry monsters that live in the sky only too well. But he can't stop his horses from charging right toward Leo the lion and Taurus the bull.

(PHAETON *pantomimes pulling at the reins.* LEO *and* TAURUS *move toward him threateningly.*)

PHAETON (*to his horses*). You crazy beasts! Do you want to get us all killed? Can't you see those monsters coming toward us?

LEO (*crouched, with a rumbling growl*). Aha!

The Sun Chariot has a new driver! And this one doesn't look as cunning with his whip or his steeds as the other one! He'll make a tasty hot lunch for me!

TAURUS (*stomping and snorting*). Not so fast, sky-cat. This one's mine.

LEO. Yours, you bovine bundle of fireflies? What do you want with him?

TAURUS. Why, to impale him upon my horns, of course.

LEO. But you're no flesh-eater.

TAURUS. It's a matter of sport, that's all. Now kindly stand aside.

LEO. Wait a minute. Perhaps we can both get something out of this. Some sport for you, some meat for me.

TAURUS. I kill him, you eat him?

LEO. Exactly!

TAURUS. Splendid idea! Allow me to turn him into a nice, fresh corpse!

(TAURUS, LEO, *and* PHAETON *all freeze.* URANIA *steps forward.*)

URANIA. But Taurus and Leo have dallied too long, and the horses have carried the chariot beyond their reach. This doesn't mean that Phaeton is free and clear, however. Oh, far, far from it.

(TAURUS *and* LEO *exit.*)

URANIA. Our hero now sees a dire threat indeed—not just to himself, but to all earthly life.

(PHAETON *unfreezes, pantomiming the reins again.*)

PHAETON (*desperately, to the horses*). No! Not down! Not toward the earth! We'll set the world on fire! Up! Up, please, I beg you! Back to the sky-path!

(CANCER *enters at one side of the stage, waving imaginary claws.*)

URANIA. Now another sky monster appears. In his current straits, Phaeton finds even a monster a welcome sight.

PHAETON (*calling out to* CANCER). Cancer! The crab! You can help me!

CANCER. I?

PHAETON. Cut the horses' traces with your claws! Set them loose from the chariot! It's my only hope!

CANCER. But you're not the god who usually drives this chariot. Who are you to ask for such a favor?

PHAETON. I'm Phaeton—the son of Helios, the Sun god.

CANCER. But not the Sun himself?

PHAETON. It doesn't matter who I am!

CANCER (*haughtily*). I'm not accustomed to taking orders from the gods themselves, much less from an underling. Besides, if I cut loose your horses, they might come after me. And with their flaming breath, they could cook me alive! I'm afraid you're on your own.

(CANCER *turns away and exits.*)

PHAETON. Wait! Don't go! Can't you see what will happen if I strike the earth? Have pity!

URANIA. Monsters seldom do what we want them to. Sometimes they even have a way of not being monstrous enough.

(SCORPIO *enters on the opposite side of the stage, also waving imaginary claws.*)

URANIA. This next beast, for example— a massive scorpion with a deadly, poisonous tail.

PHAETON (*calling out again*). You! Scorpio! You've got claws, too! Cut my horses' traces.

SCORPIO (*with vanity*). What, and risk breaking a claw? Oh, I hardly think so.

PHAETON. Then use your tail to kill my horses!

SCORPIO. But what have these poor beasts done to offend me?

PHAETON. Don't act like you've got a heart. You don't, and the whole world knows it. You yearn to kill every creature you meet.

SCORPIO (*with a cruel chuckle*). Yes, you're absolutely right. But consider this. I'll kill many, many more creatures than I ever dreamed of, just by letting your horses live and run amok. In fact, I'll preside over the end of all life everywhere! That's a spectacle I don't want to miss.

PHAETON. Then kill me.

SCORPIO (*surprised*). What?

PHAETON. You heard what I said. I don't want to live and see what happens next. Sting me with your tail. End it for me.

SCORPIO. It's tempting . . . but no. I believe I'll let you die in torment. It'll be much more fun.

(SCORPIO *turns away and exits.*)

PHAETON. Somebody, please listen! Please help! Where are you, Father? I was a fool, I know that now. I should never have asked to drive this chariot. You can punish me however you see fit. But won't you show the world some mercy?

(PHAETON *turns away, standing with his back to the audience.*)

URANIA. Do the gods hear Phaeton's call for help? If so, they show no sign of it—not yet, anyway. And just as Phaeton feared, his chariot plummets earthward, destroying everything in sight.

(*The* NEWSCASTER *enters.*)

NEWSCASTER (*with emotion*). It's every journalist's nightmare—to report the end of the world. How many people still live to hear my words? I have no idea. Everywhere I look, I see fire. The Sun Chariot has skidded across the mountaintops, causing them to explode like volcanoes, raining ash and lava everywhere. Now the chariot ravages the valleys, turning all farmland to glowing coals. Rivers all over the world are boiled dry. The lakes, seas, and oceans vanish in titanic clouds of steam, leaving cooked fish lying everywhere. And the towns— oh, the humanity! One by one, the greatest cities in all civilization are instantly vaporized. Hundreds of millions of people perish by the very second. And now . . . the inevitable has come! I see the blazing chariot hurtling toward me, drawn by its insane steeds! The light is blinding, the heat unendurable! In just another second . . .

(*The* NEWSCASTER *freezes.*)

URANIA. No mortal voice can be heard now. They're all drowned out by the roaring flames. The creatures who remain alive huddle helplessly in nooks, caves, and ditches—any refuge they can find from the deadly fire, smoke, and heat.

(*The* NEWSCASTER *exits.* MOTHER EARTH *enters and freezes.*)

URANIA. But another voice rises up to the heavens. No mortal can hear it, but the gods in Olympus can. It is the voice of Mother Earth herself.

(URANIA *steps to one side.* MOTHER EARTH *unfreezes and speaks with pain and fury, facing straight ahead.*)

MOTHER EARTH. Zeus, ruler of all the universe, what is the meaning of this madness? What have I done to deserve this punishment by fire? Have I insulted you? If so, I demand to know how! Long have I endured the presence of these two-legged creatures you have loosed upon me, long have I suffered their endless wounds and insults. They've cut my flesh with plows, disemboweled my mountains, poisoned the air and water that surround me. And yet, as you commanded, I give them life and nurture them. And this is your thanks—to turn one of these miserable animals loose in the Sun

Chariot. My hair, my skin, my sinews, and my very bones are burning to a cinder. Do you wish my death? Kill me, then! Do it yourself; don't parcel out the job to some incompetent fool. And do it quickly! Do it now!

(MOTHER EARTH *freezes.* URANIA *comes forward.*)

URANIA. Now this is a voice the gods cannot ignore. And as you can well imagine, Olympus is already in great turmoil because of what's happening below.

(MOTHER EARTH *exits.* ZEUS, HERA, *and* HELIOS *enter and freeze.*)

URANIA. Helios has been called onto the carpet by Zeus and Hera, the king and queen of the gods.

(ZEUS, HERA, *and* HELIOS *come to life. For a few moments,* HERA *stands to one side and observes the other two gods disdainfully.*)

ZEUS. What do you have to say for yourself, Sun god?

HELIOS. Nothing . . . except that I'm sorry.

ZEUS. You're sorry? You've passed the most destructive power in the universe into half-mortal hands, and you say you're sorry?

HELIOS. I swore an oath by the river Styx. You made the same mistake with Semele.

ZEUS. Semele! How dare you throw Semele in my face at a time like this! The two situations have nothing in common. That poor girl asked only

to look me in the face, not to wreak universal destruction!

HELIOS. That's not what my son intended.

ZEUS. It's certainly what he's doing.

HERA. You men! Always arguing when decisions must be made and action must be taken. The Sun Chariot is rising back up into the sky, setting the heavens on fire. We'll all be broiled alive while the two of you bicker away like children.

ZEUS. If you're so much wiser, dear, perhaps you can suggest a plan of action.

HERA. Indeed, I can. Kill the boy, and be quick about it.

HELIOS. What!

HERA. You heard what I said. It will be no great loss. His very existence was a mistake to begin with.

HELIOS. You're inhuman.

HERA. Exactly. And so are you. And so is my husband. We're gods, remember? And if you ask me, we spend entirely too much time concerning ourselves with human business. Particularly you men, who find mortal women so awfully attractive. Well, this is what it leads to. I hope you've both learned a lesson.

ZEUS. No lectures, Hera, please.

HELIOS. And no more talk of killing my son.

HERA. Oh, I'm so sorry. I had no idea that the little fool's life was of such value. By all means, let him live, and let the rest of the human race perish! Let poor Mother Earth die—and us gods, as well! Let Phaeton be the sole survivor of his own folly! It's only just.

ZEUS (*to* HELIOS). What choice do I have? I can spare your son, or spare the universe. Which do you seriously expect me to do?

HELIOS (*to* ZEUS). You have half-mortal children, too. Think of Dionysus. Think of Heracles. Could you bring yourself to kill either of them, for any reason?

ZEUS. I'd never have given them my thunderbolt, as you've given Phaeton your chariot. I always let my boys make it on their own.

HELIOS. There must be some other way.

ZEUS. Then kindly tell me what it is.

(PHAETON *turns around, pantomiming the reins again.*)

PHAETON (*desperately*). Father, where are you? Can't you hear me?

HERA (*turning toward* PHAETON). Listen. He's calling out again.

(ZEUS *and* HELIOS *turn toward* PHAETON *and listen, too.*)

PHAETON (*in agony*). The chariot's a raging furnace! Sparks are flying everywhere, blistering and burning me all over! My hair is on fire! Do something! Save me!

ZEUS (*to* HELIOS). He's calling to his father for help. What do you intend to do for him?

HELIOS (*to* ZEUS). Have pity! Spare him!

HERA. So that's how it is. Zeus could kill him in a painless instant, but you'd rather he died slowly from the smoke and flames. And you call it pity! A fine father you are.

HELIOS (*bitterly*). A fine father, indeed.

PHAETON. My eyes are full of soot and ashes. I can't see! The air scorches my lungs. And the smoke . . . (*Coughing*) I can't breathe! Zeus, Father of the Gods—

HERA. That's you, darling.

PHAETON. —end it for me. Slay me with your thunderbolt.

ZEUS (*to* HELIOS). Should I deny him his wish?

HELIOS (*quietly*). No. Do as he says.

(ZEUS *raises his arm, as if aiming a javelin at* PHAETON.)

PHAETON. Father, if you can hear me, please forgive me!

HELIOS. Forgive *me*, son.

(ZEUS *hurls his imaginary javelin.* ZEUS, HERA, *and* HELIOS *freeze.* PHAETON *slowly crumples to the ground as* URANIA *speaks.*)

URANIA. Phaeton tumbles from the chariot, and the horses break loose from their traces. They dash madly in all directions until they finally plunge into the sea. Its axle broken, the Sun Chariot lurches and careens about, then smashes into fiery pieces.

(ZEUS, HERA, *and* HELIOS *exit.*)

URANIA. At last, Phaeton tumbles into the river Eridanus—one of the few watery places left in the world. The river gently washes him, then places him on its banks where his father and mother can find him.

(HELIOS *and* CLYMENE *come to life.*)

CLYMENE. Here he is. Here's our boy. *(Touching* PHAETON*)* Oh, poor Phaeton. So badly burned! Come home with me. Let me bandage your wounds, soothe them with a healing balm. I'll take care of you. Soon, you will be well again.

HELIOS. He's not coming home, Clymene.

CLYMENE. You're a god. You can make him live.

HELIOS. I can't.

CLYMENE. Why not? You told him how powerful you were. You promised him whatever his heart desired. And now you say you can't give him life again!

HELIOS. What the Fates decide even the gods cannot change.

CLYMENE. Is that another *rule* you gods live by? Like not breaking an oath by the river Styx?

HELIOS. I had to keep that oath.

CLYMENE. Was it better to kill your son? Couldn't you stop being a god for just a moment and be a father?

HELIOS. I couldn't. No.

CLYMENE. You're powerless, then. You can fill the daytime sky with radiant light, nourish the earth with comforting warmth, perform miracles past reckoning. But even so, you're

powerless. I wouldn't be a god—not for anything in the world. We mortals have more choices.

HELIOS. Clymene, come home with me. Let's try again. We still have daughters. We can be a family again.

CLYMENE. Oh, Helios, Helios, haven't you heard? When our daughters learned that their brother was dead, they wept and wept and wept. They would have wept until the end of time, but some magical being showed them mercy, hushed them by turning them into poplar trees.

HELIOS. Perhaps I can bring *them* back.

CLYMENE. Why? So they can weep again? They're no longer in pain. Their tears have hardened into amber. I wish I were so blessed. Come. I'll show you where they're standing. They're not far from here.

(CLYMENE *takes* HELIOS *by the hand. They freeze.*)

URANIA. The next day doesn't come. Helios refuses to drive across the sky—swears never to fly again. All creation grows cold and dark. Helios' horses return to their stable, and the god of the forge makes a new Sun Chariot, but no other deity can drive it. One by one, the gods of Olympus beg Helios to end the perpetual night. At last, Helios relents and brings back the day. It's not easy for a god to change his nature.

(CLYMENE *and* HELIOS *exit.* CHARON *enters and freezes.*)

URANIA. But my story isn't quite over. You see, there is a world apart from our own world—a world which was unscathed by Phaeton's chariot, which scarcely noticed the blazing destruction. Phaeton is about to receive a visitor from this world.

(CHARON *comes to life. He speaks to* PHAETON.)

CHARON. Wake up, young fella. It's time for us to get moving.

PHAETON (*looking up at* CHARON). Who are you?

CHARON. Well, now—considering that you're freshly dead and all, who do you guess I am?

PHAETON. Charon, the ferryman of the river Styx.

CHARON. At your service.

PHAETON. And you've come to take me to the world of the dead.

CHARON. Yep.

PHAETON. Can't I go tell my mother where I'm going?

CHARON. Oh, I reckon she's figured that out by now. Besides, she'll be along herself before she knows it. Life's a lot shorter than folks realize. Let's get going, now. Mustn't waste eternity.

PHAETON. Wait a minute. What's death like?

CHARON. Well, that depends on a person's taste. For some, it's dankness and gloom and sorrow all the time. For others, it's green fields and pastures. What do you *want* it to be like?

PHAETON (*with a smile*). An adventure.

CHARON. Then that's what it'll be, son.

PHAETON. Do you promise?

CHARON (*smiling*). Sure, I promise. I promise by the river Styx.

(PHAETON *and* CHARON *begin to laugh, then freeze.*)

URANIA. Phaeton's spirit follows after Charon, but his bones and ashes remain beside the river Eridanus, where they rest to this very day. And there my story ends.

(PHAETON *and* CHARON *exit.*)

URANIA. But I can tell by your faces that you don't believe what I've told you—not much of it, anyway. Well, don't take my word for it. Go to the river Eridanus yourself and find the stone that marks Phaeton's grave. It bears an inscription that reads . . . (*Stopping and smiling*) No. I believe I'll let you read it for yourself. And when you're there, say hello to Phaeton's sisters—four small, slender trees growing near the grave. They stopped weeping ages ago, but they still get lonely for visitors. Tell them I sent you. Good-bye . . . and travel safely.

(URANIA *exits.*)

PLAYWRIGHT'S POSTSCRIPT

Some myths and legends have as much to say today as they did to the people who first heard them. The story of Phaeton seems startlingly contemporary. For example, the story partly deals with what it's like to grow up in a broken family. People today can surely understand this situation as well as people of ancient Greece and Rome—perhaps even better.

So I've tried to give this play a contemporary feeling, making the characters seem almost like people you might know. In Ovid's version, Phaeton's mother, Clymene, is a nymph and the wife of a king. Since there are different earlier traditions concerning Phaeton's parentage, I've felt free to portray her as an ordinary mortal—what we'd call today a single mother.

Today we are also more worried than ever about dangerous forces falling into the wrong hands. Nuclear power and weaponry are examples. Environmentalists question the safety of nuclear power plants, and we all worry about what will happen if terrorists get control of nuclear weapons. Again, I've hinted at such contemporary anxieties in my version of this story.

CONNECTING TO OTHER CULTURES

Cultures all over the world regard the sun with awe, respect, and sometimes fear. In a Native American story, the trickster Old Man tries to wear the fiery leggings of the Sun, only to burn himself very badly.

DEMETER AND PERSEPHONE

SETTING THE STAGE

Ancient peoples were deeply concerned with the cycles of nature. After all, their lives depended on understanding the seasons. They especially needed to know exactly when to plant and harvest crops. Like everything else in the universe, the seasons were thought to be caused by gods and goddesses.

The cycles of nature suggested something quite terrifying about how the universe worked—that the gods themselves sometimes suffered and even died, just like mortals. For example, the Greeks believed that Dionysus, the god of the vine, had been slain, torn to pieces, and then resurrected, much as the vine itself died and returned to life once every year.

The most famous story of nature's cycles is that of the earth goddess, Demeter, and her daughter, Persephone. It comes down to us in two important versions. One is the Homeric "Hymn to Demeter," a Greek poem written around the 8th or 7th century B.C. The other is a passage from *Metamorphoses*, an epic poem written by the Roman poet Ovid in the 1st century A.D.

The story of Demeter and her daughter is one of great sorrow and suffering, so it is introduced here by Melpomene, the Muse of tragedy. But Melpomene understands that great tragedy is life-affirming, not dour and dreary. She would agree with the 19th-century German philosopher Friedrich Nietzsche, who wrote that tragedy teaches us that "life is at bottom indestructibly powerful and joyful . . . "

MUSING ABOUT THE MYTH

The natural world has been a challenge to scientists and philosophers throughout the ages. As you read, note how mythology explains the way seasons and other aspects of nature came about.

DEMETER AND PERSEPHONE

CHARACTERS:

MELPOMENE (mel pom′ e nē), the Muse of tragedy

HADES (hā′ dēz), the ruler of the Underworld

KORE (kō′ rē), a young goddess, later known as PERSEPHONE (per sef′ ō nē)

APHRODITE (ăf ro dī′ tē), the goddess of love and beauty

EROS (er′ ōs), the god of love, Aphrodite's son

DEMETER (de mē′ ter), the goddess of the earth and agriculture

KORE'S COMPANIONS:
LIGEIA (li jā′ a)
MOLPE (mōl′ pē)
TELES (tel′ us)

VOICE OF TYPHON (ti′ fon), a monster

HECATE (hek′ a tē), a goddess of magic and sorcery

HELIOS (hē′ lē ōs), the Sun god

FOUR PASSERSBY

CALLIDICE (ka lid′ i sē), a young girl

HERMES (hur′ mēz), the messenger god

OTHER NAMES MENTIONED IN THE PLAY:

APOLLO (a pol′ ō), the god of light and wisdom

ARES (a′ rēs), the god of war

ARTEMIS (ar′ te mis), the goddess of the hunt and the moon

ATHENA (a thē′ na), the goddess of war and wisdom

CELEUS (sē′ le us), the ruler of Eleusis, Callidice's father

ELEUSIS (e lū′ sis), a town in Greece

HEPHAESTUS (he fes′ tus), the god of the forge

HERA (hir′ a), the queen of the Olympian gods

HESTIA (hes′ ti a), the goddess of the hearth

IRIS (ī′ ris), the messenger goddess

METANEIRA (met a nī′ ra), Celeus' wife and Callidice's mother

MOTHER EARTH

POSEIDON (pō sī′ don), the ruler of the sea

ZEUS (züs), the king of the Olympian gods

SETTING: *Sicily, Greece, and the Underworld*

TIME: *No time in particular*

(Upstage center is a low wall shaped in a semicircle, projecting toward the audience. It is about four feet across. During the play, it will represent different objects and locations—the front of a chariot, the crater of a volcano, a caldron, a desk, and a spring. A number of props are concealed behind it. Otherwise, the stage is completely bare. The stage is dimly lit as MELPOMENE enters.)

MELPOMENE. My name's Melpomene, and I'm the Muse of tragedy. That's right, our play is going to be a tragedy. I'm sure you'd prefer something light and frothy, but kindly keep your grumbling to a minimum.

You probably expect a lot of death and destruction, doom and gloom, Greek choruses tearing their clothes and pulling their hair, yelling "Aiiieee!" or "Alas!" or "Woe is me!" or something equally heartrending. Oh, and a king who puts his own eyes out, maybe. Or some beautiful sorceress who murders her own children. And a whole lot of depressing talk about destiny and fate and such—how things are bad all over, and how it's going to get worse before it gets any better.

Is our play going to be like that? I don't know. I never know until a play gets underway. The creative process is very unpredictable. So sit tight, grit your teeth, and prepare for whatever.

Excuse me if I sound defensive. It's just that people keep asking me, "Why can't we just have action-adventure or romantic comedy all the time? What use is tragedy, anyway?"

Well, a certain philosopher named Aristotle—I wonder if he's still around?—had a theory about that. He said that tragedy stirs up pity and terror so we can let off steam, get rid of bad feelings that might otherwise make us extremely cranky. Other experts say that a tragedy gives us a useful moral to take home with us, like "Watch your temper" or "Soothsayers are always right" or "Never offer your own daughter as a human sacrifice." *(With a shrug)* Maybe they're right; maybe they're wrong. What do I know? I'm not a philosopher, just a simple teller of stories. So let's get on with this one. To begin, I'll take you to a meadow in Sicily, an island off the southern coast of Italy.

(The lights warm and brighten.)

MELPOMENE. A lovely spring day, isn't it? A warm afternoon sun. A cool, gentle breeze. Blooming, colorful flowers. It's always spring here.

(HADES enters and steps behind the wall. He freezes in a pose of driving a chariot.)

MELPOMENE. This imposing gentleman is Hades, Lord of the Dead, Ruler of the Underworld. He's hurtling across Sicily in his golden chariot, snapping the iron-colored reins of his deathless black stallions, calling out their names in fierce command.

(HADES comes to life, calling to his horses.)

HADES. Faster, Vortex! You, too, Darkstar! I want to cover every hill, river, and valley on this island before nightfall! *(He freezes again.)*

MELPOMENE. And why, you ask, is this monarch of gloom driving through a sunlit meadow, far above his kingdom? Well, Sicily has a lot of seismic activity, which is to say that earthquakes are common. The earth itself is liable to burst wide open at any moment. And Hades doesn't want even the tiniest ray of sunlight spilling into the world of the dead. So he often patrols this island, looking for faults, cracks, fissures, and tectonic trouble spots.

(KORE *enters, carrying a basket and wearing a colorful sash. She freezes directly in front of* HADES *and the chariot, posing as if picking a flower.*)

MELPOMENE. Now, if tragedy teaches us anything, it's to watch out for moving vehicles. But this pretty young woman doesn't seem to have watched enough plays like this one. Otherwise, she'd have learned that lesson.

(KORE *comes to life, speaking to a flower on the ground.*)

KORE. How sad you look, drooping lily! Wouldn't you be happier up in my basket? Come on, then. *(She pantomimes picking the flower, then freezes again.)*

MELPOMENE. She's wandered away from her companions, so she's vulnerable, alone. Which reminds me—tragedy *also* teaches young people never to talk to strangers.

(MELPOMENE *steps aside to watch.* HADES *and* KORE *come to life.* HADES *pulls wildly on his reins.*)

HADES (*to his horses*). Whoa, halt, both of you! Darkstar, don't rear up like that, you'll topple us all! Easy, Vortex, easy!

KORE. You should get better control of your horses.

HADES. Better control of my—? Confound it, girl, what are you doing in the middle of my path? Why didn't you get out of the way?

KORE. I didn't notice you coming.

HADES. Didn't *notice?* You didn't hear the stomping of hooves, the screeching of the axle, the grinding of wheels? You should have felt my horses' hot breath a mile away or more—and the shaking of the ground, too.

KORE. My mind was on other things. *(To another flower)* Hello there, pretty daffodil. Do you mind if I pick you today? Oh, that's very kind of you. *(She picks the flower and puts it in her basket.)*

HADES. You could have been killed.

KORE. I doubt that.

HADES. Why?

KORE. I'm a goddess—Kore, daughter of Demeter.

HADES. Oh, yes. Haven't seen you since you were a baby. As it happens, we're related. I'm—

KORE. Hades, ruler of the Underworld. Yes, I guessed that. *(To some more flowers)* Oh, what a charming cluster of pansies! Would you all like to come with me? Thank you ever so much. *(She picks the flowers.)*

HADES. And now—get out of my way.

KORE. No, I don't think so.

HADES. Why not?

KORE. This meadow is full of crocuses, irises, hyacinths, lilies—every kind of flower you can think of. Your horses and chariot were going to cut a swath right through them. Who knows how many you would have destroyed? *(To some more flowers)* Sorry to disturb you, daisies, but you're being threatened by the god of death. Do you mind if I get you out of harm's way? Yes, I think that's wise. *(Picking the daisies, she speaks to* HADES *again.)* Why, Vortex and Darkstar might have crushed that rosebush over there without even feeling its thorns.

HADES. It can't be helped.

KORE. Oh, yes, it can. You can just go around the meadow.

HADES. And what if I don't find that convenient?

KORE. Perhaps you'd find it convenient to run me down.

HADES. Do you want me to tell your mother you're being a nuisance?

KORE. Do you want me to tell her you're being a bully?

*(*APHRODITE *and* EROS *enter.* EROS *carries a bow and wears a quiver on his back. They look on, unseen by* HADES *and* KORE.*)*

HADES. Let me remind you that I rule one-third of the universe.

KORE. Not *this* third.

HADES. Insolent girl!

KORE. Cruel man!

*(*HADES *and* KORE *fall silent, pantomiming their argument as* MELPOMENE *speaks.)*

MELPOMENE. They haven't noticed that they've got visitors—and no ordinary visitors. Aphrodite, the goddess of love, is watching and listening. So is her son, Eros—sometimes known as Cupid. He's got his bow and arrows handy, which means that someone is about to fall in love. And when someone falls in love, that means

trouble. And when there's trouble—need I even say it?—there's also tragedy.

APHRODITE. Bicker, bicker, bicker! It's sad, isn't it, Eros?

EROS. If you say so, Mother.

APHRODITE. Of course I say so! Why, here we have two healthy, attractive deities, both single, and all they can do is argue! It's such a waste! Let's do something about it.

EROS. Do you think that's wise, Mother?

APHRODITE. We're deities of love, dear. We're not supposed to be wise.

EROS. But shooting my arrows at mere mortals is one thing. Shooting them at gods and goddesses is another.

APHRODITE. Don't tell me you're scared of bigger game.

EROS. When deities fall in love, the consequences can be somewhat—well, cosmic.

APHRODITE. All the more reason to make it happen. We need to throw our weight around from time to time. We don't get the proper respect. Why, did you hear what Hades just said? *(Mocking* HADES' *voice and manner)* "Let me remind you that I rule one-third of the universe." Such presumption! Hades with his Underworld, Poseidon with his seas, Zeus with his heavens—they think they're kings of all creation!

EROS. They *are* kings of all creation.

APHRODITE. Not at all, not at all. Our kingdom—yours and mine, dear—is greater than all their kingdoms put together. Love reigns over all! And here we have a god and a goddess who know nothing of love. Teach them a lesson, Eros. A well-aimed arrow, that's all it will take.

EROS. If you insist, Mother.

(While HADES *and* KORE *continue their argument aloud,* EROS *takes an imaginary arrow out of his quiver, puts it in his bow, and aims.)*

HADES. Out of my way, I tell you.

KORE. Gladly—when I finish picking these flowers.

HADES. *Now,* I say.

KORE. And I say no!

HADES. You're risking my wrath.

KORE. Sounds like you're plenty angry already.

HADES. You've not even seen my anger yet.

*(*EROS *shoots. Stricken,* HADES *shuts his eyes.)*

KORE. What's the matter? You look like someone punched you.

HADES. Pierced me to the heart, rather.

KORE. I don't understand.

HADES. Neither do I. *(Opens his eyes)* Why, Kore, you're—you're not at all as I saw you before.

KORE. I *have* grown up since you last saw me.

HADES. I mean a *moment* before. You've changed. You're so—so—

KORE. So what?

EROS *(to* APHRODITE*).* Another arrow for Kore, Mother?

APHRODITE. Wait. I want to see how this plays out.

HADES. That luscious red flower in your basket—what is it?

KORE. A rose, of course.

HADES *(holding his hand toward her).* May I have it?

KORE. Certainly not. It's for Mother.

HADES. May I at least hold it for a moment?

KORE. I suppose so. But only if you promise not to trample this meadow.

HADES. I promise.

(Still holding her basket in one hand, KORE *offers the rose to* HADES *with the other. But* HADES *seizes her by the wrist.* KORE *staggers and drops her basket.)*

KORE. What are you doing?

HADES. Come with me. Be my queen.

KORE. I won't!

HADES. You have no choice.

KORE. My companions will come looking for me soon.

HADES. And?

KORE. And they'll tell my mother I'm missing. And—and she'll know who carried me off!

HADES. Why should I care if she knows?

KORE *(calling out).* Ligeia! Molpe! Teles! Mother! Come help me!

*(*HADES, KORE, APHRODITE, *and* EROS *freeze.)*

MELPOMENE. Hades pulls Kore up into his chariot. The earth opens. The deathless black stallions dive headlong into the void. Kore, a child of sunlit fields and flowers, now belongs to sorrow, darkness, and death. I'd call that tragic, wouldn't you?

(HADES *and* KORE *exit.*)

MELPOMENE. A crime has been committed—but whose crime? Is Hades truly guilty? Or should we blame the two onlookers?

(EROS *and* APHRODITE *come to life.*)

EROS. I didn't get a chance to shoot *her.*

APHRODITE. No matter.

EROS. But she doesn't love him.

APHRODITE. She will in time.

(APHRODITE *and* EROS *exit.* MELPOMENE *steps forward. The lights dim a little.*)

MELPOMENE. Now, if tragedy teaches us anything, it's that parents worry themselves sick if their children don't come home when they're expected. The goddess Demeter is no exception, now that evening is approaching. Here she comes now.

(MELPOMENE *steps to one side as* DEMETER *enters, looking around anxiously. She sees the fallen basket.*)

DEMETER. Oh, no! (*Picking up the basket*) What are you doing on the ground, you wicked vessel of cane and wicker? Didn't you promise me never to let go of her hand? What happened? Where did she go? Come now, the truth! And speak up, don't whisper and rustle like that. What, don't you know? I don't believe it! Lying thing! (*Looking at the ground*) Picked flowers—roses, crocuses, violets, hyacinths, clover, poppy blossoms— why do you lie scattered here? Why

did you abandon my daughter? What made you flee? What frightened you so? And where is Kore? Speak up! I can't hear you! (*She freezes.*)

MELPOMENE. "The Gentle Goddess," they call her, because she is so kind to all living things. Oh, the gifts she has brought to humankind! She gave laws so people could live peacefully together. She gave fruit and vegetation and taught people to sow and harvest them. She is the deity of health, birth, and marriage—a happy goddess, tender, loving, life-affirming. She has never been known to lose her temper—not until now.

(DEMETER *comes to life and speaks to the flowers again.*)

DEMETER. What? Won't speak, will you? Won't tell me what you know? Die then—all of you! (*She waves her hand over the flowers. There is a flash of light. Then the stage grows still darker. She rises to her feet and looks around.*) And what of those *other* flowers, the ones with arms and legs—my daughter's companions? They went out with her this morning. Where have they gone? Where are they now? Not far, I think. In fact, I sense their presence nearby! (*Calling out*) Ligeia!

(LIGEIA *enters cautiously.*)

LIGEIA. Here, m'lady.

DEMETER. Molpe!

(MOLPE *enters.*)

MOLPE. Here, m'lady.

DEMETER. Teles!

(TELES *enters.*)

TELES. Here, m'lady.

DEMETER. Hiding from me, were you?

MOLPE. Oh, no!

TELES. Not hiding!

LIGEIA. Not at all!

DEMETER. Where's my daughter?

LIGEIA, MOLPE, and TELES *(together).* We don't know, m'lady.

DEMETER. Don't know! Isn't it your responsibility to always stay near her?

MOLPE. We try.

TELES. Really, we do.

LIGEIA. But she's always wandering away.

DEMETER. When she does, you're to wander with her.

TELES. Yes, m'lady.

LIGEIA. We're sorry, m'lady.

DEMETER. Exactly when did you plan to tell me she was missing?

MOLPE. We'd hoped she *wasn't* really missing.

TELES. We'd hoped to find her.

DEMETER. That's exactly what you'd better do, and quickly—unless you want to wind up dead, like these flowers here.

MOLPE. Oh, don't kill us, please!

TELES. We've searched the meadow high and low.

LIGEIA. And the surrounding foothills, too.

DEMETER. Search all the earth then. And the seas and skies as well.

MOLPE. But how can we?

LIGEIA. We can't fly through the air!

(DEMETER *waves her hand again, and there is another flash of light.*)

DEMETER. Now you can.

(LIGEIA, MOLPE, *and* TELES *flutter around the stage, making bird-like movements.*)

LIGEIA. I have wings!

TELES. I have feathers!

MOLPE. I have talons instead of toes!

TELES. We've become birds!

DEMETER. Except for your heads.

MOLPE. Oh, it's true!

LIGEIA. We still have the faces of girls!

TELES. What awful freaks we are!

LIGEIA. Change us back, m'lady!

MOLPE. Please, change us back!

DEMETER. Gladly—once you've found my daughter and brought her back to me. Fly far and wide, north and south, east and west. Pry into every nook and cranny, every square inch of creation. Leave no stone unturned, no bush or blade of grass uncombed, no grain of sand unsifted, no living thing unasked.

LIGEIA. But what if we cannot find her?

DEMETER. Then stay as you are— forever! My curse upon you if you do not bring her back. May you pass the rest of your days on some desolate island, dreaded and feared. May you sing sailors to their deaths. Sirens, let you be called—"Those Who Wither."

(LIGEIA, MOLPE, *and* TELES *rush about frantically, then exit.* DEMETER *freezes, and*

MELPOMENE *steps forward. As she speaks, she puts the basket behind the wall.)*

MELPOMENE. Not that Demeter intends to leave the search to Kore's friends. She sets out herself as night falls, climbing the steep slope of Mt. Etna—the highest volcano in Europe, more than 10,000 feet tall.

    Before we continue, a word or two about volcanoes. You may have heard that a volcano is caused by the pressure of subterranean steam, hot gases, and molten rock forcing their way through the earth's crust. Pseudoscientific rubbish! In fact, volcanoes are caused by giants who have been buried alive. One such giant, more than a hundred miles long, lies underneath Sicily. His name is Typhon, and he was put there because he rebelled against the gods. The flames from the crater of Mt. Etna are caused by his fearful breath.

(While MELPOMENE *has been speaking,* DEMETER *has come to life and walked beside the wall, which now represents the crater of Mt. Etna. The stage has become quite dark. Red and yellow light glows from behind the wall, suggesting fire and molten lava. As* MELPOMENE *steps aside to watch, the voice of* TYPHON *is heard, perhaps amplified by speakers.)*

TYPHON. Who's there?

DEMETER. Greetings, Typhon, unhappy giant. I am Demeter, goddess of the grain.

TYPHON. Ah, an Olympian. Come to pay me a visit, eh? Do you intend to release me from these depths?

DEMETER. My Lord Zeus put you there. It's not in my power to set you free.

TYPHON. But you'll agree, won't you, that my punishment is most unjust?

DEMETER. It's not my place to question the will of Zeus.

TYPHON. Evasive.

DEMETER. If you wish to call it so.

TYPHON. I do. Be off. You have no business with me, nor I with you.

DEMETER. But Typhon—

TYPHON. Away, I say! Or I'll spew ash, lava, and fire upon you.

DEMETER. Do it then. I don't care. I'll not move from this spot until you help me. My daughter vanished from a meadow. I have no idea where she has gone. I gave wings to her friends to search for her, but I don't expect them to return. My instinct tells me that she's not to be found anywhere upon the earth.

TYPHON. And so—you suspect she's somewhere *beneath* the earth.

DEMETER. Do you know?

TYPHON. Perhaps. Perhaps not. In any case, why should I tell you?

DEMETER. I'm beginning to understand what it is to suffer, now that Kore is missing. So tell me what you know— one suffering soul to another.

*(*KORE*'s sash flutters up from the crater.* DEMETER *seizes it.)*

TYPHON. Something of your daughter's, perhaps?

DEMETER. Her sash! How did you get it?

TYPHON. It found its way to me through the cracks and crevasses of this island. It's just as you feared—she was swallowed by the earth itself.

DEMETER. But where is she now? And who caused this to happen?

TYPHON. I have no idea. But I *do* know one thing—you and I both have a grievance against the earth.

DEMETER. Yes, Mother Earth, whom I have blessed and cherished and nurtured all my days. How she has betrayed me!

TYPHON. Trapped as I am, I can do nothing to revenge myself. But you—free as you are—

DEMETER. Revenge, yes! Let the quenching rain fall no more! Let the sun's light shed no warmth upon the living! Let the flourishing grain wither on the stalk! Let the buried seeds stay buried always and never send forth shoots to peep at the sky! Let the ground grow too hard for the strongest plow to crack! Let the world know famine and misery until I see my daughter again!

TYPHON. Let the earth suffer, as we suffer!

DEMETER. Yes!

TYPHON. Oh, thank you, gentle goddess. Thank you for this fleeting satisfaction in the midst of my misery.

DEMETER (*walking away from the wall*). Farewell, Typhon. May Lord Zeus release you from these depths someday.

(DEMETER *freezes.* MELPOMENE *steps forward.*)

MELPOMENE. So in the twinkling of an eye comes winter—the first winter the world has ever known. Crystalline fingers of frost seize and shake the boughs and branches. Within minutes, leaves yellow and fall. The life-bringing crops bend numbly beneath the northern wind. All things that creep, crawl, or walk hurry for whatever shelter they may find, for fear of death by freezing.

(HECATE *steps beside the wall, which now represents a caldron. She is holding a ladle.*)

MELPOMENE. Has the gentle goddess's heart hardened fully and forever? Will she truly let all earthly life perish? Perhaps—if she never finds her daughter. But still she searches, wandering through the night. And presently, she arrives at a crossroads, where she encounters a deity of magic and sorcery.

(MELPOMENE *steps aside to watch as* HECATE *and* DEMETER *come to life. Steam rises out of the brew in the caldron, which* HECATE *stirs with her ladle.*)

HECATE.
Simmer, simmer, seethe and shimmer;
Heat the pot, ye flames a-glimmer!

DEMETER. Hail, Hecate, goddess of crossroads.

HECATE. Hush! I'm at a particularly ticklish stage in the recipe! (*stirring and tossing in imaginary ingredients*) Now we add a raven's eye,

DEMETER AND PERSEPHONE

Steeped in a farmer's worried sigh;
A wildcat's claw, a weasel's ear,
A starving baby's dying tear;
Vulture's tongue and lizard's tail—
And last, a grieving mother's wail;
I'll leave you for an hour or so
To bubble gently, boil low.
Simmer, simmer, seethe and
  shimmer;
Heat the pot, ye flames a-glimmer!

(She stops stirring.) There, that's all for now. Sorry to keep you waiting, Demeter, dearie. But whatever are you doing out on a cold night like this? We've not had weather like this—well, since *never*, I suppose. You must be chilled to the bone, poor thing! Won't you have a taste of my piping hot brew? It's not quite done, but it's already delicious, if I do say so myself.

DEMETER. No.

HECATE. Are you sure? You look rather peaked.

DEMETER. I'm sure.

HECATE. What can I do for you, then?

DEMETER. My daughter has disappeared.

HECATE. What! Pretty little Kore?

DEMETER. Yes.

HECATE. Whatever happened?

DEMETER. She was picking flowers in a meadow, and the earth opened and took her.

HECATE. Oh, shades of night! Then it was *her* voice I heard!

DEMETER. You heard her?

HECATE. She cried out.

DEMETER. What were her words?

(KORE's voice is heard as HECATE mouths the words.)

HECATE/KORE. "Ligeia! Molpe! Teles! Mother! Come help me!"

DEMETER. Oh, my poor baby! If only I had heard her!

HECATE. And if only I had known it was her! This is dreadful, dearie, truly dreadful. To be swallowed up alive like that, and in the bloom of youth! Why, she must have been frightened out of her wits. If I were you, I'd punish the earth quite sharply. But— what am I saying? You're punishing the earth already, aren't you? Of course, that explains this ghastly weather! Well, good for you. Mother Earth will think twice before pulling such a trick again.

DEMETER. Mother Earth doesn't go swallowing up young maidens for no reason. She must have done it at the bidding of some god.

HECATE. But who?

DEMETER. Oh, Hecate, please help me, I implore you! Help me learn exactly what happened and who is responsible!

HECATE. I'd love to, dearie—really, I would. But what can I do? My magic is powerful, but I'm not exactly omnipotent. I don't see all and know all. But wait! I know someone who very nearly does!

DEMETER. Who?

HECATE. The Sun god!

DEMETER. Helios, of course! He sees everything that happens as he rides his chariot through the sky.

(HECATE *and* DEMETER *freeze as* MELPOMENE *steps forward. As* MELPOMENE *speaks,* HELIOS *enters with a stool and a chart. He sits behind the wall as if it were a desk, spreads the chart before him, and freezes.*)

MELPOMENE. It's night, remember— which means that Helios is not riding above the earth. He's in his office in India, poring over flight plans for tomorrow's journey. Now, India is a very, very long way from Sicily. But if you're a sorceress like Hecate, distances don't matter much. Just a little incantation and—*voilà!*—you're there!

(HECATE *and* DEMETER *come to life as* MELPOMENE *steps aside to watch.* HELIOS *remains frozen.*)

HECATE.
Miles and miles of rough-paved road,
Paths that no one ever strode,
Craggy mountains, barren moors,
Iron gates and office doors—
Vanish all, without a trace!
Evaporate, both time and space!
And let's give Helios a shock,
For I'm not one who likes to knock!

(HECATE *claps her hands. The lights suddenly brighten, and* HELIOS *comes to life.*)

HELIOS. Great heavens! Hecate and Demeter! Where did you two come from? Why, I was so wrapped up in my work, I didn't hear my secretary announce you.

HECATE. She didn't announce us.

HELIOS. Ah, I see. Always making a magical entrance, aren't you, Hecate? You have only to say "abracadabra" or "alakazam" or "presto change-o" or some such hocus-pocus, and you pop up anywhere you like. Always wished I could do that. Well, what brings you ladies to this corner of the cosmos?

HECATE. Demeter has a problem.

HELIOS (*to* DEMETER). Do you, now? I hear you've caused some rather nasty weather. What's that all about, eh? I hope you won't stop my light from shedding warmth upon the earth when I go up tomorrow.

DEMETER. Where's my daughter?

HELIOS. Pardon?

HECATE. You heard what she said.

HELIOS. Oh, yes, your daughter—Kore's her name, isn't it?

DEMETER. She disappeared from a meadow. I know she was carried underground. Who took her and why?

HELIOS. Why are you asking me?

HECATE. Don't insult our intelligence. You see everything from your chariot. You know what happened.

HELIOS. Well, it is true that I miss very little, at least on a clear day. Perhaps I saw something, perhaps I didn't. In either case, I must regretfully say that I'm not at liberty to discuss it.

HECATE. And why on earth not?

HELIOS. Why, ethical considerations, of course. Just because I peer into the private affairs of an entire planet doesn't give me any right to blab about it.

DEMETER. Whom would you hurt by telling me the truth?

HELIOS. As I said, I'm not at liberty—

DEMETER. How can you be so unfeeling? You lost a son once—lost him by a foolish promise.

HELIOS. Don't probe that old wound, I beg you.

DEMETER. You let him drive your chariot, and he lost control of it. He had to be destroyed before he burned earthly creation to ashes. You grieved, and plunged the world into darkness for a time—just as I have plunged the world into coldness. How can you, of all gods, look upon my distress so unfeelingly?

HELIOS. I'm not unfeeling. Really, I'm not. If there's anyone in the universe who can understand your anguish, it's I. But please try to understand, the issues are larger than you can possibly know. It's a matter of—

(HECATE *claps her hands, and* HELIOS *freezes.*)

HECATE.
You who can see everywhere,
Tell us what you wouldn't dare.
Who seized Kore, what do you
  know?
Where is she now, where did she go?
Say what you saw that day in flight;
Yes, tell the truth and tell it right.

(HECATE *claps her hands again.* HELIOS *speaks in a trance.*)

HELIOS. It was Hades.

DEMETER. Hades! The Lord of the Dead!

HELIOS. He was riding through the meadow in his chariot. He seized her by the wrist and carried her off. The earth opened, and they disappeared below.

DEMETER. Is she still with him—down there?

HELIOS. I cannot see into the Underworld. But I've not seen her upon the earth since. So that's where she must be.

HECATE. What else do you know?

HELIOS. Nothing.

HECATE. Well, then . . .
You told the truth and did not err,
So be exactly as you were.

(HECATE *claps her hands again, and* HELIOS *snaps out of his trance, speaking exactly where he left off.*)

HELIOS. —confidentiality, don't you see? I have a duty—a *sworn* duty—to keep quiet about whatever I see. Do try to understand.

DEMETER. Oh, yes. I understand perfectly.

HELIOS. That's good of you, Demeter— truly good of you. And now, I've really got to get back to my flight plans. There's an equinox coming up, and that requires some careful navigation.

HECATE. We'll leave at once.

HELIOS. Oh, Demeter, before you go, I—I believe I can tell you one thing without violating my oath. Your daughter was taken away against her will. She and you have been done a terrible injustice. It can't be helped, so you must bear your loss with resignation. But as one bereaved parent to another, I want to say . . . I'm sorry.

DEMETER. Thank you.

(HELIOS, DEMETER, *and* HECATE *freeze.* MELPOMENE *steps forward.*)

MELPOMENE. So now the awful truth has been told. Perhaps Demeter knew it all along, somewhere deep inside. Perhaps she wasn't ready to face the truth. But now she has no choice.

(HELIOS *exits with his stool and chart. The lights dim, and* HECATE *steps beside the wall, which represents the caldron again. She freezes.*)

MELPOMENE. Our goddesses' business with Helios is through, and Hecate is anxious to get back to her cooking. She doesn't want her brew to burn or boil over! Just another little incantation takes them back to the crossroads. But poor Demeter—she's reeling from the shock of what she has heard.

(MELPOMENE *steps aside to watch, and* HECATE *and* DEMETER *come to life.* HECATE *stirs the brew with her ladle.*)

DEMETER. She belongs to Hades now. She's the bride of death—Queen of the Underworld.

HECATE. So it would seem, dearie, so it would seem. (*Tossing imaginary ingredients into her caldron*)

Grain of sand and burning coal
And pain from some tormented soul;
Crust of stale and moldy bread,
A teensy little pinch of dread.
Just an ounce or two of sweat
Mixed with droplets of regret.

DEMETER. How can this have happened? Why doesn't Lord Zeus himself stand up against such injustice?

HECATE. He's taken Hades' side, I imagine. They are brothers, you know.

DEMETER. Of course. The whole universe has turned its back upon my daughter and me. Such heartless indifference!

HECATE. Blame no one but yourself.

DEMETER. Myself? What can you mean?

HECATE. What a poor excuse for a mother you were—never to have taught your daughter fear.

DEMETER. How could I have done that?

HECATE. Why, by frightening her, of course. By denying her food to teach her hunger. By locking her in a closet to teach her darkness. By forcing her from hearth and home at nights to teach her despair. By pinching her to teach her pain. By turning your back upon her to teach her sorrow and rejection.

DEMETER. How cruel!

HECATE. Was it less cruel to let her wander through life unafraid? And look what it has led to! How could she have hoped to escape the clutches of Hades? (*Still stirring ingredients into her caldron*)

Simmer, simmer, seethe and
  shimmer;
Heat the pot, ye flames a-glimmer!
Just one more stir—oh, yes, just one.
That's enough—my brew is done!
(Tasting her brew) Mmm, delicious!
Care for a taste?

DEMETER. No.

HECATE. Are you sure? It's good for
what ails you.

DEMETER. No.

(DEMETER and HECATE freeze. MELPOMENE steps forward.)

MELPOMENE. Hecate's magic has
nothing more to offer, nothing more
to show. Demeter wanders away from
the sorceress and her crossroads.
Would that she could wander away
from the truth as well!

(HECATE exits. The stage brightens as MELPOMENE speaks, but the light is cold.)

MELPOMENE. What does a goddess do
in the depths of hopeless, helpless
grief? Where does she go when all
the world is her enemy—when every
bush, tree, or stone seems to say,
"Away with you! You are not
welcome here!" She roams far and
wide, without goal or destination,
never eating, never sleeping. And she
yearns for that one gift that gods and
goddesses have never yet possessed—
death.

(MELPOMENE steps aside, and DEMETER comes to life. During the following speech, DEMETER's posture shrivels from that of a proud goddess to that of a hunched old woman.)

DEMETER. Kore, Kore, Kore, Kore.

Can you hear me call your name?
Does my voice pierce the frozen
earth and reach you in the kingdom
below? I'll breathe my warm breath
upon the soil, thaw just a patch. Then
I'll plow a furrow ever so deep and
plant my voice down where you are,
and it will grow in your ear like the
sprout of baby grain, spread through
your mind like the tendrilled vine.
But, no. Even my breath cannot
unfreeze this cold, cold world.

Oh, Kore, Kore.

Do you know how much I love
you? I once believed that I loved you
more than any mother ever loved her
child—more than any mother ever
could. But I was wrong. If I had
loved you fully, I would have
leavened my kindness with just a
touch of cruelty. I would have taught
you pain and fear.

Oh, Kore, Kore.

I wanted to think that the world
was as sweet and good as you. So I
lied to us both, allowed us to believe
the world was just a huge meadow
blooming with spring flowers. Now
we both know the truth. And now
you are lost to me forever.

Oh, Kore, Kore, I am sorry.

I once thought it was a happy
thing to be a goddess. But if even the
gods know suffering, what use is it to
be divine? Let me have no more of
it. Farewell, nectar and ambrosia,
givers of immortality and slayers of
death. I'll taste the food and drink of
the gods no longer. I'll eat the scraps

of bread that mortal beggars eat. And
like any beggar, I'll die, unknown,
forgotten. And then . . .

Oh, Kore, Kore.

In Hades' depths, I'll find you at
last.

(DEMETER *has pulled a shawl up over her
head. Her transformation into an elderly beggar
woman is now complete. She freezes, and*
MELPOMENE *steps forward.)*

MELPOMENE. Can a goddess willingly
choose mortality? Can she truly
waste and wither away and die? Now
that would certainly be the stuff of
tragedy. We'll find out—all in good
time.

(DEMETER *exits.)*

MELPOMENE. But what of Kore herself?
We've seen nothing of her since her
disappearance. How is she faring in
the world below? Is her lot as bleak
and unhappy as her mother's? Let's
see.

(*The lights dim somewhat.* MELPOMENE *steps
aside as* HADES *and* KORE *enter.)*

HADES. Why so sad, my darling?

KORE. Why do you suppose?

HADES. You miss your mother.

KORE. Of course.

HADES. And the world of light and the
living.

KORE. Yes, I miss all that, but—

HADES. But what?

KORE. There's something else that makes
me sad.

HADES. Tell me.

KORE. You wouldn't understand.

HADES. I might. Please tell me.

KORE. Those flowers I dropped when
you carried me away—I keep
thinking about them, lying on the
ground like that. I feel awfully sorry
for them.

HADES. Sorry? For flowers?

KORE. I said you wouldn't understand.

HADES. I'm trying.

KORE. Flowers are living things, and I
always ask their permission before
picking them. Sometimes they agree.
Sometimes they say no.

"If you pick me, I'll soon die," a
crocus might say. "And I don't want
to die."

"Fair enough," I'd reply and pass
on.

Or we might discuss things a bit.

"If you pick me, will you put me
in a pretty vase?" an iris might ask.

"Yes," I'd say.

"With fresh, cool water?"

"Yes," I'd say.

"And on a windowsill in the
sun?"

"If you like," I'd say.

"And in a nice arrangement, too?
With baby's breath and daisies for
company?"

"Certainly," I'd say.

"Go right ahead, then," the iris
would say with a nod.

I made promises to those flowers
I'd picked that day. I broke those
promises.

HADES. You couldn't help it.

KORE. The flowers never knew that. They expected a nice home with someone to love them. Instead, they wound up scattered on the ground and nobody ever touched them again.

HADES. I'm sorry. I didn't understand. I'll go back and gather them up for you.

KORE. It's too late. They're all dead now.

HADES. Don't you like the gardens here in my realm? Don't you like the blossoms that surround you here?

KORE. I don't see any blossoms. Just cold, hard jewels.

HADES. Oh, but they're not like the jewels back in the world you come from. They grow, just like flowers. Look, here's a baby purple amethyst, still in the bud. And here's a blossoming cornflower-blue sapphire. And here's an elderly green emerald, waning on the vine. Go on, choose a jewel. Take one for yourself.

KORE (*bending toward an imaginary jewel*). Hello, bright red ruby. My, you're so heavy and full! You're ready to drop right off the stem. You must be tired from holding on so tight. Won't you let me pluck you loose and take you away?

HADES. What does it say?

KORE. "Yes, by all means."

HADES. Well, then.

(*KORE pantomimes picking the stone.*)

KORE. Oh, it's like ice! It chills my fingers to the bone! And it has no fragrance.

HADES. But look at it more closely.

KORE. I see a flame inside. More than that—a little world of dancing, laughing light. How strange, that fire can be so cold. How sad, too. All these lovely gems—they're born, they grow, they die, and yet they never really live. (*She laughs softly.*)

HADES. If it's sad, why do you laugh?

KORE. I don't know. At the world, perhaps. At life—and death.

HADES. You're starting to feel at home here.

KORE. Yes, I suppose I am.

HADES. You'll make a splendid queen. But your name, Kore—it just won't do. It's so simple, not nearly grand enough, not truly regal. I have it. From now on, let's call you Persephone.

KORE. That's pretty. What does it mean?

HADES. *Bringer of Destruction.*

KORE (*laughing again*). I rather like that.

(HADES *and* KORE—*now* PERSEPHONE—*exit.* MELPOMENE *steps forward.*)

MELPOMENE. A certain Irishman named Oscar Wilde—I wonder if he's still around?—once said that "behind sorrow there is always a soul." That's true as far as it goes, I think. But he might have said more. Laughter that breaks forth from behind sorrow *is* soul—the purest soul itself. (*With a smile*) Surprised to hear the Muse of tragedy praising laughter? I'm liable to surprise you again before our play is through.

(The stage brightens, but the light is cold again. DEMETER *enters.)*

MELPOMENE. Meanwhile, Demeter wanders throughout the world, unrecognized by gods and mortals alike. And the world is a cold place, indeed.

*(*MELPOMENE *steps aside as a* PASSERBY *enters.* DEMETER *holds out her hand.)*

DEMETER. Oh, pardon me, but could you spare just a little crust of bread?

1ST PASSERBY. Away with you, idle beggar woman.

(The 1ST PASSERBY *exits, and another* PASSERBY *enters.)*

DEMETER. Some charity, please! A copper coin, that's all, to buy a warm new shawl.

2ND PASSERBY. I work for what I have. So should you.

(The 2ND PASSERBY *exits, and another* PASSERBY *enters.)*

DEMETER. I'll work for something to eat—anything you need done around your house.

3RD PASSERBY. I already have a maid.

(The 3RD PASSERBY *exits, and another* PASSERBY *enters.)*

DEMETER. I'm so very cold. Could I please come home with you, spend just a few moments warming myself by your fire?

4TH PASSERBY. There's no room by my fire for a beggar.

(The 4TH PASSERBY *exits.)*

DEMETER. Ah, how kind you are, all of you! How merciful! With every rebuke, with every refusal, I feel this burden of flesh grow lighter. You're giving me the death I'm yearning for—and the quicker the better. *(She sits on the edge of the wall, which now represents a spring.)*

MELPOMENE. But death does not come quickly, despite cold, hunger, and thirst. Demeter wanders for days and days, for nights and nights. She winds up on the outskirts of Eleusis, a village in Greece. There she sits at the edge of a spring, hoping never to move until she dies.

*(*CALLIDICE *enters, carrying a pitcher.)*

CALLIDICE. Good afternoon, ma'am. *(Pause)* Good afternoon. *(Pause)* Maybe you're deaf. *(Walking over to the spring, directly in front of* DEMETER*)* Would you like some water?

*(*DEMETER *doesn't look up at her.)*

CALLIDICE. Maybe you're blind, too. *(Pause)* What's your name?

DEMETER. It doesn't matter.

CALLIDICE. Of course, it matters. Names matter a lot. How could people ever make friends without knowing each other's names? *(Extending her hand to* DEMETER*)* My name's Callidice. How d'you do?

*(*DEMETER *doesn't move.)*

CALLIDICE. You're not from around here, are you? That's not really a question. I know you're not. I know everyone in Eleusis, and I don't know you, so that means you're not *from* Eleusis, doesn't it? Would you like some water?

DEMETER. No.

CALLIDICE. All right. I'm just getting some for my family. Hope I'm not bothering you. My father's name is Celeus. Maybe you've heard of him. He's the ruler of Eleusis. He's really worried because of this awful weather. So is everybody, but Papa worries most because he's responsible for everything. It's cold, and the grain is dying in the fields. Nothing like this has ever happened before. Folks say it's because the goddess Demeter is angry. No one knows what about. *(Dipping her pitcher into the spring)* The water's so cold! It's liable to freeze soon.

DEMETER. What's your mother's name?

CALLIDICE. Metaneira.

DEMETER. That's a pretty name.

CALLIDICE. I think so, too.

DEMETER. Has she raised you well?

CALLIDICE. I guess so. She's sweet. She can be strict at times. I suppose that's a good thing.

DEMETER. Did she teach you how to be afraid?

CALLIDICE. What do you mean?

DEMETER. Children need to learn to fear danger. Did she teach you that?

CALLIDICE. Well, she told me never to talk to strangers.

DEMETER. She was wise.

CALLIDICE. 'Course, that's what I'm doing right now—talking to a stranger. Oh, dear, maybe I shouldn't. I don't think I've ever met a stranger before, so it just slipped my mind.

DEMETER. You should do as your mother says.

CALLIDICE. Maybe, but it's too late now. Besides, I'm sure she didn't mean strangers like *you*. She meant mean, nasty strangers.

DEMETER. She meant all strangers.

CALLIDICE. Oh, I'm sure she didn't. *(Holding the pitcher toward DEMETER)* Here. Have a sip.

DEMETER. I don't want it.

CALLIDICE. You look like you could use it. I hope you don't mind my saying so.

(DEMETER sips some water out of the pitcher, then hangs her head.)

CALLIDICE. Are you crying?

DEMETER. I don't know how to cry.

CALLIDICE. Everyone cries. Only the gods can't cry.

DEMETER. I should have told her not to talk to strangers.

CALLIDICE. Told who?

DEMETER. My daughter.

CALLIDICE. You have a daughter?

DEMETER. I did.

CALLIDICE. What happened to her? *(Pause)* Where are you from?

DEMETER. It doesn't matter.

CALLIDICE. Right, just like your name. You're a very hard person to get to know. *(Pause)* Listen, are you looking for a place to live? And a job, maybe?

Because Mama says we could use somebody at home. Just the usual sort of work—cooking, housecleaning, taking care of my baby brother. We'll give you a room of your own. You'll have plenty to eat—at least I hope so. Papa says there's going to be an awful famine if this weather keeps up. Then *none* of us will eat, I guess. That's a scary thought. Anyway, we'll treat you as well as we can. Won't you come home with me? I'd be awfully glad if you did.

(Pause. DEMETER*'s shoulders shake a little.)*

CALLIDICE. You *are* crying, aren't you?

DEMETER. Yes. I've never cried before.

CALLIDICE. I'm sure that's not true.
(Pause) I didn't mean to make you sad.

DEMETER. No. You're very kind. There won't be any famine in Eleusis. This town will always have plenty to eat. This town is blessed.

CALLIDICE. How do you know? *(Pause)* Will you come home with me?

DEMETER. Yes.

CALLIDICE. That's good.

*(*DEMETER *rises to her feet; then she and* CAL-LIDICE *freeze as* MELPOMENE *steps forward.)*

MELPOMENE. "There won't be any famine in Eleusis," she promised. "This town is blessed," she said. But a frail, dying woman cannot bless and preserve a town and its people. So Demeter must taste ambrosia and nectar again—become a goddess reborn.

(As she speaks, MELPOMENE *lowers* DEME-TER*'s shawl.* DEMETER *stands upright again, then freezes.)*

MELPOMENE. And when the people of Eleusis see the goddess in all her splendor, they worship and adore her. They build her a magnificent temple in which she makes her home. Though sad, Demeter is glad to have a home—especially one so far away from Olympus and its callous gods.

(Continuing her speech, MELPOMENE *takes a folded robe from behind the wall. She unfolds it and drapes it over* CALLIDICE*'s shoulders.)*

MELPOMENE. She chooses a handful of men and women to be her priests and priestesses. And she teaches them her sacred Mysteries—secret and solemn rites and rituals, unknown to other mortals and even to the gods. And as a long year passes, she keeps her promise to Callidice. For even as the world slowly freezes, the little town of Eleusis thrives and prospers.

*(*CALLIDICE *and* DEMETER *come to life as* MELPOMENE *steps aside to watch. Still holding the pitcher,* CALLIDICE *kneels before* DEMETER*.)*

CALLIDICE. Great Mother, may I beg a word with you?

DEMETER. Arise, my dear. When we are alone together, you need not kneel before me. And you need beg nothing of me—you have only to ask. I shall always see you as that kindly child who gave me a home when I had none. And you must always see me as that wretched beggar with no friend in the world but you.

CALLIDICE. Thank you, Mother. *(Rising to her feet)* I've just been to the spring where we first met. I went there to get water.

DEMETER. Indeed?

CALLIDICE. And I looked beyond the spring, beyond the outskirts of Eleusis. I saw a barren, wasted expanse as far as my eye could see. Not one blade of grass grew anywhere; no living creature crept upon the ground. I wondered—is all the world dead, except Eleusis? Then, as if in reply, a cold wisp of wind carried a sound to my ear—the sound of weeping. Oh, Mother, it was such a terrible sound, so full of fear, pain, and mourning! I wanted so much to offer help.

DEMETER. You couldn't, child. There was nothing you could do.

CALLIDICE. Must the world suffer so? Must all things die?

DEMETER. I'm sorry—but yes.

CALLIDICE. Can nothing persuade you otherwise?

DEMETER. No.

CALLIDICE. Not even the gods?

DEMETER. You've seen for yourself that they cannot. They've come here one by one—seven or eight of them by now, I believe. And they all pleaded with the same tired words. But I'll never relent—not until Kore returns to me. And Zeus will never allow that. He'll never deprive his own brother of his queen.

CALLIDICE. I feel sorry for them.

DEMETER. For the gods? How strange!

CALLIDICE. They suffer, just as mortals suffer. I wonder if they might even die.

DEMETER. Gods don't know how to die. I'm living proof of that.

CALLIDICE. Are you sure? So few mortals are left alive. Can the gods go on living with no one to believe in them?

DEMETER. Let things unfold as they must, Callidice. Perhaps everything *will* pass away—the depths of the sea, the bowels of the earth, the heights of the sky, those kingdoms of Poseidon, Hades, and Zeus. But there is a fourth kingdom now—the kingdom of Eleusis, my own realm. Eleusis will never pass away.

CALLIDICE. I'm afraid of the surrounding cold.

DEMETER. Don't be. Our hearts are warm, yours and mine. All the cold in creation cannot put out the fire of a single warm heart. *(Looking offstage)* But who do I see coming here? Another god, I believe. Yes, it's Hermes, Zeus' messenger. Hardly any surprise. He's just about the only deity I hadn't heard from.

(HERMES enters.)

HERMES. Greetings from Olympus, gentle goddess. Almighty Zeus, wielder of the thunderbolt, sends praises and commendations.

DEMETER. Kneel, Hermes.

HERMES. Oh, Demeter, really—

DEMETER. This is my realm, and I rule here. You'll find that even Lord Zeus, wielder of the thunderbolt, isn't so "almighty" in this corner of the cosmos.

HERMES *(reluctantly kneeling).* I bring an urgent message.

DEMETER. Of course you do. But it's nothing I haven't already heard from—let's see, which gods have stopped by to visit me? First came Iris, then Athena and Hephaestus. Then in fairly rapid succession arrived Artemis, Hestia, Apollo, and Aphrodite. After that, there was Hera, and—oh, yes—Ares. They all said much the same thing, and I'm sure you will, too.

HERMES *(rising).* But, goddess—

DEMETER. You are not at liberty to rise, lowly messenger.

HERMES. I didn't come here to be insulted.

DEMETER. You should have thought better of coming here at all. It pleases me to have you kneel.

(HERMES kneels again.)

DEMETER. "Why do you punish the earth so?" the gods all pleaded. "Can't you see that your daughter's marriage does honor to both her and you? Now she is queen of one-third of the universe! She rules in glory in the Underworld and even has a grand new name—Persephone! Isn't that good? And isn't it harsh of you to reward good fortune with cruelty? And—oh, please, gentle goddess!— won't you show some mercy?" This is your message, too, I fancy. So off with you.

HERMES. Actually, goddess, that is *not* my message.

DEMETER. No?

HERMES. No.

DEMETER. You've piqued my interest.

HERMES. I've come to ask you this: *If your daughter is returned to you, will you let the world live again?*

DEMETER. I don't understand.

HERMES. You heard the question. Answer it.

DEMETER. Certainly, I would, but—

HERMES. Is that a promise?

DEMETER. A solemn promise, but—

HERMES *(rising to his feet and turning to go).* All right, then. I'll be off now, just as you ordered.

DEMETER. Where are you going?

HERMES. Why this sudden interest in the doings of a "lowly messenger"?

DEMETER. Tell me.

HERMES. I'm headed for the Underworld. I'm going to tell Hades that he's under strict orders from Lord Zeus to send your daughter home immediately.

DEMETER. Don't toy with me.

HERMES. It's true. Lord Zeus realizes that something must be done, or your cold heart will freeze us all. Now that you've promised to relent, I'll go and demand your daughter's return.

CALLIDICE. Oh, Great Mother, you've won!

DEMETER. It can't be that simple. I'm sure there's a catch.

HERMES. Actually, there is. Your daughter cannot be yours again if she has eaten anything in the Underworld.

DEMETER. Oh, yes, that old rule. How ridiculous!

HERMES. Ridiculous or not, the three Fates have decreed it. Even Lord Zeus can't defy the Fates.

CALLIDICE *(to* DEMETER*).* Then there's no hope, after all! She's been down there for more than a year. How could she have gone all this time without eating something?

DEMETER. Don't worry, child. There's no food in the Underworld. No one eats there.

HERMES. Gentle goddess, for your own sake, don't hope too much. Lord Hades is a wily, cunning fellow. If he *knows* of this decree—

DEMETER. It makes no difference if he does. I'm positive that Kore has been perfectly wretched there. She's been far too unhappy to eat a single bite of food.

HERMES. How can you know?

DEMETER. Because I am her mother.

HERMES. You've not seen your daughter for a long while. She's surely changed in ways you can't reckon on.

DEMETER. Don't presume to tell me that my daughter has changed. She *hasn't* changed. She'll never change. And now, be on your errand. Waste no more time about it.

*(*DEMETER, CALLIDICE, *and* HERMES *freeze as* MELPOMENE *steps forward.)*

MELPOMENE. Ah, the little self-deceptions of motherhood. Demeter's daughter isn't *perfectly* wretched in the Underworld, as we've already seen.

*(*DEMETER, CALLIDICE, *and* HERMES *exit. The lights dim.)*

MELPOMENE. And as for Hades—well, he may live beneath the earth, but he doesn't exactly bury his head in the sand. He can't very well rule a third of the universe without having a pretty good idea of what's going on elsewhere—especially an Olympian endeavor to take his wife away from him. And he's not likely to let that happen if he can help it.

*(*MELPOMENE *steps aside as* HADES *and* PERSEPHONE *enter.* HADES *holds a small cloth pouch, and* PERSEPHONE *holds a necklace.)*

PERSEPHONE *(talking to the necklace).* Hello, pretty little stones. You look so happy, strung together like that. You must enjoy one another's company.

HADES. You like it, then?

PERSEPHONE. I do—truly, I do. Why, each gem is shaped exactly like the others. It's so perfect!

HADES. I told the royal gardener to choose the stones very carefully.

PERSEPHONE. And so he did. It's just that—

HADES. What? Is something wrong?

PERSEPHONE. Oh, Hades, please don't take this badly. But you've given me so much jewelry already, and although I love every last bit of it, your generosity sometimes overwhelms me a little.

HADES. You deserve more treasures than the earth can possibly contain.

PERSEPHONE. That's sweet of you to say. It's just that—well, when I look at this necklace, I can't help thinking how nicely it would suit Mother. It would bring out the color in her face and hair so perfectly. Isn't there any way to—? *(Pause)* No, of course not. I'm sorry for asking.

HADES. I have another little gift for you—something rather special, I think.

PERSEPHONE. What is it?

(HADES hands the pouch to PERSEPHONE. She opens it and takes out a pomegranate.)

PERSEPHONE. A pomegranate! I haven't seen a piece of real fruit since I've been here.

HADES. I thought maybe you missed that sort of thing. I brought it here at considerable trouble and expense, if I may say so.

PERSEPHONE. How thoughtful of you. It's lovely—it really is. I'll find a nice place to put it, where we can look at it always.

HADES. No, my dear. You must eat it.

PERSEPHONE. Oh, but how could I, when you've gone to so much trouble to get it?

HADES. How could you not? It's ripe, my dear—perfect for eating. Soon it will spoil, and it won't even be pleasant to look at.

PERSEPHONE. It seems so sad to eat it—the only pomegranate in our realm.

HADES. How do you suppose the pomegranate feels?

PERSEPHONE *(to the pomegranate).* Tell me, luscious fruit—may I break you open? May I taste you?

HADES. What does it say?

PERSEPHONE. "Yes, by all means."

HADES. Well, then.

(PERSEPHONE and HADES freeze as MELPOMENE steps forward.)

MELPOMENE. If tragedy teaches us anything, it's to exercise caution before tasting a piece of fresh fruit. It's as likely as not to be forbidden for one reason or another.

(PERSEPHONE exits, while HADES remains frozen. As she continues her speech, MELPOMENE walks around him, studying him.)

MELPOMENE. But, ah, poor Hades! I know, he's the villain of our piece, or so he seems. Even so, I pity him. For he's our only character who has no real power to do what he wants. We've heard no soliloquy from him, and he hasn't said much—that's not his style. Still, it's not hard to guess what he's thinking and feeling, and it's very tragic. To fall in love unwittingly—well, that's happened to us all, and there's probably no other way to fall in love. But to feel genuine love, to want nothing but good things for your beloved, and yet to know that you've won her and kept her by coercion and deception—that's surely very painful. How cruel love is, when it makes us do cruel things to those we love.

You can leave our story now, Hades. I do feel sorry for you.

(HADES exits.)

MELPOMENE. I'm going to skip an episode or two, if you don't mind. Hermes' arrival in the Underworld, Hades' reluctant farewell to his queen, Persephone's journey back to the world of the living—they add little to our story, and you can fill them in with your imaginations. What matters most, I think, is the reunion between mother and daughter.

(PERSEPHONE and DEMETER enter—PERSEPHONE still wearing the necklace, and the pouch tied to her wrist. They stand several feet apart, facing each other, then freeze. The stage brightens—cold light again.)

MELPOMENE. A certain author named Thomas Wolfe once wrote a book entitled *You Can't Go Home Again.* I've not read it, so I'm not sure what he meant by the title. Sounds tragic though. Is it true?

(MELPOMENE steps aside to watch as DEMETER and PERSEPHONE come to life, still looking at each other.)

DEMETER. Daughter.

PERSEPHONE. Mother.

DEMETER. Can it really be you?

PERSEPHONE. Of course it is.

DEMETER. I'm afraid.

PERSEPHONE. Of what?

DEMETER. To touch you. To hold you. I'm afraid you'll vanish. I'm afraid this is only a dream.

PERSEPHONE. I'm afraid, too.

(Long pause. Then DEMETER and PERSEPHONE rush into each other's arms and hold each other tightly.)

DEMETER. I've missed you so.

PERSEPHONE. And I've missed you.

DEMETER. I've been so frightened for you.

PERSEPHONE. You didn't need to be.

DEMETER *(stepping out of their embrace).* Oh, let me look at you. Yes, it really is you! My baby is mine again!

PERSEPHONE. I've been so worried about you, Mother—worried because I knew how worried *you* were. Does that sound silly? I wanted so much to talk to you, to send you a message, at least—to let you know I was all right.

DEMETER. All right? In that awful place?

PERSEPHONE. It wasn't as awful as you think. Hades was very kind.

DEMETER. What nonsense you talk! You've forgotten what kindness and comfort really are! But you'll learn again in no time, Kore. My own darling Kore!

PERSEPHONE. Oh, Mother—

DEMETER. What?

PERSEPHONE. You mustn't call me that anymore. I'm Persephone now.

DEMETER. Oh, yes, so I've heard. What a peculiar sort of name. It isn't very pretty. What does it mean?

PERSEPHONE. You wouldn't like what it means.

DEMETER. Indeed? Then let's change it back to Kore.

PERSEPHONE. We can't. I'm not the same as when I left you. I've learned so much, I've—

DEMETER. Grown up so much?

PERSEPHONE. That, and more.

DEMETER. Yes, I *do* see a change. Your eyes—they're deeper, darker, sadder. But that will pass. We'll rid you of this melancholy streak. Just a day or two in the sunlight—

PERSEPHONE. I'll never be the girl I was again.

DEMETER. Foolish child! Do you think you know more about yourself than your mother does? Why, you're sounding just like Hermes! "She's surely changed in ways you can't reckon on," he told me—the dolt!—when anyone can see that you're really the same deep down. Why, he even said you might have eaten something in the Underworld! Who could have supposed such a thing?

PERSEPHONE. What do you mean?

DEMETER. I told him you'd refuse to eat—and so you did.

PERSEPHONE. But I did eat—just a little.

DEMETER. What?

PERSEPHONE. Hades offered me a pomegranate, and I—

DEMETER. It's not true.

PERSEPHONE. It is.

DEMETER. You lie.

PERSEPHONE. Why would I lie?

DEMETER. If you ate in the Underworld, you can't be here.

PERSEPHONE. But I *am* here. You see me. You held me in your arms.

DEMETER (*backing away from* PERSEPHONE *fearfully*). No. You're not you. You're not my daughter. I should have seen it at once. Those eyes of yours—they're strange. You are a phantom, a changeling sent by that fiend in the depths to mock me, to tell me my daughter's never coming back.

PERSEPHONE. Mother, no.

DEMETER. Show me your real face! Show me who you are!

PERSEPHONE. I'm your own daughter.

DEMETER. Can you do nothing but lie? Then let Hades himself tell me the truth. (*Falls on her knees and pounds on the floor*) Open the earth, you monster! Let me come down, down into your wretched world! What, still shut? Do you fear me? And well you should! I'll tear your face with my nails. I'll harrow the depths, steal all your treasures, free all the dead. I'll make the lower regions my own and end your reign forever. Just try to keep me out! Just try!

(DEMETER *collapses to the ground, exhausted and in tears.* PERSEPHONE *has taken the partly eaten pomegranate out of the pouch and holds it toward* DEMETER.)

PERSEPHONE. Mother, here.

DEMETER. What's this?

PERSEPHONE. If it's so evil, I don't want it. Take it. Bury it, burn it, hurl it into the sea, do whatever you must to get rid of it.

DEMETER. I don't understand.

PERSEPHONE. Look at me again, Mother. Look into my eyes. I know they've changed. They're sadder and older. But they're still your daughter's eyes. They'll always be your daughter's eyes.

DEMETER. They are! They are, indeed! And—and you didn't eat all of it?

PERSEPHONE. To tell the truth, I didn't have much of an appetite.

(DEMETER *begins to laugh. She embraces* PERSEPHONE *again and again.*)

DEMETER. So you're mine, mine, mine again—for part of the year at least!

PERSEPHONE. I still don't understand.

DEMETER. He couldn't keep you forever—not unless you ate all of it. He can have you back someday, can claim you as his own from time to time. But not until fall comes.

PERSEPHONE. What's fall?

DEMETER. It's not a what, it's a when.

PERSEPHONE. When is it then?

DEMETER. An eternity away, dear! An eternity away!

(*The light suddenly grows much warmer.* DEMETER *and* PERSEPHONE *freeze.*)

MELPOMENE. And so our goddess laughs like there's no tomorrow, and her laughter sheds new joy upon the earth. The sun's light is warm again, and the earth thaws in an instant. Within minutes, sprouts pop up through the ground, and the trees are speckled with leaves and buds. The sky is a hearty, robust blue—but off on the horizon lingers a cloud that promises a light, refreshing rain. The world knows health and happiness again.

Surprised that a tragedy should have a happy ending? It's not as unusual as you might think.

(PERSEPHONE *and* DEMETER *come to life again.*)

PERSEPHONE. Oh—I almost forgot! I brought you a present.

(PERSEPHONE *takes the necklace from around her neck and hands it to* DEMETER.)

DEMETER. What exquisite stones! Why, they're almost like flowers.

PERSEPHONE. Stones grow like flowers there.

DEMETER (*putting the necklace around her own neck*). Do they really? Who would have thought that such beauty could come out of the depths!

(PERSEPHONE *and* DEMETER *freeze again.*)

MELPOMENE. Then again, can our story be said to end at all? Fall isn't *really* an eternity away—nor are the falls, winters, springs, and summers that will follow one another, again and again and again for countless ages. Someday—and someday soon—Persephone will return to the world of the dead. And when she does, Demeter will weep like there's no tomorrow. And the sun will grow cold, and the earth will freeze, and the leaves will fall, and the crops will perish.

For if tragedy teaches us anything . . .

But to be honest, I don't really believe that tragedy teaches us a single blessed thing. It's a celebration, pure and simple—a celebration of the wise foolishness and foolish wisdom of Demeter. For how foolish-wise it is to laugh like there's no tomorrow, when sorrow certainly lies ahead. And how wise-foolish it is to weep like there's no tomorrow, when joy will certainly come again someday.

(PERSEPHONE *and* DEMETER *come to life again.*)

DEMETER. Let's go eat the rest of this pomegranate together.

PERSEPHONE. Is it safe to eat?

DEMETER. Certainly, now that you're back among the living. Besides, I'm sure that you've worked up a bit of an appetite since your return.

PERSEPHONE. Oh, yes—yes, I have!

DEMETER. But your name—are you *sure* we can't change it back?

PERSEPHONE. Persephone suits me now.

DEMETER. All right, then. But I'll make up my own meaning for it—"Bringer of Blossoms."

(PERSEPHONE *and* DEMETER *exit.*)

MELPOMENE. "In life there is really no great or small thing," that wise and foolish Irishman Oscar Wilde once said. "All things are of equal value and equal size." Tragedy celebrates all things—great and small, good and bad, joyful or painful. Tragedy makes no distinctions. It celebrates all of life—life for its own sake.

And now, I've got a special treat in store. The Mysteries of Eleusis are about to be revealed on this very stage. That's right, you are about to witness a ritual which has been kept a deep and awful secret for untold ages. But please—tell no one what you're about to see!

(*Music begins. It doesn't matter what music is used, as long as it is gleeful, life-affirming, even comical. The entire cast returns to the stage and performs a joyful dance. When the music ends, the dancers bow and leave the stage.*)

PLAYWRIGHT'S POSTSCRIPT

This is one of the world's greatest stories, and it is impossible to do it full justice in so short a play. The Homeric "Hymn to Demeter" tells more about Demeter's life in Eleusis than I have here. Still disguised as a mortal, Demeter became a servant in the house of Celeus and Metaneira, where she nursed their infant son Demophon. She loved the child so much that she decided to make him immortal. To do so, she placed him in the red-hot coals of the fireplace every night.

One night, Metaneira walked into the room just when Demeter was setting Demophon in the coals. She screamed in horror. Demeter was furious at the interruption and revealed herself to be a goddess. She explained that she had intended to free Demophon from illness and death, but now would not do so. To appease Demeter's anger, the citizens of Eleusis built a temple for her and began celebrating the Eleusinian Mysteries. Perhaps this haunting episode deserves a play of its own.

CONNECTING TO OTHER CULTURES

There are many other stories that are strikingly similar to that of Demeter and Persephone from cultures all over the world. For example, the ancient Egyptians told how the goddess Isis searched all over the world for parts of her dismembered husband, Osiris, then brought him back to life. Like Persephone, Osiris spent only part of every year among the living.

And the Native American Cherokees tell a story of a "medicine bear" who was killed by hunters but came back to life. In Cherokee stories, the bear was a godlike animal whose behavior was connected with the cycles of nature. Like Persephone, he disappeared into deathly darkness when winter came, then returned to the sunlight in spring.

ORPHEUS AND EURYDICE

SETTING THE STAGE

Euterpe, who introduces this play, is the Muse of lyric poetry. The word *lyric* means expressive of strong personal emotions; it also has to do with song. To the ancient Greeks and Romans, the legendary Orpheus was the greatest of all lyric poets and a musician of supernatural gifts. Even stones could not hear his songs without being moved.

The most famous story about Orpheus tells how he went to the Underworld in an attempt to rescue his dead wife, Eurydice. This story comes down to us in two versions. Virgil included it in his long poem *Georgics*, written during the 1st century B.C. Ovid told it in his epic *Metamorphoses*, written during the 1st century A.D. Virgil and Ovid were both Roman writers. But to keep this play consistent with the others in this collection, I've used Greek names for gods and goddesses.

In addition to being one of the world's greatest love stories, this is also the tale of a quest. In a typical quest story, a hero or heroine goes on a dangerous journey in search of something of great personal value. Jason's voyage in search of the Golden Fleece is one of the most famous quest stories.

Does Orpheus' quest for his lost love prove successful or unsuccessful? I'll let the story speak for itself.

MUSING ABOUT THE MYTH

This play pairs a romance with a quest, sending its hero into the deadly realm of the Underworld to pursue his wife. As you read, ask yourself what dangers you might be willing to endure in the name of love.

ORPHEUS AND EURYDICE

<table>
<tr><td>

CHARACTERS:

> EUTERPE (ū ter′ pē), the Muse of lyric poetry

> ORPHEUS (or′ fē us), a singer and poet

> EURYDICE (ū rid′ i sē), Orpheus' wife

> THREE WOOD NYMPHS

> THREE OFFSTAGE VOICES

> CHARON (ker′ en), the ferryman of the river Styx

> FOUR GHOSTS

> HADES (hā′ dēz), the ruler of the Underworld

> PERSEPHONE (per sef′ ō nē), Hades' wife, the queen of the Underworld

</td><td>

THE FURIES, goddesses of vengeance and punishment:

> TISIPHONE (ti sif′ ō nē)

> MEGAERA (me jē′ ra)

> ALECTO (a lek′ tō)

OTHER NAMES MENTIONED IN THE PLAY:

> ALCESTIS (al ses′ tis), a mortal queen, rescued from death by Heracles

> STYX (stiks), the river that surrounds the Underworld

> THANATOS (than′ a tos), the god of death

> ZEUS (züs), the king of the Olympian gods

</td></tr>
</table>

SETTING: *Mythical Thrace and the Underworld*

TIME: *No time in particular*

A WORD ABOUT SONGS

The "songs" in this play are really meant to be spoken, not sung. And Orpheus' lyre can be a pantomime instrument without any strings at all. Whenever he is not otherwise occupied, Orpheus should punctuate songs by strumming the lyre; a musician offstage (with a guitar, mandolin, piano, or another instrument) can accompany Orpheus' strummings with simple chords that reflect the mood of the moment. No real melody is necessary.

Of course, there would be nothing wrong with Orpheus playing real chords on a real instrument—an autoharp, perhaps. And anyone who wants to set the songs in this play to music is welcome to do so.

ORPHEUS AND EURYDICE

(The stage is bare except for two stools for actors to use as needed. On top of one stool is a folded piece of fabric. ORPHEUS *enters, carrying a lyre and wearing a rose in his lapel. He sits on the stool without the fabric and begins to play the lyre.* EUTERPE *enters, watching and listening.)*

ORPHEUS.
>With every touch upon these strings
>>I pluck a rose;
>And every note this lyre sings
>>Cries of woes.
>Such is the truth of every song,
>That life and love are short, not long;
>>My lyre knows.

*(*ORPHEUS *keeps strumming as* EUTERPE *speaks to the audience.)*

EUTERPE. Here's a charming sight—a young man in a meadow, strumming his lyre and singing. And what a singer he is! Look how forest animals have gathered around to listen. Even the rocks have crept closer to hear. And there didn't used to be trees in this meadow, but there are now. They've picked themselves up by the roots and walked here to listen to the young man's song.

ORPHEUS.
>A rose was cut before her time;
>>A single cry,
>So mournful and yet so sublime,
>>Filled up the sky.
>How sad and strange it seems to me
>For beauty to blend with misery
>>When roses die.

*(*ORPHEUS *keeps strumming as* EUTERPE *speaks.)*

EUTERPE. And a sad song it is. I love sad songs, don't you? I suppose everybody does. Strange, isn't it? It's almost as if people enjoy being sad.

*(*ORPHEUS *freezes as* EUTERPE *continues.)*

EUTERPE. For your information, that's a very fine musical instrument—a regular Stradivarius as lyres go. It was a gift from Apollo, the god of poetry and music. And the lad himself is pretty remarkable. His name is Orpheus, and he's a true artistic genius. I have to admit I'm a bit prejudiced. I'm Euterpe, the Muse of lyric poetry, and I happen to be his aunt. I must warn you, the story I have to tell about him is quite sad. Still, I don't imagine that's a problem. We all love sad stories, don't we?

*(*ORPHEUS *rises to his feet.* EURYDICE *enters and stands beside him, followed by three* WOOD NYMPHS. *They all freeze.)*

EUTERPE. It begins in a meadow in Thrace. Orpheus is getting married. His lovely bride is Eurydice, and her bridesmaids are wood nymphs. It's a simple, rustic ceremony—nothing fancy, just two young people in love, exchanging their vows.

*(*ORPHEUS *takes the rose out of his lapel and hands it to* EURYDICE.*)*

ORPHEUS.
>My dearest, with this rose
>>I thee wed.

EURYDICE.
>It's a poor gift you chose—
>>This rose so red!

ORPHEUS.
>But what could be so fine

95

In this sweet hour?
There's nothing more benign
Than a flower.

EURYDICE.
This rose you've cut away
Will soon be dead.
You should give me this day
A ring instead.

ORPHEUS.
A ring? A hollow ring
Of lifeless gold?
Oh, no! Not such a thing
So crass and cold.
Believe me, dearest wife,
This gift's not wrong.
It's fragrant, full of life.

EURYDICE.
It won't live long.

ORPHEUS.
It will, it will. I pray
To the gods above—
Fresh and alive let it stay
As long as our love.

EURYDICE.
I like this prayer of yours.
Will it be granted?

ORPHEUS.
The gods adore my verse;
My song's enchanted.

EURYDICE (*pinning the rose to her dress*).
Then let there be no rift
Between me and you;
For with this lucky gift
I wed thee, too.

(ORPHEUS, EURYDICE, *and the* WOOD NYMPHS *freeze. Weeping,* EUTERPE *dabs her eyes with a handkerchief.*)

EUTERPE. Oh, look at me! Aren't I a mess? I always cry over symbolism! A bright red rose, cut and waiting for death. And isn't that the case of all mortals? Just like the rose, they know they must die sooner or later. But they hope to find love before they fade away.

(*A rumble of thunder. The stage grows a bit darker.* ORPHEUS *exits, leaving* EURYDICE *and the* WOOD NYMPHS *frozen.*)

EUTERPE. Oh, it's a beautiful ceremony, all right. So beautiful, no one seems to have noticed that the weather is hardly perfect. The wedding god did not arrange for a bright, sunny day. In fact, it looks like there's a storm coming up.

(*As* EUTERPE *steps aside to watch,* EURYDICE *and the* WOOD NYMPHS *come to life.* EURYDICE *begins to walk away from her companions.*)

1ST WOOD NYMPH. Eurydice, where do you think you're going?

EURYDICE. For a little walk.

2ND WOOD NYMPH. But it's going to rain.

EURYDICE. So? Let it rain.

3RD WOOD NYMPH. But you just got married. And Orpheus is looking for you.

EURYDICE. So? Let him look.

1ST WOOD NYMPH. He'll be angry when he finds you.

EURYDICE. How little you know about men!

1ST WOOD NYMPH. And when did you get to be such an expert?

EURYDICE. It's commonsense male

psychology, that's all. I disappear right after the wedding, just when he least expects it. He worries himself sick for a little while, and when he finds me at last, he'll be more in love with me than ever.

1ST WOOD NYMPH. Hope you're right.

(Thunder)

2ND WOOD NYMPH. There's a serious storm coming.

EURYDICE. A little rain never hurt anybody.

2ND WOOD NYMPH. No, but I hear getting struck by lightning hurts quite a lot.

EURYDICE. I won't get struck by lightning.

2ND WOOD NYMPH. What makes you so sure?

EURYDICE. I live a charmed life.

3RD WOOD NYMPH. Well, watch your step anyway. The sky's awfully dark, and it's hard to see.

EURYDICE. Relax. I know this meadow like the back of my hand. *(Lifting her foot)* Ouch!

1ST WOOD NYMPH. What's the matter?

EURYDICE. I stepped on a thorn. Strange, I was sure there weren't any thorns around here.

2ND WOOD NYMPH *(pointing to the ground)*. That's no thorn, that's—

(EURYDICE collapses to the ground, unconscious.)

2ND WOOD NYMPH. —a snake!

1ST WOOD NYMPH *(kneeling beside EURYDICE)*. Oh, heavens!

3RD WOOD NYMPH. What happened?

2ND WOOD NYMPH. The snake!

1ST WOOD NYMPH. It bit her!

3RD WOOD NYMPH. Is she—is she—?

2ND WOOD NYMPH. Don't even think it!

1ST WOOD NYMPH. It's just the excitement of the wedding. It made her faint.

2ND WOOD NYMPH. Still, someone had better go find Orpheus.

3RD WOOD NYMPH. I'll go. *(3RD WOOD NYMPH exits.)*

1ST WOOD NYMPH. Wake up, Eurydice, dear. You're frightening us half to death.

2ND WOOD NYMPH. I'll bet she's just pretending.

1ST WOOD NYMPH. Of course she is! Why, everybody knows that none of the snakes around here are poisonous.

2ND WOOD NYMPH *(to EURYDICE)*. Orpheus is going to be here any second. And male psychology notwithstanding, he's going to throw a royal fit over this stunt of yours.

1ST WOOD NYMPH. This is wicked of you, Eurydice. Truly wicked. Now, wake up, won't you? It's not the least bit funny.

(ORPHEUS and the 3RD WOOD NYMPH enter. The 1ST and 2ND WOOD NYMPHS step aside as ORPHEUS kneels beside EURYDICE.)

2ND WOOD NYMPH. She needs a good scolding, Orpheus.

1ST WOOD NYMPH. That's right, she's just pretending.

2ND WOOD NYMPH. Why, just a minute ago, she was bragging about how she was going to give you a really good scare.

1ST WOOD NYMPH. She's certainly given us *all* a good scare.

ORPHEUS. Eurydice, my love, what's the matter? Your hands, they're so cold. Your cheeks, they're so pale. And not the slightest breath . . . *(To the* WOOD NYMPHS*)* What happened to her?

2ND WOOD NYMPH. A snake.

1ST WOOD NYMPH. It bit her.

ORPHEUS. A snake? Where?

3RD WOOD NYMPH *(pointing).* I see it. It's wriggling in the grass, right there.

1ST WOOD NYMPH. It's so brightly colored.

2ND WOOD NYMPH. I've never seen one like it in the meadow before.

ORPHEUS *(walking over to the snake and peering down at it).* No, I'm sure there's never been such a snake here. It was sent by the Fates to destroy my bride.

3RD WOOD NYMPH. But why?

ORPHEUS. Who can know the reasons of the Fates?

*(*ORPHEUS *kneels and picks up the imaginary snake.)*

2ND WOOD NYMPH. What are you doing?

1ST WOOD NYMPH. It already bit *her.* Isn't that enough?

*(*ORPHEUS *observes the imaginary snake wrapping itself around his wrist.)*

ORPHEUS.
Cruel snake—so sweet
Is your embrace.
My eyes you greet
With smiling grace.
You lick my wrist,
Your fangs withdrawn—
Soft as a kiss
Of a lover fond.
Where is the sting
You gave to her?
To life I cling.
I wish you were
More kind to me.
You deny—but why?—
To set me free,
To let me die.

*(*ORPHEUS *lowers his hand to the ground.)*

2ND WOOD NYMPH. It didn't bite him.

1ST WOOD NYMPH. It's creeping off his wrist.

ORPHEUS. The Fates won't take me. How strange. How wrong.

(Thunder, lightning, and the sound of rain. The stage darkens more.)

3RD WOOD NYMPH. Oh, the storm!

1ST WOOD NYMPH. It's here!

2ND WOOD NYMPH. Quick, find shelter!

3RD WOOD NYMPH. We'll all be struck by lightning!

(The WOOD NYMPHS *exit.)*

ORPHEUS. Wait! Don't leave me! I need your help!

EUTERPE *(to the audience).* Ah, wood nymphs—not the most steadfast creatures in the world, nor the bravest. Remember that in case you ever have to depend on them in a pinch.

(More thunder and lightning, and the sound of rain continues. ORPHEUS *kneels by* EURYDICE *again.)*

ORPHEUS. Let's go, Eurydice. The storm is here. Do you want to get wet? Do you want to get struck by lightning? Look—the birds are fleeing to their leaf-sheltered nests. The hare is running to his warm burrow. A parade of ants is marching to the anthill. Don't you have the sense of a bird, a hare, an ant? Don't you know when to come out of the rain? *(Holding her hand)* No one is here. This body is like an abandoned house. Even the earth beneath us is more alive. Oh, why should a bird, a hare, an ant have life— and you no breath at all? *(Unpinning the rose from her dress)* But your rose— it's still bright and fragrant. And so is our love! My darling, you haven't died, not really. You'll never die as long as our love is alive. *(Putting the rose in his lapel)* The Fates have failed. Even the snake they sent cannot kill you. And wherever you are now, I'll find you. I promise to find you and make you mine again.

(Thunder, lightning, and the sound of rain continue. As EUTERPE *speaks to the audience,* ORPHEUS *takes the folded cloth from the stool. He unfolds it and carefully covers* EURYDICE. *She will remain covered until she is brought to life again.)*

EUTERPE. Alone in the rain, Orpheus buries the empty form that once was Eurydice. He has only one thought in his mind—where to look for her, how to bring her back. Now, we all have ideas about where people go when they die. And we all know of one bitter law—that we can't follow them there, not until we die, too. But Orpheus won't accept this law. He's ready and willing to break it. But where does he go? How can he begin his search? When one's mind is set on doing the impossible, there's really only one way to start—with a prayer.

*(*ORPHEUS *rises to his feet and calls to the heavens.)*

ORPHEUS.
Apollo, god of verse and song,
Who gave to me this lyre I play—
Direct me as I walk along,
And take me to my love, I pray.

EUTERPE. And through the storm he wanders, until he finds the entrance of a cave. A mysterious light glows within. Orpheus steps inside.

(The lightning, thunder, and rain stop. The lighting grows warmer and a bit brighter. ORPHEUS *gazes all around.)*

ORPHEUS. Torches all along the walls, to light the way. And such a steep path down! What sort of cave is this, and where does it lead?

*(*OFFSTAGE VOICES *are heard.)*

1ST VOICE. Hold!

2ND VOICE. Do not come this way!

3RD VOICE. Go back!

ORPHEUS. Who are you? *Where* are you?

1ST VOICE. We are the cavern drafts.

2ND VOICE. We howl among limestone icicles.

3RD VOICE. We groan over calcite pedestals.

1ST VOICE. We murmur amid gypsum columns.

2ND VOICE. We whisper above groundwater lakes.

3RD VOICE. We whistle through mazes and passageways.

ORPHEUS. Then tell me where these caverns lead.

VOICES (*together*). That is not for you to know.

ORPHEUS. Why not?

1ST VOICE. You breathe.

2ND VOICE. You feel.

3RD VOICE. Your blood is warm and flowing.

ORPHEUS. You won't tell me because I'm alive.

VOICES (*together*). Yes.

ORPHEUS. So these caverns lead down to the land of the dead. That's just what I wanted to know. Apollo has guided me to the place I seek. (*He starts to walk on.*)

1ST VOICE. Wait!

2ND VOICE. You mustn't!

3RD VOICE. Trouble awaits you!

ORPHEUS. I'm not a warrior or a monster slayer, just a poet and musician. I don't claim to be strong and brave. Still, I've never been a man to be frightened of a gust of wind—especially when a god is watching out for me.

1ST VOICE. You'll find grief.

2ND VOICE. You'll find sorrow.

3RD VOICE. Greater grief and sorrow than you've ever known.

ORPHEUS. I've lost my love. There is no greater grief or sorrow.

(ORPHEUS *freezes.* EUTERPE *steps forward.*)

EUTERPE. Ah, Orpheus, be careful what you say. It's wise to pay heed to drafts and winds when they take a mind to speak. They have a way of knowing what they're talking about. Down, down, down into the depths our hero goes. The path is clearly marked by torches, but the way is long indeed, and the cavern drafts cry out warnings with his every step.

(CHARON *enters, carrying a tin can. He pantomimes bailing water out of a boat.*)

EUTERPE. At last, he reaches the banks of a river—the river Styx. And there he meets the ferryman Charon.

(EUTERPE *steps aside to watch.* ORPHEUS *comes to life.*)

ORPHEUS. Is this the boat that crosses to the land of the dead?

CHARON. Yep. The *Quagmire Queen.* A beauty, ain't she?

ORPHEUS. It—*she* leaks.

CHARON. I reckon she does a little.

ORPHEUS. She leaks a lot.

CHARON. Not all that much.

ORPHEUS. Are you sure she's safe?

CHARON. She's never sunk once—not in umpteen thousand years of service.

ORPHEUS. There's a first time for everything.

CHARON. Not in these parts. Things stay the same, mostly. Life's pretty predictable when you're dead. Still, it wouldn't hurt if you'd help me bail on the way over.

ORPHEUS. I guess I'd better come aboard.

CHARON. Now wait a minute. Wait just a little tiny minute there. What are you in such an all-fired rush about? You've got to pass the test first. Open your mouth.

(ORPHEUS *does so.*)

CHARON. Say "ah."

(ORPHEUS *does so.*)

CHARON. Sorry. Can't take you.

ORPHEUS. Is it because I'm alive?

CHARON. Alive, are you? Can't say I noticed.

ORPHEUS. Because if that's the problem, maybe I should explain why I—

CHARON (*interrupting*). Strictly speaking, no live folks are allowed on the far shore. Not that it matters to me. Live folks, dead folks, they're much the same, far as I can see.

ORPHEUS. So what's the problem?

CHARON. You're supposed to have a coin on your tongue.

ORPHEUS. Pardon?

CHARON. Price of passage, so to speak.

ORPHEUS. Is this some sort of law?

CHARON. It's *my* law anyhow.

ORPHEUS. Does Lord Hades know you're taking bribes?

CHARON. You can ask him when you see him.

ORPHEUS. The river doesn't look all that deep. I think I'll wade across.

CHARON (*laughing*). Suit yourself.

ORPHEUS. Do you know something I don't?

CHARON. That wouldn't take much, would it? Go on, start wading. I'll watch. Give me a little entertainment. (*Pause*) No? Maybe you're smarter than you look.

(ORPHEUS *strums his lyre.*)

ORPHEUS.
You can't take it with you, they say,
But it seems you'd best jolly well try;
I have learned with misgiving
That the high cost of living
Goes up quite a bit when you die.
I know that I really should pay
For my voyage of passage below;
But if it's tradition
That death charges admission,
I'd just as soon go to a show.

(*Weeping,* CHARON *dabs his eyes with a handkerchief*)

CHARON. Oh dear, oh dear.

ORPHEUS. What's the matter?

CHARON. I don't know why, but I always cry over poetry.

ORPHEUS. I'm sorry, I didn't mean to upset you.

CHARON. No, it's all right, really. Fact is, I liked it. Odd, eh? You'd think I enjoy being sad. Say, that song of yours ought to have a chorus.

ORPHEUS. So it ought, so it ought.
(*Strumming his lyre*)
I am just a poor poet, you know,

Who is often a bit short on
   dough;
     And if it's tradition
     That death charges
     admission,
I'd just as soon go to a show.

CHARON *(weeping some more).* Oh, it's so sad, so sad. How about another verse?

ORPHEUS. Are you sure you're up to it?

CHARON. Sure, I'm sure.

ORPHEUS. I'll sing it after you've taken me to the other shore.

CHARON. You've got yourself a deal, son.

(ORPHEUS and CHARON freeze. EUTERPE steps forward.)

EUTERPE. Orpheus keeps his part of the bargain, of course. And as always, he leaves his listener wanting more.

(CHARON exits.)

EUTERPE. Ah, the power of song! What may not be expected of a man who can charm animals, trees, and even rocks? The question is—can he enchant the dead themselves? Now *that's* a really tough audience. But he's going to have to win them over. He'll never get back his bride without help from others.

(FOUR GHOSTS enter, and ORPHEUS comes to life. EUTERPE steps aside to watch.)

1ST GHOST. You breathe.

2ND GHOST. You feel.

3RD GHOST. Your blood is warm and flowing.

4TH GHOST. You do not belong here.

ORPHEUS. Who are you—more drafts and breezes? No, I can see you, if only dimly.

GHOSTS *(together).* We are the dead.

ORPHEUS. Tell me more.

1ST GHOST. I am a child who drowned in a lake.

2ND GHOST. I am a wife and mother who died of the plague.

3RD GHOST. I am a husband and father who was slain in wars far from home.

4TH GHOST. I am a lover who perished of unrequited love.

ORPHEUS. I'm sorry for all your sufferings in the living world. Are things better for you here?

GHOSTS *(together).* We belong here.

ORPHEUS. How fortunate for you. Alas, I know of one ghost who doesn't. Her name is Eurydice, and she's my bride. Do you happen to know her?

(The GHOSTS shake their heads silently.)

ORPHEUS. Her death was a mistake.

1ST GHOST. So was mine.

2ND GHOST. And mine.

3RD GHOST. And mine.

4TH GHOST. Nobody wants to die.

ORPHEUS. I understand, I really do. But even so, I assure you that hers really is a special case. This rose I'm wearing, do you see it? I cut it for Eurydice when we were married. And look— it's still red, alive, fragrant, even down here among the dead! As long as it lives, so must she.

GHOSTS *(together).* We do not know where she is.

ORPHEUS. But surely you can help me find her.

ORPHEUS AND EURYDICE

1ST GHOST. I cannot find my mother and father.

2ND GHOST. I cannot find my children and husband.

3RD GHOST. I cannot find my family.

4TH GHOST. I cannot find my love.

ORPHEUS. Are they still among the living?

GHOSTS *(together).* No, they are dead.

ORPHEUS. Then why can't you find them here?

1ST GHOST. There are so many dead.

2ND GHOST. Many more dead than there are living.

3RD GHOST. We might search forever and not find our loved ones.

4TH GHOST. So how can we help you find your bride?

ORPHEUS. Couldn't you introduce me to King Hades and Queen Persephone?

1ST GHOST. We could.

2ND GHOST. But why?

3RD GHOST. This realm is full of the lonely and the wretched.

4TH GHOST. Why should we want to help *you*?

ORPHEUS. Because I'm a stranger. Isn't that enough? In the world you left behind, it's proper to treat strangers with kindness. Isn't it so here?
(Strumming his lyre)

Oh, do not say you now forget
Some wandering stranger you once
　met
Craving shelter from cold and harm;
The fire you built to make him warm;
The loaf of bread, the spiced red wine;

The pleasant prattle long and fine;
The plate of savory roast beef;
The hot bath for his bones' relief;
The pleasing, deep, and downy bed;
The feather pillow for his head
To rest upon in soothing sleep.
Does no one in these regions keep
The law that Zeus himself once
　made—
To offer strangers ease and aid?

1ST GHOST. Yes.

2ND GHOST. Yes.

3RD GHOST. Yes, we remember that good law.

4TH GHOST. We'll take you to our king and queen.

(The GHOSTS *and* ORPHEUS *freeze.* EUTERPE *steps forward.)*

EUTERPE. Before you get the idea that the realm of the dead is all darkness and gloom, let me tell you a little about the palace of Hades and Persephone.

(The GHOSTS *exit.)*

EUTERPE. The depths of the earth are full of treasures beyond reckoning, beyond imagination. Rubies, amethysts, diamonds, sapphires, topaz, jade—they're all found in abundance there. Oh, and gold and silver, too. None of these have been spared in building the palace. Imagine how its great halls must sparkle and glitter when lit by thousands—nay, millions—of torches and candles!

*(*HADES *and* PERSEPHONE *enter, then freeze. The lights brighten.)*

ORPHEUS AND EURYDICE

EUTERPE. However, the very flames are cold—and so, I'm afraid, is the hospitality of the king and queen.

(HADES, PERSEPHONE, and ORPHEUS come to life. EUTERPE steps aside to watch.)

HADES *(studying ORPHEUS)*. A mortal—a living, breathing mortal. It's been a long time since someone like you came our way. *(To PERSEPHONE)* Who was the last, dear?

PERSEPHONE. Heracles, perhaps.

HADES. Oh, yes, Heracles. A troublemaker. He took our three-headed watchdog, Cerberus—although he gave him back eventually. But let me see if I understand you correctly. You've come here in search of your bride—what was her name again?

ORPHEUS. Eurydice.

HADES. Eurydice, yes. And you want me to restore her to life again.

ORPHEUS. That's right.

HADES. A rather exceptional request. Oh, it's been done before. Heracles once rescued a queen from death—Alcestis was her name, I think. He wrestled the death-god Thanatos to get her back. But Heracles is quite a hero, and he succeeded by sheer dint of strength. And you—well, if you don't mind my saying so, you don't look like much of a wrestler. Why should I return your bride to you?

(While HADES has been speaking, PERSEPHONE has walked over to ORPHEUS.)

PERSEPHONE *(to ORPHEUS)*. What a lovely rose. May I have a look at it?

(Before ORPHEUS can protest, PERSEPHONE snatches the rose from his lapel.)

PERSEPHONE. So fresh, so fragrant. And such soft petals. I love flowers—I really do. And none ever grow here. Amazing, that this one is still alive. May I have it?

ORPHEUS. I'm sorry—but no.

PERSEPHONE. What?

ORPHEUS. It's very important to me, Your Highness. You see—

PERSEPHONE. I don't want to hear it. *(She brusquely hands the flower back to ORPHEUS, then walks back toward Hades.)*

PERSEPHONE *(to HADES)*. Make him go away. I don't like him.

HADES. At least we could hear him out.

PERSEPHONE. No. I want him gone.

HADES. But, dear—

PERSEPHONE. We've got a crowding problem as it is. More and more dead show up every day. And if the *living* start coming around all the time, imagine the mess we'll have.

HADES *(to ORPHEUS)*. You seem like a nice young fellow. But really, it's out of my hands. The Fates themselves decided that your bride must die. And not even I can disobey the Fates.

ORPHEUS *(strumming his lyre)*.
With scissor sharp, with words unspoken,
Her thread of life the Fates have broken;
It was too soon, it was too soon.

104

But grant me just this trifling token
And let Eurydice be woken;
    Ask I too much to ask this boon?

HADES. A pretty song.

PERSEPHONE *(with some surprise).* A very pretty song.

HADES. But learn to count your blessings. You were parted in the bloom of youth. You never had to watch each other grow old and gray. You will always remember her as young and beautiful—and so she will remember you.

ORPHEUS *(strumming his lyre).*
Youthful beauty is but flimsy,
A veil that's woven out of whimsy;
    It hides the heart, it hides the
      soul.
But with the years, the veil that
  flatters
Falls away in shreds and tatters;
    A lovely spirit sparkles whole.

PERSEPHONE *(to* HADES*).* Oh, darling, he does have a point.

ORPHEUS.
To feel the fire of youth turn colder,
Yet love still more as we grew older—
    This was a bliss we never knew.
So I have traveled near and yonder,
And now into these depths I wander
    Praying this last prayer to you.

PERSEPHONE *(to* HADES*).* It's true, it's true! You've never lived among the living, and I have. You don't know how devoted mortal couples can be in their old age. It's really quite touching.

HADES. Be that as it may, there's nothing I can do. The Fates, Orpheus. The Fates.

ORPHEUS *(strumming his lyre).*
It's true, her thread the Fates did
  sever,
But must that mean we part forever?
    Surely such rules were made to
      break.
To tie the thread is all that's needed;
A little knot and the Fates are
  cheated;
    A little knot—for lovers' sake.

(PERSEPHONE *is weeping openly now, and even* HADES *appears to have trouble keeping his composure.)*

PERSEPHONE *(to* HADES*).* He's right. You know he is. Rules are made to be broken. Didn't you break the rules yourself when you brought me here to be your bride?

HADES. But, my pet—

PERSEPHONE. No "buts," please! You simply must bring his beloved what's-her-name back to life. If you don't, I'm—I'm going home to Mother!

HADES. You go home to Mother once a year.

PERSEPHONE. Well, then, I'll—

HADES. No need for threats. The truth is, he's won me over, too. *(Walking to where* EURYDICE *lies covered)* You can cheat the Fates for a time, Orpheus. But you cannot win in the end.

ORPHEUS. I know it.

HADES. I can re-tie the thread of life, but the thread will wear and fray with age.

ORPHEUS. I know it.

HADES. And when it breaks again, I cannot tie another knot.

ORPHEUS. I know it—and I want it no other way.

HADES *(uncovering* EURYDICE*).* Getting her back to the world of the living will prove most perilous.

ORPHEUS. I'm ready for anything.

HADES. I hope so, for your sake.

*(*EURYDICE *rises to her feet, looking very disoriented.)*

ORPHEUS. My darling—!

EURYDICE *(lifting her foot).* Ouch!

ORPHEUS. What's the matter?

EURYDICE. I stepped on a thorn. Strange, I was sure there weren't any thorns around here.

ORPHEUS. But, Eurydice—

EURYDICE. Oh, Orpheus, you found me! How sweet of you to come looking so quickly! I know, it was wicked of me to wander off like that. I just wanted to give you a little scare, that's all—and make you love me even more. Can you forgive me?

ORPHEUS. I don't understand.

EURYDICE. How bright the meadow is! And just a moment ago, we thought a storm was coming. Oh, our wedding day is perfect, after all! But where are my bridesmaids? They ran off to find shelter from the storm, I'll bet. Come back, you silly things! Can't you see the storm is gone? It's sunny now.

ORPHEUS *(to* HADES*).* What have you done to her?

HADES. Nothing at all. She's new to this realm, and she's bewildered. Newcomers often can't understand that they're dead. They learn after a while. But since you're determined to take her back to the living— well, I'm afraid she'll be doubly confused.

ORPHEUS *(to* EURYDICE*).* Listen very carefully. You're not in the meadow anymore. And you didn't step on a thorn. You were bitten by a snake.

EURYDICE. A snake?

ORPHEUS. Its poison killed you.

EURYDICE. Now you're just talking nonsense.

ORPHEUS. I'm not. Look around. What do you see? The halls of a palace, all studded with precious jewels and lit by candles and torches.

EURYDICE. What palace is this?

ORPHEUS. The palace of Hades and Persephone, the king and queen of the dead.

EURYDICE. No.

ORPHEUS. It's true. The king and queen themselves are standing right before you.

EURYDICE. Then I *am* dead! And you are, too!

ORPHEUS. Neither one of us is dead— not anymore. I've come to bring you back to the world of sunlight, the world of the living.

EURYDICE. But how—?

*(*ORPHEUS *takes the rose from his lapel and hands it to* EURYDICE.*)*

ORPHEUS. This rose—do you remember

the vows we made with it? As long as it lives, so will our love. Do you understand?

(EURYDICE *nods uncertainly.*)

ORPHEUS (*to* HADES *and* PERSEPHONE). Thank you. We must go now.

PERSEPHONE. Oh, but what's the rush? Couldn't you sing a little something first? A sad song, please. I do love sad songs. I wonder why that is.

ORPHEUS. Not now, Your Highness, I implore you. Your husband says that our journey will be difficult, so we'd better get started.

PERSEPHONE. Is this how you repay our kindness?

HADES. Let him go, dear. You can't blame him for not wanting to waste precious living moments among the dead.

PERSEPHONE (*to* ORPHEUS). But when will we see you again?

ORPHEUS. All mortals arrive here sooner or later.

PERSEPHONE. But how long will that be? I'm so anxious to hear another song. Oh, Orpheus, please die very soon! Couldn't you die tomorrow— or the next day, at the very latest?

ORPHEUS. I'm afraid it's not for me to decide. Let's see what the Fates have in mind.

PERSEPHONE. Oh, the Fates! Always the Fates!

ORPHEUS. I'm sure I'll be back before you know it. You live in eternity, and a lifetime is much shorter for you than for mortals.

HADES. It's true, Persephone. Let them be on their way.

PERSEPHONE. If I must.

ORPHEUS (*to* HADES). Thank you, Your Highness. (*Taking* EURYDICE's *hand*) Come on, my dear. I know the way.

HADES. One moment, Orpheus. I'm afraid it's not that simple.

ORPHEUS. Well?

HADES. First, turn your face away from Eurydice.

ORPHEUS. But—

HADES. You must.

(ORPHEUS *does so.*)

HADES. Now do not look in her direction until you reach the world of the living.

ORPHEUS. That's impossible!

HADES. Impossible or not, it's the only way.

ORPHEUS. Why did you give me hope, only to trick me like this?

HADES. It's not a trick. I'm doing all I can to help you cheat the Fates. But there are rules that even I can't change, and this is one. You simply must not look at Eurydice until you both stand in the open air again.

ORPHEUS. And if I fail?

HADES. She'll return to the dead, and there will be no bringing her back.

ORPHEUS. I've not come all this way to falter now. Follow me, Eurydice. And be very careful not to step in front of me.

EURYDICE. But, Orpheus, my foot hurts

so badly. Please—help me get rid of this thorn.

HADES. She's still lost between two worlds, between life and death.

ORPHEUS (*speaking to* EURYDICE *without looking at her*). Eurydice, I'm sorry about the pain, but I'm sure it will go away in time. In the meantime, you must follow me. And you mustn't drop behind, because I can't turn back for you. Do you understand?

(*Not looking at* ORPHEUS, EURYDICE *nods uncertainly—but of course,* ORPHEUS *cannot see her.*)

ORPHEUS. Eurydice!

EURYDICE. Yes, I think so. But everything seems so very strange.

ORPHEUS. I know. And if I speak to you sharply, it's only because I love you. I'll do whatever it takes to get us home again. (*Strumming his lyre*) Do you hear my lyre?

(EURYDICE *nods again.*)

ORPHEUS. Eurydice!

EURYDICE. I hear it.

ORPHEUS. I'll keep playing it. Pay close attention to its chords. Try to think of nothing else. Just follow my lyre.

EURYDICE. I'll try.

HADES. Good luck, Orpheus.

PERSEPHONE. And come back soon!

(HADES, PERSEPHONE, ORPHEUS, *and* EURYDICE *freeze.* EUTERPE *steps forward.*)

EUTERPE. And so begins the perilous return. Orpheus is faced with a task that gives new meaning to the phrase "a matter of life and death."

(HADES *and* PERSEPHONE *exit. The lights darken somewhat.*)

EUTERPE. Crossing the Styx again is simple enough. Charon the ferryman is glad to take them across for a song. But the climb through the caverns— ah, that's not so easy! It must be a law of physics that the way up is always much longer than the way down. Gravity isn't always our friend. And don't forget—our hero can't look back at his beloved, or he'll lose her forever.

(EUTERPE *steps aside to watch.* ORPHEUS *and* EURYDICE *come to life.*)

EURYDICE. I'm tired, Orpheus. And my foot hurts so much. Can't we stop and rest?

ORPHEUS. Not until we reach the sunlight.

EURYDICE. But where *is* the sun? The day has gotten so dark and cloudy again! It's liable to rain any moment. Shouldn't we find shelter?

(*The* OFFSTAGE VOICES *are heard again.*)

1ST VOICE. Dark and cloudy?

2ND VOICE. Rain?

3RD VOICE. Shelter?

1ST VOICE. What on earth is she talking about?

2ND VOICE. The poor thing must be deranged.

3RD VOICE. Quite out of her head.

EURYDICE (*to the* VOICES). Who are you?

ORPHEUS. They're the cavern drafts.

1ST VOICE. Howling.

2ND VOICE. Groaning.

3RD VOICE. Murmuring.

1ST VOICE. Moaning.

2ND VOICE. Whispering.

3RD VOICE. Whistling.

ORPHEUS. Pay no attention to them. Listen only to my lyre.

EURYDICE. But *where* are they?

1ST VOICE. In the tunnel behind you.

2ND VOICE. In the opening to the right of you.

3RD VOICE. In the passage to the left of you.

ORPHEUS. Don't try to go after them. Follow me, and only me. Do you hear me?

EURYDICE. I hear you. You don't have to use that tone of voice. I don't know why you're so angry with me. You won't even look at me.

ORPHEUS. Eurydice, try to remember I can't look at you or you'll die.

1ST VOICE. Poor young fellow!

2ND VOICE. Didn't we tell you?

3RD VOICE. Didn't we warn you?

1ST VOICE. You'll find grief.

2ND VOICE. You'll find sorrow.

3RD VOICE. Greater grief and sorrow than you've ever known.

ORPHEUS. That hasn't happened yet. And it won't, not if I can help it. My lyre, Eurydice. Listen to it. Think of nothing else. Follow nothing else.

(A terrible sound fills the air, like the flapping wings of gigantic bats. The sound grows louder and louder.)

1ST VOICE. Oh, no!

2ND VOICE. *They* are returning!

3RD VOICE. Flee!

1ST VOICE. Hide!

2ND VOICE. Seek cover!

3RD VOICE. Seek safety!

(The sound of wings becomes very loud—then suddenly stops. Total silence.)

EURYDICE. Orpheus?

ORPHEUS. Yes?

EURYDICE. What's happening?

ORPHEUS. I don't know. But whatever it is, it frightened the cavern drafts themselves into silence.

EURYDICE. Then perhaps we should be frightened, too.

ORPHEUS. True.

(The FURIES—TISIPHONE, MEGAERA, *and* ALECTO—*enter.)*

TISIPHONE. Outlaws!

MEGAERA. Fugitives!

ALECTO. Felons!

FURIES *(together).* We've got you now!

EURYDICE. Oh, Orpheus, these creatures—they're horrible! They've got huge bat wings! And snakes for hair!

ORPHEUS *(to* FURIES*).* Who are you, with your canine faces and bloodshot eyes?

TISIPHONE. I am Tisiphone.

MEGAERA. I am Megaera.

ALECTO. I am Alecto.

TISIPHONE. We are sisters.

MEGAERA. The punishing goddesses.

ALECTO. Born from the blood of Heaven.

EURYDICE. Born from the blood of Heaven? Orpheus, they're the Furies—the Angry Ones! They're avenging goddesses, older than Zeus himself!

ORPHEUS. I've heard of them, yes. But what are they doing here?

TISIPHONE. We are returning from the world of the living.

MEGAERA. We had some business there.

ALECTO. A murderer had escaped human justice.

TISIPHONE. We hounded him from town to town.

MEGAERA. We stung him with whips of conscience.

ALECTO. We plagued him with pangs of despair.

TISIPHONE. We drove him hopelessly mad.

MEGAERA. Our job is done.

ALECTO. Now we are going home.

ORPHEUS. Home?

EURYDICE. I've heard that they live down in the lowest depths of the earth—even below the realm of Hades.

ORPHEUS (to EURYDICE). You sound quite clear-headed all of a sudden.

EURYDICE. Oh, yes. Coming face to face with the most frightful creatures in the universe concentrates the mind wonderfully.

ORPHEUS (to FURIES). We're not criminals. Kindly let us pass.

TISIPHONE. But you *are* criminals.

MEGAERA. Do you take us for fools?

ALECTO. Why else have you fled the realm of the dead?

ORPHEUS. Because we are alive.

TISIPHONE. A likely story!

MEGAERA. If you're alive, what were you doing there in the first place?

ALECTO. We know all about your kind.

TISIPHONE. You're wayward dead who refuse to stay where you belong.

MEGAERA. The living world is full of ghosts like you.

ALECTO. And now we've got you!

EURYDICE (to ORPHEUS). It's no use, we're done for. There's no reasoning with them. They're a law unto themselves, and even Zeus is helpless against them. The best we can hope for is a quick, painless death.

TISIPHONE. An intelligent young lady.

MEGAERA. Indeed, we *are* quite adamant.

ALECTO. We'd strike the sun if it strayed from its path.

(ORPHEUS *strums his lyre.*)

EURYDICE. Really, dear, this is hardly the time to break into song.

ORPHEUS (to FURIES).
I know your name.
All the captains, all the kings—
Even the gods—tremble before
  Your fearful fame.
They know and dread your righteous
  stings.
But I, mere poet, know something
  more;
  I know your name.

EURYDICE. Of course, we know their name! They're Furies! What do you

think you're doing, Orpheus? This is
futile and dangerous.

ORPHEUS.
>Daughters and sons
>With parents' blood upon their hands
>Flee you in fear, calling you
>>"The Angry Ones."
>I know what else you're called, by
> chance,
>And I believe it is more true—
>>"The Kindly Ones."

TISIPHONE. Kindly Ones.

MEGAERA. Yes.

ALECTO. That is our truer name.

FURIES *(together).* You are a wise poet.
Very wise.

(The FURIES *fold their arms, bow their heads,
and fall silent and still.)*

EURYDICE. They've closed their wings
and shut their eyes—like sleeping
bats. How did you do it?

ORPHEUS. I sang of their secret.

EURYDICE. But how did you *know* their
secret?

ORPHEUS. I didn't. But it seemed to me
that they must be kindly deep down.
After all, they love justice so much,
they're willing to turn themselves
into monsters in order to uphold it.
But let's get on our way before they
wake again.

*(*ORPHEUS *and* EURYDICE *freeze.* EUTERPE
steps forward.)

EUTERPE. The worst dangers are surely
past. Our hero and heroine aren't
likely to face any threats more fearful
than the Furies.

(The FURIES *exit.)*

EUTERPE. And yet—the very absence of
danger can be dangerous. Perhaps
that's why so many accidents happen
close to home. Caution becomes
most precious when confidence
grows strongest.

*(*EUTERPE *steps aside. A pool of light appears
directly in front of* ORPHEUS. ORPHEUS *and*
EURYDICE *come to life.)*

ORPHEUS. Look, Eurydice! The cavern
entrance! We're here! We're here at
last! *(Stepping into the pool of light)* Ah,
the sun! The source of all life! Thank
you, Apollo! Thank you for
answering my prayers! Thank you for
bringing us back to the living world!

(Still behind ORPHEUS, EURYDICE *stumbles
and almost falls.)*

ORPHEUS. Eurydice, come quickly!
Eurydice, where are you? *(He turns
toward her.)*

EUTERPE *(to the audience).* It's
elementary male psychology, I'm
afraid. Men are always just a little
ahead of themselves—sometimes
with tragic results.

(Picking herself up, EURYDICE *does not yet see
him.)*

EURYDICE. It's all right, my love. I
stumbled a little, that's all. *(Looking at*
ORPHEUS*)* Orpheus! You're looking
at me! And I'm still in the cave!

ORPHEUS *(turning away).* No!

EURYDICE. You saw me. And now I
must die.

ORPHEUS. Oh, Eurydice, my darling,
please forgive me.

(EURYDICE *walks toward* ORPHEUS.)

EURYDICE.
> Forgive you, dear?
> That's one thing I can't do, I fear.
> Forgiveness is
> Not fitting for a time like this.
> Can I forgive
> Your wanting so much for me to
> live,
> Your ardor led
> You down among the doleful dead?
> Or for having forsook
> That dire commandment not to
> look—
> So much you yearned
> To see my face when we returned?
> Oh, no—I can't
> Such leniency give or grant.
> Accept instead
> More thanks and love than can be
> said.

(EURYDICE *places the rose in* ORPHEUS' *lapel, then exits.* ORPHEUS *freezes.* EUTERPE *steps forward.*)

EUTERPE. So back to the dead Eurydice goes. And Orpheus? Well, devastated is too mild a word.

(CHARON *enters with his tin can, then freezes.*)

EUTERPE. But as you might guess, it's not his way to take disaster lying down. Pretty soon, he goes down into the cavern again. But things don't go well. You wouldn't think he'd have much trouble dealing with Charon the ferryman, but he does.

(EUTERPE *steps aside to watch.* CHARON *and* ORPHEUS *come to life.*)

CHARON (*bailing water out of his boat*). *You* again! What do you want this time?

ORPHEUS. To be taken across, of course.

CHARON. Huh-uh. No can do.

ORPHEUS. Why not?

CHARON. You're alive.

ORPHEUS. I thought you didn't care about that.

CHARON. Didn't used to. But the boss chewed me out something fierce after the last time. Said I'd be out of a job if I ever took live folks across again.

ORPHEUS. Surely we can work out some kind of a deal.

CHARON. Nope.

ORPHEUS. I'm better prepared this time.

CHARON. How do you mean?

ORPHEUS (*sticking out his tongue*). Ahhh.

CHARON. So? You've got a coin in your mouth. What is this, some kind of magic trick?

ORPHEUS. Price of passage.

CHARON. Don't know what you're talking about.

(ORPHEUS *reaches into his pocket and pulls out a handful of coins.*)

ORPHEUS. I can make it worth your while.

CHARON. I'm shocked—shocked, d'you hear me?—to be offered a bribe!

ORPHEUS. What about a song, then?

CHARON (*bailing*). Don't want to hear it.

ORPHEUS (*strumming his lyre*).
> They've been saying since I don't
> know when

That this place is as dismal as sin.
    Reads a sign front and center,
    "Give up hope ye who enter."
I can't help it—I want to get it in!

CHARON (*bailing faster*). I'm not listening.

ORPHEUS. You're crying.

CHARON. No, I'm not.

ORPHEUS. Oh, yes, you are. I see a tear right there on your cheek.

ORPHEUS. What if I am? Sing all the sad songs you like. I'm not taking you, and that's that.

(ORPHEUS *and* CHARON *freeze.* EUTERPE *steps forward.*)

EUTERPE. It's said that Orpheus can change the courses of rivers with his songs. But he can't change Charon's mind—not this time, not after the ferryman puts in a pair of earplugs. For seven whole days, Orpheus wanders the Styx's shore, but in vain. He can't get across.

(CHARON *exits.* ORPHEUS *sits down on a stool and strums on his lyre.*)

EUTERPE. Which brings us back to where we started—with a young man in a meadow, strumming his lyre and singing. Forest animals have gathered to listen—and so have rocks and trees. But there's more to Orpheus' story. Perhaps you'd like to hear the rest of it in his own words. (*To* ORPHEUS) Sing it for us, won't you?

ORPHEUS (*strumming his lyre*).
    I came back to the world of life
    And rested in this field.

I wept and sang till meadows rang,
    But my soul never healed.
I would not speak to anyone;
    My heart I would not yield.

I would not yield my heart to love,
    Yield prayer to any god.
When lovely maidens came to me,
    I scarce gave them a nod.
When gods performed their miracles,
    I was not touched nor awed.

Then some god saw I was not awed;
    This gave offense to him.
He called his maiden worshippers
    And swore his sentence grim.
The maids with might, by darkest night,
    Tore me limb from limb.

They tore me limb from limb, I say,
    And scattered me far and wide.
The Muses forlorn—how they did mourn!
    They gathered me while they cried.
The nightingale sings sweetest near
    The tomb where I abide.

EUTERPE. Now that I think of it, Orpheus—I find it rather puzzling to hear you singing about your own death. And right in the very meadow where it took place!

ORPHEUS. But Aunt Euterpe, you know it happened. You even helped bury me.

EUTERPE. Yes, I know. But if you really were torn limb from limb, scattered far and wide, then buried in a tomb—well, how can we possibly be having this conversation?

ORPHEUS. You ought to understand
better than anybody. You *are* the
Muse of lyric poetry. Death can't take
me. I'll live forever in song and story.
*(Rising to his feet and strumming his lyre
again)*
Life and love are short, not long,
    As we've all heard;
Such is the truth of every song,
    Rest assured.
But verse and song are long indeed;
To live forever, you but need
    A simple word.

*(EURYDICE enters as ORPHEUS continues
strumming his lyre.)*

EURYDICE.
In magic springs of song we swim,
    My love and I.
Now we are bathed in singer's hymn,
    In poet's sigh.
We've washed away all marks of
    death;
As long as a poet draws a breath,
    We'll never die.

*(ORPHEUS hands the rose to EUTERPE. Then
he and EURYDICE exit hand in hand.)*

EUTERPE. But of course! And that must
be why everyone loves sad songs.
Because they belie their very sadness.
They render everything and everyone

they touch immortal. And if that's
true—well, let's try a little
experiment, shall we?

*(EUTERPE steps forward and addresses the
audience, accompanied by offstage chords.)*

EUTERPE.
Keep still, sit tight;
I promise you,
I will not bite.

My treatment, it's true,
May hurt a little;
All good things do.

But pain is brittle
And soon made nil,
Just like a riddle

Solved with skill
By someone bright.
Sit tight, keep still,

While I recite
This little song
And death takes flight.

May you live strong,
May you live well,
May you live long—

No, *always*! My spell
Is done; farewell!

(EUTERPE exits.)

PLAYWRIGHT'S POSTSCRIPT

The story of Orpheus' descent into the Underworld has been retold countless times. The 18th-century German composer Christoph Willibald Gluck wrote an opera about it, as did the 19th-century French composer Jacques Offenbach. And in 1959, a movie called *Black Orpheus* told the story yet again with a Brazilian setting.

Echoes of the story can also be heard in countless poems and songs up to the present day. The idea of love attempting to defy death has an endless appeal to poets and songwriters. As Elizabeth Barrett Browning concluded a famous sonnet, "if God choose, /I shall but love thee better after death."

CONNECTING TO OTHER CULTURES

In Japanese mythology, the goddess Izanami died and went to the Underworld, and her husband Izanagi followed her there in a vain attempt to rescue her. The Native American Blackfoots told of a man who journeyed into the land of death to find his lost wife, only to lose her again. And according to the Nez Percé Indians, the trickster Coyote almost succeeded in rescuing his wife from death. But like Orpheus, Coyote broke a sacred rule; he embraced his wife before they arrived in the world of the living, and so he lost her.

EROS AND PSYCHE

SETTING THE STAGE

As we've already seen, the gods of classical mythology were all-too-human in their moods and feelings. So it was inevitable that sometimes gods fell in love with mortals. Usually, this resulted in disaster, especially when Zeus' eye was caught by a beautiful but unlucky woman. But in at least one story, a god and a mortal found lasting happiness.

The story of Eros' love for the mortal princess Psyche was told by the Roman writer Apuleius in his prose work *The Golden Ass*, written in the 2nd century A.D. This tale is only a small part of *The Golden Ass*, which tells the story of a young man who was magically turned into a donkey.

When retold, this story is usually called *Cupid and Psyche* because Apuleius used the Roman names for the gods. To be consistent with the other plays in this collection, I have used Greek names for all the gods, so the play is titled *Eros and Psyche*. Besides, Apuleius spent part of his life in Greece, where he possibly first heard this story with Greek names.

MUSING ABOUT THE MYTH

Gods and mortals aren't supposed to fall in love, but in legends and myths they sometimes do. As you read, think about the spoken and unspoken rules that influence relationships. What are the consequences of breaking such rules?

EROS AND PSYCHE

(The visible stage is bare except for two stools. Upstage, a long bench is concealed behind a curtain. PSYCHE *enters and speaks to audience.)*

PSYCHE. How deep is the earth? How high is the sky? What are the stars made of?

*(*PSYCHE *freezes.* ERATO *enters and addresses the audience.)*

ERATO. A young woman's curiosity—that's my theme. We've heard such stories before, haven't we? You may remember Pandora, who just couldn't keep her itchy fingers off the lid of that jar. And so she released all kinds of evils into the world. And, oh, there was Eve, too. She just had to find out what that apple tasted like, and so Paradise itself was lost! Ah, women and their curiosity! They've brought such terrible trouble to us all, there's no doubt about it. And yet . . . I wonder if we're only getting one side of the story. Has no good ever come from feminine curiosity? I wonder . . . *(Pause)*

Oh, excuse me. I'm getting way ahead of myself, as usual. I'm Erato, and I'm the Muse of romantic love. Now, you hear all sorts of popular songs about falling in love, falling out of love, unrequited love, betrayal in love. Well, I inspire those songs. I've been doing it for millennia. It's a thriving business, always has been. Love's an endless topic—and one to inspire great curiosity, isn't it? I mean, who really understands it? And who doesn't want to know more about it? Now, when we talk about love, the whole issue of beauty is sure to come up sooner or later. This man is handsome, that one is ugly. This woman is pretty, that one is plain. One oughtn't care one way or the other about people's looks—but one does. And beauty plays a crucial role in the story I'm about to tell.

(The KING comes onto the stage. He freezes near PSYCHE.)

ERATO. In a kingdom somewhere in Greece, there lives a king with a very beautiful daughter named Psyche. Not that Psyche's beauty brings her any happiness. Far from it!

(The KING and PSYCHE come to life.)

PSYCHE. No, Papa.

KING. But, Psyche—

PSYCHE. I won't do it, that's all.

KING. They're calling your name. Listen.

PSYCHE. Yes, I hear them. And every day, I go out on the balcony and let them have a look at me. It's humiliating, Papa. I just can't do it anymore.

KING. Is it so terrible that they think you're beautiful?

PSYCHE. They think all kinds of things about me. They think I'm a goddess. They even *pray* to me! I'm just a human being, Papa. I don't have any business being prayed to. Can't you do something to stop it?

KING. I've tried everything I could think of. I've made laws forbidding people to worship you. I've sent priests and scholars throughout the land to tell people you're *not* a goddess. But no one believes it. And they keep coming here.

PSYCHE. I can't do *anything* anymore. I can't leave the palace, not even to go shopping or to take a walk in the forest. When I do, I'm mobbed by people. I'm a prisoner here. Even the servants look at me like I'm some kind of freak.

KING. Nobody thinks you're a freak. They think you're the most beautiful creature alive. Is that so bad? Why, every young woman in the world must envy you. Can't you enjoy all the praise and attention, just a little?

PSYCHE. No. It's a curse. I don't think of myself as beautiful. I do my best to not *be* beautiful. Look at the way I keep my hair. Look at how I dress. I try to look ordinary—even homely. Why can't people see me that way?

KING. Because, my dear daughter, you *are* beautiful—whether you want to be or not.

PSYCHE. Maybe I could pour a bucket of mud over myself.

KING. To make yourself ugly? It won't work. Your beauty is something you carry inside. No matter how you try to look, people will always find you beautiful.

PSYCHE. But it's terrible to live this way—and terrible for you, too. My poor Papa, because of me, your whole kingdom is completely out of control. Whatever can we do?

KING. What about taking a husband, Psyche? If you married, perhaps this fascination with your beauty would simply fade away.

PSYCHE. No one will marry me. No man would dare marry a goddess. Not that I've ever met the man I *would* marry. Men are all so dull. I've never met one with an interesting idea in his head—or who can answer any of the questions I yearn to have answered.

KING. But *nobody* can answer your questions, child! Your curiosity is boundless—and completely unreasonable. "How deep is the earth?" you keep asking people. And "How high is the sky?" And "What are the stars made of?" Why, only a god could answer such questions!

PSYCHE. Then perhaps some day I should talk with a god.

KING (*shaking his head sadly*). You're such a dreamer, Psyche.

PSYCHE. Yes, I suppose I am.

KING. But now—*please* step out onto the balcony! I'm afraid they'll break into the palace.

(PSYCHE *walks directly downstage and presents herself to an imaginary crowd.* VOICES *are heard from offstage.*)

VOICES. Hail, Psyche, of surpassing beauty! Hail, Psyche, our immortal goddess!

(PSYCHE *freezes.*)

ERATO. An immortal goddess, they call her. Dangerous words. For you see, *real* gods and goddesses have a way of resenting such talk.

(PSYCHE *exits.*)

ERATO. Not that it's the least bit Psyche's fault. The gods aren't always just, that's all.

(EROS *enters carrying a bow, with a quiver slung over his shoulder, then freezes.*)

ERATO. Take a look at this strapping young winged fellow with the bow and arrow. You've probably heard him called Cupid and have seen him portrayed as a little winged baby. The ancient Greeks knew him by the name of Eros, and as you can see, he's actually a handsome young man. A lot of people blame him for all the confusion and craziness of romantic love—and with good reason, I think. You see those arrows of his? If he hits you with one—even if it just grazes your skin—you'll fall hopelessly in love.

(*While* ERATO *has been speaking,* EROS *has unfrozen and taken an imaginary arrow out of his quiver. He puts it in his bow and draws the string tightly, pointing the arrow directly at the audience.)*

ERATO. Look out! He's aiming right at you!

(EROS relaxes his pull and puts the imaginary arrow back in the quiver. He freezes.)

ERATO. Oops, sorry. False alarm. He was just exercising his biceps. If only he'd practice his *aim* from time to time! I swear, sometimes he seems to shoot those arrows purely at random.

(APHRODITE comes onto the stage and freezes.)

ERATO. Anyway, right now he's got other things on his mind. He's been summoned by his mother, Aphrodite—the goddess of love. She's got something urgent to discuss with him.

(ERATO steps aside to watch. EROS and APHRODITE come to life.)

EROS. Hello, Mother.

APHRODITE. Hello, Eros, dear. Do sit down.

(EROS sits on a stool.)

APHRODITE. Have you noticed anything amiss lately?

EROS. Like what, Mother?

APHRODITE. Like a lapse of public interest in my goddessness, perhaps. Hardly anyone is worshipping at my temples these days. And how long has it been since anyone offered a sacrifice to me? You *have* noticed this little problem, haven't you?

EROS. Yes, I suppose I have, Mother.

APHRODITE. It just won't do, dear. A goddess must have worshippers and sacrifices to maintain her prestige. What will the other Olympians think if mortals stop fawning over me altogether? Would you happen to know the cause of this unfortunate situation?

EROS *(mumbling).* Well, I've heard . . .

APHRODITE. Speak up, dear. I can't hear you.

EROS *(a little louder).* I've heard that there's this very beautiful young woman who—

APHRODITE *(interrupting).* Beautiful? How beautiful?

EROS. Um, extremely beautiful.

APHRODITE. As beautiful as me?

EROS. That's what people say.

APHRODITE. Astonishing! Do continue.

EROS. Some people say that she *is* you—that the goddess Aphrodite has appeared on earth in mortal form. People are traveling from all over the world just to get a look at her.

APHRODITE. And so people have forgotten all about the real *me*.

EROS. That's what I hear.

APHRODITE. Yes, I've heard much the same thing. Well, Eros, a dreadful mistake has been made. I mean, I *am divine*—and unmistakably so, I think. Why, even my birth was miraculous. I sprang from the foam of an ocean wave—a creation of the waters!

EROS. I know, Mother.

APHRODITE *(ignoring him).* Can this mere girl claim any such marvelous birth? No! She's a creation of mere flesh—of vulgar earth, that's all. Filthy, sooty, clumpy, smelly *dirt*. This attention she's attracting—it's not just sacrilegious, it's unhygienic. We've got to do something about it right away. But what?

EROS. I'm sure you've got an idea, Mother.

APHRODITE. Well, yes, I suppose I do, dear. I want you to find the girl right away. Wound her with one of your arrows. Then make sure that she falls madly, hopelessly in love with the ugliest, must repulsive creature imaginable. That will make an example of her, once and for all.

EROS. But, Mother—

APHRODITE. I know, it sounds harsh. But we've got to be ruthless, if only to teach her a lesson. I hope you don't think it's a matter of vanity, dear. I hope *nobody* thinks I've got a vain bone in my body! It's the principle of the thing. Why, if we let this go, we'll soon have mortals pretending to be Zeus, Hera, Hermes, Athena, and all the rest. The cosmic order will go all topsy-turvy. We've got to put a stop to it immediately.

EROS. But, Mother—

APHRODITE. *What*, dear? Do speak up!

EROS. Is it really her fault she's so beautiful?

APHRODITE. Is it really her—? Such a question! Eros, I believe you've missed the entire point of our little talk. *Of course*, it's her fault she's so beautiful! It's anybody's choice to make. I myself could be fearfully ugly if took a mind to it—not that I ever would, since being beautiful is my sacred duty. Why, if the girl would only wear a bag over her head, I'd have no quarrel with her. But if she's being mistaken for *me*, it can only be deliberate. But what makes you say such a thing? You're not falling in love with her yourself, are you?

EROS. Of course not. I've never even seen her.

APHRODITE. And you *are* devoted to your dear mother?

EROS. Of course, I am.

APHRODITE. Always and forever?

EROS. Yes.

APHRODITE. Eros, *say* it.

EROS *(wearily—he has to say this a lot).* I *am* devoted to my dear mother, always and forever.

APHRODITE. What a precious little winged darling you are to me! Now—get to work!

(EROS and APHRODITE exit. ERATO steps forward.)

ERATO. Did I happen to mention that Psyche has two older sisters? No, I don't believe I did. They're fairly beautiful, but nothing like Psyche. And they're married, but not especially happily.

(OPAL, BERYL, and the KING come onto the stage, then freeze.)

ERATO. In fact, they live what you might call in-between sorts of lives. As you can imagine, it's hard to live an in-between life when your sister is being worshipped as a goddess.

(ERATO *steps aside to watch.* OPAL, BERYL, *and the* KING *come to life.*)

OPAL. Father, dear, this whole "goddess" thing has gotten completely out of hand.

KING. I quite agree, but what's to be done?

BERYL. Couldn't she just look a tad less beautiful?

OPAL. Maybe even a little bit ugly?

KING. That's not a solution, and you know it.

BERYL. What about marriage, then?

KING. You know your sister. She has extremely high expectations for a husband.

OPAL. Tut-tut, the girl always wants the moon and the stars.

BERYL. An ordinary man just won't do for her.

OPAL. *I* settled for an ordinary man, and I have no complaints—or at least not many.

BERYL. She has to learn to live with lower expectations, like the rest of us.

KING. I just don't know what to do.

OPAL. If you ask me, this is a good time to go to the oracle.

BERYL. Yes! At the very least, the oracle can tell you whom Psyche should marry.

(OPAL, BERYL, *and the* KING *freeze.* ERATO *steps forward.*)

ERATO. "What's an oracle?" you're asking. Well, it's a kind of fortune-teller. And like most fortune-tellers, oracles are notoriously vague.

(OPAL, BERYL, *and the* KING *exit.*)

ERATO. Let's say you ask an oracle "How long will I live?" The oracle is liable to reply "Red's your favorite color." Or suppose you ask "Will I ever be rich?" The oracle just might say "You're very fond of animals."

(*The* ORACLE *comes onto the stage and freezes.*)

ERATO. But when the king goes to the local oracle to ask about his daughter, the reply is frighteningly clear.

(ERATO *steps aside to watch as the* ORACLE *delivers her prophecy. She can either recite or sing. She can also dance a bit.*)

ORACLE.
A husband for your daughter—
Now just who might he be?
My answer will prove odder
Than you may now foresee.

Prepare her for a wedding,
But in no gown of white.
For terror and for dreading
A black dress will do right.

A monster fierce and frightful
Will take her by the hand.
His claim on her is rightful,
So don't scorn his demand.

And give up all resistance;
It lies beyond your scope;

123

And yearn for no assistance;
And also give up hope.

At dawn, you must awake her
And bid her to be meek;
Then to the mountain take her
And guide her to its peak.

Then leave her there—yes, leave her.
It's not for you to see
The one who'll come to thieve her
From your company.

Then go home and forget her—
Forget her if you can.
Forgetfulness is better
Than trying to understand

The strange and untold reason
For her to have to go.
She was yours for a season;
Content yourself just so.

(The ORACLE *exits.* ERATO *steps forward.)*

ERATO. Horrible words! And oracles are not to be doubted or disobeyed—at least not when they make some sense. But as you can imagine, the king is reluctant.

(The KING *and* PSYCHE *enter.)*

KING. No. It's impossible.

PSYCHE. Papa, I've got to go. It's the oracle's command.

KING. But to give you to a monster! How can I do that?

PSYCHE. Poor Papa, you're crying! But you mustn't cry—not now. The time for crying was when I was cursed with such terrible beauty. But soon I'll be free!

KING. Free? To marry a monster?

PSYCHE. Why do you think that's bad? Did the oracle say I wouldn't be happy with a monster? After all, what am I but a kind of monster? A monster might make a perfect husband for me.

KING. But you don't know.

PSYCHE *(laughs).* Whoever *does* know what they're getting into when they marry? I'll make the best of whatever happens. But now you've got to follow the oracle's instructions. You've got to take me to the mountaintop tomorrow morning.

KING. If I must. But the oracle also told me to do something I swear *never* to do.

PSYCHE. What's that?

KING. She told me to forget you. But I won't ever forget you.

PSYCHE *(holding his hand).* Nor I you, Papa.

(The KING *and* PSYCHE *freeze.* ERATO *steps forward. As she starts speaking,* OPAL *and* BERYL *enter and freeze near the* KING *and* PSYCHE.)*

ERATO. So the next morning, the king leads a grim procession escorting Psyche to the mountaintop. It looks more like a funeral than a wedding.

(The KING, OPAL, BERYL, *and* PSYCHE *come to life and pantomime their farewells while* ERATO *continues speaking. Then all except* PSYCHE *exit.* PSYCHE *steps downstage and freezes.)*

ERATO. Everybody is very sad as they say their farewells to our young heroine. Even Psyche's sisters cry a little—or at least they appear to. Then, as the oracle ordered, the procession turns and goes back down the mountain, leaving Psyche all alone. She stands at the edge of a cliff, looking out over the valley.

(ERATO *steps aside to watch.* PSYCHE *comes to life.*)

PSYCHE *(turning slowly and calling out).* Hello! Is anybody there? You can come for me now. Everybody is gone. And I'm not afraid. *(To herself, uneasily)* Or at least not very.

(*As* ERATO *is speaking,* PSYCHE *pantomimes being thrown off balance.* ZEPHYR *enters, dressed in a black robe and a black hood to suggest invisibility. He steps behind* PSYCHE *and guides her outstretched arms in imaginary flight.*)

ERATO. At that moment comes a powerful gust of wind. Before Psyche can catch her balance, she topples from the cliff. But does she fall to her death in the valley below? No!

PSYCHE. I'm not falling! I'm flying!

ZEPHYR. To be more precise, I'm *wafting* you.

PSYCHE. But who *are* you? *Where* are you? I can't see you.

ZEPHYR. My name is Zephyr.

PSYCHE. I've never been wafted before. It's a wonderful feeling. Are you a bird? An angel?

ZEPHYR. I'm the west wind.

PSYCHE. Are you my husband?

ZEPHYR. I wish I were. I work for your husband. He gave me orders to waft you.

PSYCHE. But *where* are you wafting me?

ZEPHYR. Where would you like to be wafted?

PSYCHE. Oh, look! Deep down in the valley by a running stream, there's a splendid palace surrounded by beautiful gardens! I'd love to be wafted there!

ZEPHYR *(with a chuckle).* As luck would have it, that's just where I'm supposed to waft you. It's your husband's home.

(ZEPHYR *lets go of* PSYCHE's *arms and exits. No longer flying,* PSYCHE *gazes around at an imaginary garden.*)

ERATO. Zephyr wafts her gently into the garden, and Psyche winds her way through its pathways to the magnificent palace gates.

PSYCHE. Well, this must be home.

(PSYCHE *knocks on an imaginary door. Her hand movement is accompanied by offstage knocks.*)

PSYCHE. Is anybody here?

(*The* GATEKEEPER *enters—dressed, like* ZEPHYR, *in a black robe and hood to suggest invisibility. He opens the imaginary door.*)

GATEKEEPER. Step right this way, madam. We've been awaiting you.

PSYCHE. A talking door?

GATEKEEPER. No, an invisible gatekeeper.

PSYCHE. Invisible?

GATEKEEPER. Yes. That doesn't displease you, I hope.

PSYCHE. No. It's just a bit of a surprise. Is the master—er, is my husband in?

GATEKEEPER. Not at the moment. He seldom comes around during the day. He'll arrive later this evening.

PSYCHE. Oh. What's his name, by the way?

GATEKEEPER. With due apologies, madam, I'm not at liberty to say.

PSYCHE. I guess he'll tell me when I meet him.

GATEKEEPER. Perhaps so, madam. Do you have any bags I can assist you with?

PSYCHE. No, I, uh—decided to travel light.

GATEKEEPER. A wise choice. I'm sure you'll not lack anything here. Would you like me to show you to your room?

PSYCHE. Not just yet. Would it be all right if I looked around a bit?

GATEKEEPER. By all means, you are at complete liberty. It's your house, after all. And if you need anything, just call.

PSYCHE. Thank you. You're very kind.

(The GATEKEEPER exits.)

PSYCHE. What an extraordinary home! Why, Papa's palace is nothing to this! Such a high ceiling! And such beautiful paneling! I wonder what it's made from.

(TWO SERVANTS enter, also dressed in black robes and hoods.)

1ST SERVANT. Cedar.

2ND SERVANT. And ivory.

PSYCHE. Who's there?

1ST SERVANT. We beg your pardon, madam.

2ND SERVANT. We didn't mean to alarm you. You see, we're—

PSYCHE. Don't tell me. Invisible servants.

1ST SERVANT. Quite so, madam.

PSYCHE. Are there any . . . *visible* people hereabouts?

1ST SERVANT. Well . . .

2ND SERVANT. . . . to be perfectly truthful . . .

1ST and 2ND SERVANTS (together). . . . No.

PSYCHE. Not even my husband?

1ST SERVANT. With all due apologies, madam—

PSYCHE. You're not at liberty to say.

2ND SERVANT. Quite correct.

PSYCHE. This could take some getting used to.

1ST SERVANT. We regret the inconvenience, madam.

2ND SERVANT. Yes, and we do apologize.

PSYCHE. Oh, don't apologize. I just need to be flexible, that's all.

1ST SERVANT. And now—can we serve you in any way?

2ND SERVANT. Something to eat, perhaps?

PSYCHE. No, thank you. I had breakfast before I left home.

1ST SERVANT. Some tea, then?

PSYCHE. Yes, that would be very refreshing.

EROS AND PSYCHE

(The 2ND SERVANT *pulls a cup out of her robe and presents it to* PSYCHE.*)*

2ND SERVANT. Your tea, madam.

PSYCHE. Thank you. *(She sips the tea.)* Do tell me more about this beautiful place. There's so much to see! How can I take it all in?

1ST SERVANT. You have plenty of time, madam.

2ND SERVANT. All the time in the world.

PSYCHE. So I do! So I do!

*(*PSYCHE *freezes. The* SERVANTS *exit, taking the cup.)*

ERATO. A delightful day passes as Psyche tours the seemingly endless palace and its grounds. And Zephyr gives her an enchanting waft through the surrounding valley. But shortly after nightfall, something rather alarming happens in the palace.

(The lights suddenly dim as ERATO *steps aside to watch.* PSYCHE *comes to life.)*

PSYCHE. The lamps and candles! They've been blown out! Zephyr, did you do that? If so, it wasn't a very funny joke. Servants, come quickly, I can't see a thing! Won't somebody light a single candle?

*(*EROS *enters, dressed in a black robe and hood.)*

EROS. Good evening, Psyche.

PSYCHE. Um—good evening. Who are you?

EROS. I'm your husband.

PSYCHE. I can't see you.

EROS. I know. You must never see me.

PSYCHE. Why not?

EROS *(with a slight laugh).* You're very curious, aren't you?

PSYCHE. Isn't it natural to want to know what one's husband looks like?

EROS. It's just not possible. I'm sorry.

PSYCHE. Is it because you're a monster?

EROS. Would you be horrified to learn that I'm really a monster?

PSYCHE. Not at all. You have a pleasant voice. You'd surely be a very gentle monster. But I don't think you *are* a monster. What are you, really? *(Pause)* What's your name?

EROS. I can't tell you that.

PSYCHE. A husband without a name? Oh, come on, now. This is getting just a little ridiculous.

EROS. I just can't.

PSYCHE. What should I call you then?

EROS. Whatever you choose to call me.

PSYCHE. Well, I'll just have to call you "Whoever-You-Are." Will you answer to "Whoever-You-Are"?

EROS. Certainly.

PSYCHE. All right then, Whoever-You-Are.

EROS. Is there anything I can bring you?

PSYCHE. What about a nice, lighted lamp?

EROS. Sorry.

PSYCHE. No, of course not. May I ask you a question, Whoever-You-Are?

EROS. Of course.

PSYCHE. Why did you bring me here?

EROS. Because I love you. Because I want you to be my wife. And I hope . . . *(Pause)* Well, I know it's too soon to say, but—

PSYCHE. You hope I'll learn to love you, too?

EROS. That's right. *(Pause)* And now, what can I do for you? You can have anything your heart desires. I'm very rich, as you've surely noticed.

PSYCHE. I've noticed. But my heart's desires are very simple.

EROS. Really? Isn't there anything you've longed for all your life, but could never have?

PSYCHE. Yes. Someone to talk to. Someone who can answer the questions I yearn to have answered.

EROS. Such as?

PSYCHE. How deep is the earth?

EROS. The earth is unfathomably deep. No mortal can ever reach its center. And yet, the earth is not so much as a speck of dust in the vastness of the sky.

PSYCHE. How high is the sky?

EROS. The sky has no edge or boundary. It is so vast that you cannot begin to see all its stars—not even on a brilliant summer night. And the stars you *can* see are unthinkably far away. The very light from them has taken hundreds, thousands, even millions of years to reach your eyes.

PSYCHE. And what are the stars made of?

EROS *(with a slight laugh).* You really *are* full of curiosity, Psyche. How many questions have you got for me?

PSYCHE *(happily).* I've got a whole mortal lifetime full of questions, Whoever-You-Are—as many questions as there are stars in the sky. And you, I think, are the answer to my heart's desires.

(EROS and PSYCHE freeze as the lights come up again. ERATO steps forward.)

ERATO. And so Psyche's life as a married woman begins—and it couldn't be happier. Her invisible servants help her set up a laboratory where she can conduct all kinds of experiments. And the mysterious "Whoever-He-Is" brings her piles upon piles of books from all the world's great libraries and bookstores.

(EROS and PSYCHE unfreeze. EROS takes a book out of his robe and gives it to PSYCHE, then steps to one side and freezes. PSYCHE sits on a stool and reads eagerly.)

ERATO. So Psyche's days are filled with study and thought—and her nights with wonderful talk. Of course, when her husband comes home and the lights go out, it *is* difficult to read . . .

(The lights suddenly dim again as ERATO steps aside to watch.)

PSYCHE. Hey! I was in the middle of a very interesting chapter!

EROS. Sorry. I could go away for a while so you can have some more light.

PSYCHE. Oh, please don't go, my darling Whoever-You-Are! I didn't mean to snap at you. Let's talk. I was just looking at a very interesting drawing. It shows that the moon is big and round and covered all over with mountains, valleys, craters, and such.

EROS. That's true, I hear.

PSYCHE. How very curious! The moon looks so small and flat and smooth from here on earth—like a little piece of polished stone. I wish I could see it better.

EROS. Would you like a telescope?

PSYCHE. I'd love to have one!

EROS. I'll bring it tomorrow night.

PSYCHE. You're so incredibly kind to me, Whoever-You-Are. You give me everything I could possibly want or need, and you know the answers to so many questions. Sometimes I feel like . . .

EROS. What?

PSYCHE. Well, like I have nothing to offer you in return.

EROS. You give me joy. It's very beautiful to watch your mind range far and wide over so many questions and mysteries. I take delight in helping you to satisfy your curiosity.

PSYCHE. But can't I do the same for you? Isn't there some question troubling you that only I can answer?

EROS. Yes, I suppose there is.

PSYCHE. What is it?

EROS. What's it like . . . to know that you will someday die?

PSYCHE. You don't know?

EROS. No.

PSYCHE. You are immortal, then? *(Pause)* What kind of being *are* you?

EROS. Psyche, please—

PSYCHE. I'm sorry. I forgot. Well, then . . . what *is* it like? I wish I could find the words for it. Death is a mystery, that's all. It's a mystery that haunts the future.

EROS. Does it frighten you?

PSYCHE. Sometimes it does. Sometimes it doesn't seem frightening at all. Sometimes it just seems like some grand adventure lying ahead.

(Pause)

EROS. *I'm* frightened, Psyche— frightened for you.

PSYCHE. Whatever for?

EROS. Because I think your end might be near.

PSYCHE. Why?

EROS. There are two people who wish you ill, and they have the power to hurt you.

PSYCHE. Who?

EROS. Your sisters. Every day, they've been going to the mountaintop where you disappeared. They've been calling for you, asking where you've gone.

PSYCHE. The poor things! They must be worried sick!

EROS. No, Psyche. They mean you harm.

PSYCHE. Oh, but you're wrong, Whoever-You-Are! They're my sisters, and they love me, and they're desperate to find out if I'm alive or dead! And I've been so selfish, I've hardly given them a thought all this time—or my poor father, either! I've got to go see them.

EROS. No, Psyche.

PSYCHE. Why not? Can't Zephyr take me up to the mountaintop?

EROS. You mustn't go there.

PSYCHE. Well, then, can't Zephyr bring them down?

EROS. They mustn't come here.

PSYCHE. But what harm could they possibly do me?

EROS. They could turn you against me.

PSYCHE. Nothing could turn me against you.

EROS. Don't say that, Psyche. You don't understand the danger you're in.

PSYCHE. No, *you* don't understand how worried my sisters are. Please, let me see them. Let me show them that I'm all right.

(*Pause*)

EROS. I'll send Zephyr for them tomorrow morning.

PSYCHE. Oh, thank you, Whoever-You-Are!

EROS. Don't thank me. I fear I'm making a terrible mistake.

(EROS *and* PSYCHE *freeze. The lights come up again, and* ERATO *steps forward.*)

ERATO. As you might imagine, Psyche barely sleeps at all that night, she's so anxious to see her sisters.

(EROS *exits, taking the book.*)

ERATO. And sure enough, the very next morning Zephyr wafts Opal and Beryl down into the valley, and they visit Psyche at home.

(ERATO *steps aside to watch as* OPAL *and* BERYL *enter.* PSYCHE *comes to life.*)

BERYL. Goodness, what a descent!

OPAL. I thought I was going to die every second of the way!

BERYL. You must admit, it was rather exhilarating.

OPAL. Exhilarating, my foot. I believe I'm going to be sick.

PSYCHE. Oh, please don't be sick. Would you like something to settle your stomach? Some tea, perhaps? Have you had any breakfast?

OPAL. Don't even *talk* about food! What *was* that unholy contraption that tossed us down here?

PSYCHE. My friend Zephyr, the west wind.

BERYL. So we're making friends with the winds now, are we?

OPAL. It makes for an awfully bumpy ride. Terrible turbulence.

BERYL. Maybe you ought to have an elevator put in.

(*Pause*)

PSYCHE (*rather timidly*). I'm—very glad to see you.

OPAL (*embracing* PSYCHE). Oh, listen to how we're complaining so!

BERYL (*embracing* PSYCHE). We're so sorry!

OPAL. We can't tell you what a relief it is to see you alive and well.

BERYL. A *tremendous* relief!

OPAL. It's just that . . . well, it's all so strange.

BERYL. So *very* strange!

PSYCHE. Yes, I know. Sometimes I still find it pretty strange, myself.

OPAL. We've been so worried about you!

BERYL. So *awfully* worried!

OPAL. Nobody had any idea what had happened to you after you disappeared off that mountaintop.

BERYL. Everybody said you were dead.

OPAL. Everybody except Beryl and me, of course.

BERYL. Oh, no. We *never* gave up hope.

PSYCHE. I'm so glad. Won't you have a seat?

BERYL. That would be nice.

PSYCHE (*calling out to* SERVANTS). Two chairs, please.

(*The* TWO SERVANTS *enter.*)

1ST SERVANT. Right away, madam.

2ND SERVANT. At your service, madam.

(*The* SERVANTS *move the stools toward* OPAL *and* BERYL, *then exit.*)

OPAL (*sitting*). What have we here?

BERYL (*sitting*). Mechanical furniture?

PSYCHE. No. Invisible servants.

OPAL. I'm not sure I'd much like that. Call me old-fashioned, but I like to be able to *see* the help. When I scold somebody, I want to look them in the eye. How else can you keep them from getting sloppy?

PSYCHE. The servants are always perfect. I never have anything to scold them for.

OPAL. If you say so, dear. I'm sure you're much too lenient.

PSYCHE. How's Papa?

BERYL. Oh, he's well.

OPAL. But worried about you.

BERYL. Yes, *very* worried.

PSYCHE. I'm so sorry. Please tell him I'm all right.

OPAL. We'll be sure to do that.

BERYL. So you're a married woman now, are you?

PSYCHE. Yes.

OPAL. Well, it's about time. The family just about gave up hope. Can we meet your husband at long last?

PSYCHE. I'm afraid not. You see, he's . . . Well, he travels a lot.

BERYL. On business?

PSYCHE. That's right.

OPAL. What does he do?

PSYCHE. Um—he's in imports and exports.

BERYL. Goodness!

OPAL. Well, what does he look like, dear?

PSYCHE. Oh, he's fairly young. Tall. Sandy-haired. Quite good-looking— or I think so anyway.

BERYL. And prosperous, too, from the looks of things! What a lovely mansion! Everything's so very opulent! Why, there's gold leaf absolutely everywhere! And jewels, too!

OPAL. A little gaudy for my liking.

PSYCHE. I admit, it took some getting used to. But would you like a little something to take home with you? Opal, you're fond of pearls. And Beryl, you've got a taste for rubies.

OPAL. Oh, we couldn't.

BERYL. It wouldn't be right.

PSYCHE. I insist. (Calling to SERVANTS again) Gifts for my sisters, please.

(The TWO SERVANTS enter again. The 1ST SERVANT presents a necklace to OPAL. The 2ND SERVANT presents a ring to BERYL.)

1ST SERVANT (to OPAL). A pearl necklace for you, madam.

2ND SERVANT (to BERYL). And a ruby ring for you, madam.

(The SERVANTS exit.)

OPAL. Really, dear, this is quite overwhelming.

BERYL. How can we ever thank you?

PSYCHE. Oh, it's nothing. There's plenty more if you like. What do you see that catches your fancy? Go on, take something else, anything.

OPAL. Oh, no, absolutely not.

BERYL. I'm sure your friend Zephyr has a weight limit. Why, we'd never get out of this valley!

OPAL. Your husband must be . . . extremely rich.

PSYCHE. Yes, I suppose he is.

(OPAL, BERYL, and PSYCHE freeze.)

ERATO. And, oh, such a silence falls! But if you really listen, you'll hear something in that very silence. It's the sound of jealousy and envy clicking away in two wicked sisters' brains. Can you hear it, too? Listen very closely.

(OPAL and BERYL unfreeze and speak to the audience.)

OPAL. "Quite good-looking," she says. Huh! My husband's old enough to be my grandfather, and he's as bald as an onion!

BERYL. My husband's even older than Opal's, and he's all buckled over with gout and arthritis.

OPAL. Oh, mine's rich enough—but stingier than you can imagine! Why, he's got padlocks absolutely everywhere. He doesn't even trust me with his valuables.

BERYL. Has mine ever bought me so much as a ring or a locket? Don't make me laugh!

OPAL. It's just not fair, I tell you. I am the oldest.

BERYL. And Psyche is the youngest!

OPAL. Why should she get the husband of every woman's dreams?

OPAL and BERYL (together). It makes me sick!

(OPAL and BERYL freeze again.)

ERATO. Ah, jealousy and envy! Has curiosity ever caused half the harm of jealousy and envy?

(OPAL, BERYL, and PSYCHE unfreeze.)

OPAL. What did you say his name was?

PSYCHE. I didn't say.

BERYL. Then tell us, dear!

PSYCHE. Well . . . he's got this funny, superstitious sort of thing about his name. He doesn't like anyone to say it aloud. So I just call him "Whoever-You-Are."

OPAL and BERYL (together). "Whoever-You-Are."

PSYCHE. I know it sounds silly.

OPAL. Silly isn't quite the word for it, dear.

BERYL. What a peculiar way to go through life! Calling your own husband "Whoever-You-Are"!

OPAL. What *is* his name, really?

PSYCHE. Um . . . I can't tell you.

BERYL. Oh, come on.

OPAL. Just between us sisters!

BERYL. We won't tell anyone.

PSYCHE. I just can't. I'm sorry.

OPAL. How old did you say he was, again?

PSYCHE. Oh . . . 45-ish.

BERYL. I thought you said he was young.

PSYCHE. Well, 45 isn't so old, is it?

OPAL. Old enough to be your father.

BERYL. What did you say he looked like?

PSYCHE. Medium height, black-haired—

OPAL. I thought you said he was tall.

BERYL. And sandy-haired.

PSYCHE. Well, sort of in between.

OPAL. And what did you say he does for a living?

PSYCHE. Um . . . he's a ship's captain.

BERYL. He's not in imports and exports?

PSYCHE. He does that, too.

OPAL. Now, Psyche, you've always been a terrible liar.

BERYL. We can see right through you.

OPAL. Don't you think it's time you told your big sisters the truth? You've never even seen this husband of yours, have you?

(Pause)

PSYCHE. No.

BERYL. Do you even *have* a husband?

PSYCHE. Oh, yes. He comes to me every night. It's just that he won't tell me his name, and I'm not allowed to ever see him.

OPAL. And why do you suppose that is?

PSYCHE. I don't know. But I think something terrible would happen if I ever saw him. Perhaps I'd die. Listen, could we not to talk about him any more? I've said too much already. He wouldn't like it.

ERATO. Another silence falls—and this time, Psyche's sisters exchange a glance.

OPAL (aside to BERYL). Follow my lead.

BERYL (aside to OPAL). I'm right with you.

OPAL. Psyche, I'm afraid we've got terrible news. We weren't going to say anything because we hoped it wasn't true. But from everything you say, it's clear that you're in serious trouble.

BERYL. *Very* serious!

PSYCHE. What do you mean?

OPAL. Do you remember when that oracle said you were doomed to marry a monster?

PSYCHE. But my husband's not a monster.

BERYL. Oh, but he *is*.

OPAL. He's a *dragon*, dear. He's been seen by hunters and farmers hereabouts. They say he's all coiled and serpent-shaped, with awful scales all over him. He's got fiery breath and huge, poisonous fangs.

BERYL. And he *eats* people!

OPAL. Indeed, he does! He's extremely carnivorous, and human flesh is his favorite. Why, he's eaten more than a dozen people just in the last day or two!

BERYL. And folks say that he's only fattening you up so he can eat you, too!

PSYCHE. I don't believe it.

OPAL *(tearfully)*. Oh, Beryl, listen to her! She doesn't believe her own loving sisters!

BERYL. We didn't want to believe it either, Psyche. It hurts us to tell you, but it's for your own good. Please believe us.

OPAL. Don't break our hearts, dear.

PSYCHE. But he's so kind. And gentle.

OPAL. I'm sure he seems so.

BERYL. That's the wickedness of it.

PSYCHE. No. I don't believe it. I *won't* believe it. He's my husband, and I know him. You don't.

(Pause)

BERYL. How I wish we could make you see the truth!

OPAL. Won't you let your friend Zephyr waft you away with us?

BERYL. You belong back home.

PSYCHE. No. I belong here with my husband. *(Pause)* And now, I hope you don't think it rude of me, but—

OPAL. Maybe it's time for us to leave.

PSYCHE. That's right.

BERYL. Very well, dear. But remember what we said.

OPAL. We'll be there for you whenever you need us.

PSYCHE. Thank you. And now—are you sure you wouldn't like a few more jewels?

OPAL. Well, if you *insist*.

BERYL. Just a little handful.

(OPAL, BERYL, and PSYCHE freeze. ERATO steps forward.)

ERATO. So Opal and Beryl depart, laden with a king's ransom—and quite satisfied that they've planted the seeds of their sister's destruction.

(OPAL and BERYL exit. The lights dim again.)

ERATO. And that night, when lights go out and Psyche's husband comes home, the conversation is a little— well, more strained than usual.

(ERATO steps aside to watch. EROS enters and PSYCHE comes to life.)

EROS. So how were your sisters?

PSYCHE. They seemed well. They've been awfully worried about me.

EROS. What do they think of your life here?

PSYCHE. They don't like it.

EROS. Really?

PSYCHE. They say you're a monster.

EROS. What sort of a monster?

PSYCHE. A fire-breathing dragon with poisonous fangs. They say you eat people.

EROS. They're lying.

PSYCHE. How am I to know?

EROS. They mean you ill, Psyche. I warned you. They'll do anything to destroy our love.

PSYCHE. But I've never even seen you. If you're not a monster, what can possibly be the harm in—?

EROS (interrupting her angrily). Perhaps I'm a monster, and perhaps I'm not. Either way, you are forbidden to look upon me. I thought you understood that. Didn't you? (Pause) Are you not happy with me, Psyche?

PSYCHE. Happier than I thought I ever could be.

EROS. Is not seeing me such a terrible price to pay for your happiness?

PSYCHE. No, I don't suppose it is.

EROS. Very well, then. (Pause) This conversation has left me tired. I'll go on to bed.

PSYCHE. I'll be along shortly.

(EROS exits.)

ERATO. But Psyche doesn't go to bed. She blindly roams the dark halls of the mansion wrestling with her very soul.

PSYCHE. What does my husband plan to do with me? Will he devour me some day? No, that's impossible. My sisters are wrong, that's all. They don't know him. He's not some hideous dragon that craves human flesh. But what *is* he? A creature that will never die, it seems. And what might such a creature be? (Pause) Servants! Come at once!

(The TWO SERVANTS enter.)

1ST SERVANT. At your service, madam.

2ND SERVANT. What do you wish?

PSYCHE. Bring me an oil lamp.

1ST SERVANT. A lamp?

2ND SERVANT. Whatever for?

PSYCHE. Such a question! To see with, of course! I can't sleep tonight, and I want to read awhile. But how can I read when I can't see my hand in front of my face?

1ST SERVANT. But you're not *supposed* to see at night.

2ND SERVANT. Not when the master is here.

PSYCHE (sharply). Who are you to question my orders? Am I not the lady of the house?

1ST SERVANT. Of course you are, madam.

2ND SERVANT. But—

PSYCHE. But what? Did your master tell you never to bring me a lamp at night?

1ST SERVANT. Well, no.

2ND SERVANT. Not specifically.

PSYCHE. Do you want me to tell him you've disobeyed me?

1ST SERVANT. Of course not, madam.

2ND SERVANT. We never meant to be disobedient.

(*The* 1ST SERVANT *pulls a small oil lamp out of her robe and presents it to* PSYCHE. *The lights grow slightly brighter.*)

PSYCHE. Thank you.

1ST SERVANT. Would you like us to bring your books?

PSYCHE. I won't be needing them.

2ND SERVANT. But didn't you say—?

PSYCHE. It doesn't matter what I said.

(*As* ERATO *speaks,* PSYCHE *walks upstage toward the curtain.*)

ERATO. As Psyche approaches the bed where her husband lies, what does she expect to see? A coiled dragon, as her sisters warned? Perhaps she most fears finding nothing but an ordinary man.

(*Psyche opens the curtains, revealing the long bench. Lying across it is the sleeping* EROS— *no longer robed in black, but dressed as he was when we first saw him. Beside the bench are his quiver and bow.*)

ERATO. You can be sure of one thing— she's quite unprepared for what she *does* find in that bed!

PSYCHE (*in an urgent stage whisper*). Servants!

1ST SERVANT (*whispering*). Well?

2ND SERVANT (*whispering*). What is it?

PSYCHE. Look at what I've found! A beautiful creature with great, white, folded, feathered wings!

1ST SERVANT. Yes, we know.

2ND SERVANT. He *is* our master.

PSYCHE. Why couldn't you have told me?

1ST SERVANT. We were forbidden, and besides—

2ND SERVANT. —could *you* have found words to describe him?

PSYCHE. No, of course not.

1ST SERVANT. And neither could I.

2ND SERVANT. Nor I.

PSYCHE. But who *is* he?

1ST SERVANT. We mustn't say. And anyway—

2ND SERVANT. —we think you know already.

PSYCHE. Yes, I believe I do know. But dare I say it aloud? Dare I even *think* it? He can only be Aphrodite's immortal son—the god Eros.

1ST SERVANT and 2ND SERVANT (*together*). Eros. Yes.

1ST SERVANT. And now that you know—

2ND SERVANT. —please, come away!

PSYCHE. And look—his quiver full of arrows!

1ST SERVANT. Don't touch them!

2ND SERVANT. Especially not the points!

1ST SERVANT. They're very dangerous!

PSYCHE (*with a quiet laugh*). How so? Because they'll make me fall in love? But I'm in love already! I've been in love since the moment I first heard his voice! And now, I long for nothing else than to be more and more and more in love! *(Touching the tip of an arrow)* There. It hardly hurts at all to draw a little blood—and to fall ever more hopelessly and helplessly in love with Love himself! *(Kneeling beside him)* Beloved Eros, forgive my presumption. I didn't know. But now that I do, I'll never shine the light of a lamp on you again. For you are my light—the only light I'll ever need. Let the whole world go dark forever. Let the sun and the moon and the stars all disappear. I'll be happy as long as I have you.

(PSYCHE reaches to touch his hair.)

1ST SERVANT. Don't touch him!

2ND SERVANT. You'll wake him!

(As PSYCHE draws back, the lamp shakes in her hand.)

ERATO. Then, ah, the merest trembling of a hand—and the fatal drop of hot oil, falling from the lamp!

(EROS awakens with alarm.)

EROS. My shoulder! I've been burned!

PSYCHE. I'm sorry.

EROS. You! Psyche! With a lamp!

PSYCHE. I'm so sorry.

EROS. You've seen me!

PSYCHE. Oh, my dear husband, Eros, I'm so very sorry!

EROS. You know my name!

PSYCHE. But why shouldn't I know your name? Why shouldn't I see you?

EROS. Because mortals and gods are forbidden to marry! No one must know.

PSYCHE. Not even me?

EROS. You might tell someone—and that would be fatal.

PSYCHE. Couldn't you have trusted me?

EROS. I trusted you not to look at me, and look what you've done.

PSYCHE. But why did you choose to marry me if it was forbidden?

EROS. My mother was jealous of your beauty. She sent me to strike you with an arrow and make you fall in love with some vile beast. But when I saw you, I fell in love with you myself. I persuaded the oracle to tell that story about a monster. *(Holding out his hand)* Look at this wound. I loved you so much, and I wanted to love you even more, so I pierced myself with one of my own arrows.

PSYCHE *(holding out her hand)*. I have a wound just like yours. I pierced myself for the same reason—so I could love you endlessly.

EROS. I wish you hadn't. Now both of our hearts will break. I must go.

PSYCHE. Don't go! Think of our love!

EROS. There can be no love where there is no trust. Farewell.

(EROS exits. PSYCHE freezes. ERATO steps forward as the lights come back up.)

ERATO. And as Eros flies away, Psyche's whole world vanishes into thin air—the castle, the gardens, the servants, simply everything. She finds herself alone in a desolate valley, without even Zephyr to waft her away. For days, she wanders the world, searching for her lost beloved. She asks everyone she meets where Eros might be, but no one knows.

(APHRODITE *comes onto the stage and freezes.*)

ERATO. At long last, her desperate wanderings lead her to Aphrodite's palace.

(APHRODITE *and* PSYCHE *come to life.*)

APHRODITE. Ah, Psyche! We meet at last. Let me have a look at you. (*Studying* PSYCHE) May I be frank? I find it hard to see what all the fuss is about. Oh, you're pretty enough. Even beautiful, I suppose, in a mortal sort of way. But you're nothing, really, in comparison with the average wood nymph—let alone a full-fledged Olympian goddess. How you were ever mistaken for me, I'll never understand.

PSYCHE. Nor I.

APHRODITE. I'm glad we agree. Yes, I actually feel a bit sorry for you. You're truly a victim of your own publicity, of hype gotten out of hand. It's sad, really. It's especially sad that my poor son got caught up in the whole mess.

PSYCHE. Where is he?

APHRODITE. Who?

PSYCHE. Eros. My husband.

APHRODITE. Your *husband*? Oh, you poor little fool, you're not *married* to

him. No, no! He's a god and you're a mortal. You're not of the same social status. Marriages of that sort simply aren't allowed.

PSYCHE. Please, tell me where he is.

APHRODITE. He's in his room, and he's very ill. You severely injured the poor dear. Spilling hot oil on him! How could you be so cruel?

PSYCHE. I didn't mean to.

APHRODITE. Careless then.

PSYCHE. It was just a drop. How could it have hurt him so badly?

APHRODITE. It wasn't the drop of oil so much as the *betrayal*. You promised to never look at him—and yet you did. The merest drop of betrayal is very injurious. I'm not sure he'll ever fully recover.

PSYCHE. I want to see him.

APHRODITE. So you can hurt him again? Oh, I can hardly allow that. He needs his mother's protection. He needs his mother's care. The very last thing in the universe he needs right now is you.

PSYCHE. Isn't there anything I can do?

APHRODITE. Yes. You can die. That would make me happy.

PSYCHE. I'll do anything you ask. I'll carry out any task you can name. Just let me speak to him once.

APHRODITE. An intriguing proposal. (*Pause*) Yes, now that you put it that way, there *is* a little something you might do.

PSYCHE. Then tell me what it is!

APHRODITE. Caring for my sick son has aged me, oh, a millennium or so. You'll find this hard to believe, Psyche, but I'm usually much more beautiful than this. I need some beauty to freshen me up a bit. Perhaps you could go fetch me some.

PSYCHE. Oh, yes! Just tell me where I can find it.

APHRODITE. The Underworld.

PSYCHE. The realm of the dead?

APHRODITE. That's right. The queen of the dead always keeps a stash of beauty handy. Go and ask her for some. Not much, a little box will do. I'm sure she'll be glad to oblige. Then bring it right back to me. If you'll just do me this one teensy little favor, I promise to let you see Eros.

PSYCHE. But—

APHRODITE. But what?

PSYCHE. No mortal can go down to the Underworld and—

APHRODITE. Live?

PSYCHE. That's right.

APHRODITE. So I've heard. Well, that's not *my* problem.

PSYCHE. But if I die, how am I going to bring you back some beauty?

APHRODITE. You'll just have to solve that little difficulty yourself, won't you? I think you'd better try. For if you *don't* do my bidding, I'll make your life worse than any death you can imagine.

(APHRODITE *exits.* PSYCHE *freezes.* ERATO *steps forward.*)

ERATO. How very dire things look for our heroine! But she's plucky and resourceful, and she finds her way to a cave that leads down into the Underworld. Her trials and tests along the way are many and hazardous.

(*Three actors come onto the stage to play* CERBERUS, *the three-headed dog. They freeze.*)

ERATO. Just for example—how would *you* like to come face to face with Cerberus, the gigantic, three-headed watchdog?

(*As* ERATO *steps aside to watch,* CERBERUS *and* PSYCHE *come to life.*)

1ST HEAD. Stop!

2ND HEAD. Grrr!

3RD HEAD. Who comes here?

PSYCHE. My name is Psyche.

1ST HEAD. Are you alive?

2ND HEAD. Sniff, sniff, sniff.

3RD HEAD. Or are you dead?

PSYCHE. Does it matter?

1ST HEAD. Not to me.

2ND HEAD. Rrruff!

3RD HEAD. But to you, it matters a great deal.

PSYCHE. How so?

1ST HEAD. Because if you're dead, you won't be bothered when I sink my fangs into you and tear you limb from limb.

2ND HEAD. Grrrrrowwwl!

3RD HEAD. But if you're alive, it's liable to hurt a good bit.

PSYCHE *(stepping toward* CERBERUS*)*. Oh, I'm sure you'd never bite me. Not an adorable little puppy dog like you.

1ST HEAD. Stay back!

2ND HEAD. Yap!

3RD HEAD. *Who's* an adorable little puppy dog?

PSYCHE. Why, *you* are, of course. But you poor thing! How long have you been all chained up like this? Doesn't anyone ever take you for a walk? No wonder you're in such bad temper.

1ST HEAD. Well, I'm not very well-treated.

2ND HEAD *(a whimper)*. Rooooo.

3RD HEAD. That's true.

PSYCHE. And you're hungry, too, I'll bet.

1ST HEAD. Oh, yes.

2ND HEAD. Ummummumm.

3RD HEAD. I've not been fed in a long time.

(PSYCHE produces a small loaf of bread from her clothing. She holds it toward CERBERUS*.)*

PSYCHE. How does a nice piece of barley bread sound!

1ST HEAD. Delicious!

2ND HEAD. Woof!

3RD HEAD. Please!

PSYCHE *(tearing the loaf in half)*. All right then.

1ST HEAD. No!

2ND HEAD. Arf!

3RD HEAD. I want it all!

PSYCHE. Ah, ah, ah! Not wise, not wise!

If you eat too much too fast, you're liable to get sick! Here you go.

(PSYCHE tosses half the loaf to CERBERUS. *The heads immediately start quarreling over it, and* PSYCHE *slips by them and exits.)*

1ST HEAD. Wait, it's mine!

2ND HEAD. Snarrrrrrrl!

3RD HEAD. No, she meant it for me!

1ST HEAD. Give it here, I'll share.

2ND HEAD. Grrrrrowwwl!

3RD HEAD. No, you won't!

(CERBERUS exits. ERATO *steps forward.)*

ERATO. It's a tricky business, getting into the world of the dead when you're still alive—and not winding up dead yourself!

(PSYCHE and PERSEPHONE *come onto the stage and freeze.)*

ERATO. But at long last, our heroine stands before the throne of Persephone, the queen of the dead.

(PSYCHE and PERSEPHONE *come to life.)*

PSYCHE *(bowing deeply)*. Greetings, Your Royal Highness.

PERSEPHONE. Well, bless my soul! A living, breathing young woman! Why, you must have had a very difficult time getting here.

PSYCHE *(still in a bow)*. If I may ask a favor of Your Majesty—

PERSEPHONE. Oh, do stand up, won't you? There's no need for ceremony—not after all you must have been through.

PSYCHE *(rising)*. Very well, Your Majesty.

PERSEPHONE. My, you're such a *lovely* thing! But just who *are* you? No, don't tell me. You must be young Psyche. Yes, I've heard all about you. The most beautiful woman in the world, they say. So beautiful, some people think you're really Aphrodite herself.

PSYCHE. I'm not Aphrodite.

PERSEPHONE. Oh, I can see that. I've known Aphrodite all my life. Still, I must say, your beauty *does* rival hers. But don't let it get back to her that I said that.

PSYCHE. Aphrodite sent me here.

PERSEPHONE. Really? What for?

PSYCHE. She wondered if you could let her have a little box of beauty.

PERSEPHONE. Imagine that! The goddess of love herself, asking poor little me, the lowly queen of the dead, for some beauty! What are things coming to? She must be in a dreadful state. Well, how can I say no? A box of beauty, coming right up.

(PERSEPHONE produces a small box from her clothing.)

PERSEPHONE *(handing the box to PSYCHE).* Here you go.

PSYCHE. Thank you. And now, I'd better go.

PERSEPHONE. Why the rush? You haven't told me anything about your adventures getting here. Just how *did* you do it? Why, our watchdog Cerberus ought to have torn you limb from limb!

PSYCHE. I gave him a—

PERSEPHONE *(interrupting).* But, oh, what an awful hostess I am! Why, you must be famished, and I haven't offered you a thing to eat. What about a nice, red apple? The Underworld is famous for its fruit. You won't find any so delicious in the world of the living.

(PERSEPHONE produces an apple from her clothing.)

PERSEPHONE. Here, do try it.

PSYCHE. No, thank you, Your Majesty.

PERSEPHONE. Oh, but you mustn't refuse my hospitality. You'll hurt my feelings. Come now, just one bite?

PSYCHE. May I speak frankly, Your Majesty?

PERSEPHONE. Certainly.

PSYCHE. I know what you're up to. If I eat that apple, I'll never be able to leave. I'll be one of the dead forever.

PERSEPHONE. Quite true, Psyche. Well. I hope you don't blame me for trying. You would have made a splendid catch. *(Pause)* You're very clever, aren't you? And I'll bet not many people know that. People underestimate the cleverness of beautiful women.

PSYCHE. Oh, I'm not so clever. Just curious.

PERSEPHONE. Don't be modest. Not many living people are smart enough to get this far into the Underworld— not without dying somewhere along the way. The question is, are you smart enough to make it all the way back . . . alive? I wouldn't bet money on it.

PSYCHE. We'll just have to see.

PERSEPHONE. Yes, I suppose we shall. But do take good care of that box. Its contents are extremely precious. Beauty in its pure, uncut state is wonderful, wonderful stuff. I don't suppose any mortal has ever had a chance to handle it before. But whatever you do—don't open that box! Don't look inside! *(Pause)* Farewell, Psyche. And good luck. And if you *do* happen to die, be sure to come back and talk to me. There's a bright future for a smart girl like you in a growing business like the Underworld.

(PERSEPHONE exits. PSYCHE freezes. ERATO steps forward.)

ERATO. On the way back from the Underworld, Psyche faces all the same trials and tests—including our old friend, the three-headed dog Cerberus. The other half of the barley bread takes care of that little problem. At last, Psyche reemerges from the cave, and she finds herself in the world of the living again.

(ERATO steps aside to watch as PSYCHE comes to life.)

PSYCHE. Hello, sunlight! Hello, smell of flowers and clear, fresh air! Hello, rippling stream full of colorful fish and croaking frogs! Hello, birds and clouds and bright blue sky! My, how good it is to see all of you again! The Underworld is an interesting place to visit, but I don't much care to live there—at least not until I have to. And now, all I've got to do is get this box back to Aphrodite, and I'll see my beloved Eros again! But I'll rest a minute or two first.

(PSYCHE sits on the upstage bench and looks carefully at the box.)

PSYCHE. What a pretty box. I'd love to know exactly what's inside. What did Persephone call it? Oh, yes. "Beauty in its pure, uncut state." And to think that no mortal has ever handled it before! Imagine that!

ERATO. Careful, Psyche! Remember Persephone's warning!

PSYCHE. Now, what do you suppose pure, uncut beauty actually looks like? Persephone said I mustn't open it—but really, what could be the harm? After all I've been through, I deserve a peek.

(PSYCHE opens the box, and a soft light glows from inside. As if stricken with pain, PSYCHE closes her eyes, then shuts the box lid. She lies motionless on the bench.)

ERATO. And so—our heroine dies! Tell me, did you see *this* plot twist coming? Sad, isn't it? I guess Psyche will be checking back in with Persephone, after all. Ah, feminine curiosity! Once again, it's proven fatal, and there's nothing good to be said for it.

(While ERATO is speaking, EROS enters, carrying a small jar. He kneels beside PSYCHE and gazes at her intently.)

ERATO. Or is there? Consider the life Psyche would have led if she *hadn't* looked upon the sleeping Eros. Oh, she was happy enough. But how long could she go on like that—never seeing her husband's face, never even knowing his name?

(EROS *gently applies some of the contents of the jar to* PSYCHE's *forehead.*)

ERATO. And also consider that our story isn't *quite* over.

(ERATO *steps aside.* PSYCHE *awakens and sits up.*)

PSYCHE. Eros!

EROS. Yes, my love. Everything's all right now. You're lucky, though. Mortal eyes cannot bear to look upon pure, uncut beauty.

PSYCHE. So what happened to me?

EROS. You died.

PSYCHE. Died? But why am I alive again?

EROS. I put some of this medicine on your forehead. It was enough to bring you back to life. Here. Have a taste of it.

(PSYCHE *takes some of the medicine on her fingers and tastes it.*)

PSYCHE. Mmmm. I've never tasted anything so delicious.

EROS. I thought you'd like it. So tell me—what's it like to be dead?

PSYCHE. I don't remember. Isn't that awful? I'm so sorry, I ought to have paid better attention! Perhaps I should—

EROS (*laughing*). Die again? You *would* do that, wouldn't you—just to find out what it's like!

PSYCHE (*with a shrug*). Why not?

EROS. Don't you dare!

PSYCHE. Well, I'll die *someday*, won't I? All I have to do is wait around long enough. You can ask me then.

EROS. I'm afraid things aren't going to work out that way.

PSYCHE. Why not?

EROS. That medicine I just gave you— it's ambrosia, the food of the gods. It has made you immortal.

PSYCHE. Immortal!

EROS. When I heard what had happened to you, I went to see my father, Zeus. I told him how much I loved you— how I couldn't bear the thought of living without you. (*Chuckling*) Well, he's been in love a few times himself, thanks to me. So he understood just how I felt. And he gave me some ambrosia to bring you back to life— and to turn you into a goddess.

PSYCHE. A goddess! But what will Aphrodite—?

EROS. Zeus ordered my mother never to disturb you again. All the gods of Olympus will treat you as one of their own. And now—how would you like a better look at some pure, uncut beauty?

PSYCHE. Oh, I'd love to see it! But—

EROS. It won't kill you this time. Nothing can kill you.

PSYCHE. Then open the box!

(EROS does so, and a soft light again glows from inside the box. PSYCHE gasps with delight. She and EROS freeze.)

ERATO. Ah, to be able to live forever! Now, what would *that* be like? To some people, it's a terrible thought. What would you *do* with all the time in the universe? But for the naturally curious, the idea of immortality is quite appealing. You see, the human mind can think up infinite questions. And eternity itself can simply zip by when you're asking questions.

(PSYCHE and EROS unfreeze.)

PSYCHE. Pssst!

EROS. Erato!

ERATO. What?

PSYCHE. What does the name *Psyche* mean, anyway?

ERATO. Well, it *can* mean *soul*—

EROS. Soul!

ERATO. —but it can also mean *butterfly*.

PSYCHE. Butterfly!

EROS. How lovely!

(PSYCHE and EROS exit, hand in hand.)

ERATO *(to the audience again)*. And, oh— Eros and Psyche had a baby daughter, an immortal deity, like themselves. They named her Pleasure. I hope my play has brought you a little visit from this beautiful child. Good-bye.

(ERATO exits.)

PLAYWRIGHT'S POSTSCRIPT

Apuleius' version of this story includes many more events than I could fit into this play. For example, Aphrodite actually forced Psyche to undertake a whole series of seemingly impossible tasks. One by one, Psyche accomplished them with magical assistance.

When Psyche had to sort out a huge pile of different kinds of seeds, ants came to her aid. When she had to gather the wool of a flock of fierce and dangerous sheep, she received crucial advice from a whispering reed. When she had to fetch a bottle of water from the deadly river Styx, she was helped by an eagle. After Psyche accomplished all these deeds, Aphrodite sent her to the Underworld to bring back a box of beauty.

CONNECTING TO OTHER CULTURES

Many love stories deal with broken promises, as when Psyche looked at Eros despite having sworn not to. In German legend, the hero Lohengrin married the beautiful Elsa on the condition that she never ask his name. When she broke her promise, Lohengrin had no choice but to disappear.

And of course, you probably noticed similarities between this story and the ever-popular fairy tale *Beauty and the Beast*. Like Beauty, Psyche found herself living with a mysterious creature who turned out to have a wonderful secret.

THE APPLE OF DISCORD

SETTING THE STAGE

In 415 B.C., the Athenian dramatist Euripides wrote an antiwar play called *The Trojan Women*. It dealt with the Trojan War, which, according to legend, the Greeks had fought against Troy hundreds of years earlier. Euripides' play showed how disgracefully the Greeks behaved in victory. They burned Troy and herded its women off to lives of slavery.

Euripides regarded the Trojan War as one of the great disasters of humankind. It lasted ten long years and took countless lives. In the end, it destroyed the Trojan civilization and brought lasting and bitter consequences to the Greeks.

Homer's epic poem *The Iliad*, written around the 9th century B.C., emphasized the heroic aspects of the Trojan War. His was a story of warriors and great deeds. But Euripides wanted to show the war at its most ignoble. His play raised the question of what started the Trojan War. The answer was sobering. The war began with a golden apple, the vanity of three goddesses, and men's obsession with a beautiful woman. In short, this frightful catastrophe happened for trivial reasons.

Calliope, the Muse of epic poetry, will be your rather reluctant guide through this bitter story.

MUSING ABOUT THE MYTH

The classical deities could be kind and generous, but they could also be vain and cruel. As you read, note places where gods often behave in all-too-human ways.

THE APPLE OF DISCORD

CHARACTERS:

CALLIOPE (ka lī′ o pē), the Muse of epic poetry

ERIS (er′ is), the goddess of discord and strife (has apple)

ATHENA (a thē′ na), the goddess of war and wisdom

HERA (hir′ a), the queen of the Olympian gods

APHRODITE (af ro dī′ tē), the goddess of love and beauty

HERMES (hur′ mēz), the messenger god

ZEUS (züs), the king of the Olympian gods

PARIS (par′ is), a prince of Troy

OENONE (ē nō′ nē), a water nymph

OTHER NAMES MENTIONED IN THE PLAY:

HECUBA (hek′ u ba), the queen of Troy

MENELAUS (men e lā′ us), the king of Sparta & Helen

MT. IDA, a mountain near Troy

PRIAM (prī′ am), the king of Troy

TROY, a city in what is now Asia Minor

SETTING: *Greece and Mt. Ida*

TIME: *Before the Trojan War*

(The stage is bare except for one or two stools for actors to use as needed. CALLIOPE enters and begins to walk across the stage. She stops when she notices the audience.)

CALLIOPE *(to the audience).* Oh—it's you! And you're waiting for me, aren't you? That's right, we had an appointment; it slipped my mind. I was supposed to tell you a story—an *epic* story, since I'm the Muse of epic poetry. Well, I'm sorry, but I've got to cancel. I've been invited to a banquet, and I'm on my way there right now. All the gods and goddesses will be there, and all the other Muses, and even the Fates and Graces, and one simply does *not* turn such invitations down. I hope you don't mind. But, oh, now that I think of it—why don't you come, too? I can bring guests if I like. We'll have a great time, I promise. Besides, I'm sure you don't *really* want to hear some dreary, long-winded saga of wars and heroes and battles with humongous monsters and storms at sea and shipwrecks and such. No, of course not. A banquet will be much more fun. Come along, then.

(ERIS *enters, holding a golden apple.*)

CALLIOPE. Uh-oh. There's Eris, the goddess of discord. She's always making trouble of one kind or another, and I'm sure she wasn't invited. So—not a word to her about where we're going, please! Let's just try to slip by unnoticed.

ERIS. Hello, Calliope.

CALLIOPE (*to the audience*). Oops. (*To* ERIS) Hello.

ERIS. Where are you off to?

CALLIOPE. Um, I'm just out for a walk.

ERIS. Are you going to the banquet?

CALLIOPE. Well, yes.

ERIS. Have a good time. I wasn't invited.

CALLIOPE. Nooo!

ERIS. Why the surprise? I haven't been invited to any banquets for centuries now.

CALLIOPE. Such a shame.

ERIS. It's all right.

CALLIOPE. You're not taking it hard then?

ERIS. Oh, no. I understand. I've got a bad reputation. Everybody thinks I'm a troublemaker. And they're right. I've done a lot of terrible things over the years. I've only got myself to blame. Go ahead, Calliope. Don't let me hold you up.

CALLIOPE (*to the audience*). Something doesn't smell right here. (*To* ERIS) Um, Eris, you're not planning some kind of revenge, are you?

ERIS. Like what?

CALLIOPE. Well, like a thunderstorm maybe. Or some hail. Or a hurricane. Or an earthquake. Or a volcanic eruption. Or maybe a collision between the earth and a gigantic asteroid, to be followed by months without sunlight and the rapid extinction of 70 percent of all the world's species.

ERIS. Well, *that* wouldn't be smart, would it? I'd just confirm everybody's bad opinion of me. No, I'm turning over a new leaf. I'll try to do nothing but good from now on.

CALLIOPE. That's great, Eris. There's nothing more admirable than changing for the better. And a real challenge, too.

ERIS. Oh, yes. It's very hard for deities to change. We're very fixed in our ways. But I'm really going to try.

CALLIOPE. I'll tell everybody at the banquet about your decision. And maybe you won't get left out next time.

ERIS. Would you do that for me, Calliope?

CALLIOPE. Of course.

ERIS. How sweet! And, oh—there's something else maybe you could do for me. Here.

(*She hands* CALLIOPE *the golden apple.*)

CALLIOPE. A golden apple! How pretty! And it's got something engraved on it. It says, "For the Fairest."

ERIS. Could you take it to the banquet as a gift—a token of my goodwill?

CALLIOPE. Of course. But who do you want me to give it to?

ERIS. I haven't decided. Who do *you* think should get it?

CALLIOPE. Well, there's Hera, I suppose. She's always trying to make her husband notice how beautiful she is. She'd certainly like to be called *the fairest*.

ERIS. That's true.

CALLIOPE. And then there's Athena. She's just all-around proud. I'm sure she already thinks of herself as *the fairest*.

ERIS. That's true.

CALLIOPE. And, oh, I mustn't forget Aphrodite. The goddess of love would just *hate* not to be *the fairest*.

ERIS. That's true.

CALLIOPE. To tell the truth, I don't know which of them to give it to.

ERIS. Me, neither. I'll tell you what, just take the apple and put it in front of them. Let them decide for themselves who should get it.

CALLIOPE. Um, Eris . . . that's a really bad idea.

ERIS. Why?

CALLIOPE. Well, don't let it get back to them that I said this, but those three goddesses are *all* pretty vain.

ERIS. Nooo.

CALLIOPE. And if you leave the decision to them, a huge fight is liable to break out.

ERIS. You don't say.

CALLIOPE. And when gods and goddesses start fighting, it leads to all kinds of trouble.

ERIS. I don't believe it.

CALLIOPE. Come on, Eris. You know it's true.

ERIS. But aren't *I* the only deity that ever makes any trouble?

CALLIOPE. Nobody ever said that.

ERIS. They sure make me feel like it. Anyway, I just want to make a little gesture of kindness. It's not *my* fault if those goddesses can't deal with it. Go ahead, Calliope. Just set the apple in front of them and let the cards fall as they may.

CALLIOPE. No, Eris.

ERIS. You won't even do me this one little favor? And I thought you were my friend!

CALLIOPE. I wouldn't be doing you a favor. You'd be more unpopular than ever.

ERIS. Oh, never mind. I'll go do it myself. (*She takes the apple back from* CALLIOPE.)

CALLIOPE. But they won't even let you in.

ERIS. It doesn't matter. I'll just toss the apple through the door.

CALLIOPE. Wait a minute.

ERIS. 'Bye, Calliope. Thanks for nothing. (*She exits.*)

THE APPLE OF DISCORD

CALLIOPE. Eris, come back! *(To the audience)* Oh, it's no use. There's no stopping her when she's up to no good.

This reminds me of a story. Don't worry, it's very short. Just between you and me, I get tired of epics, and a really simple little story with a clear-cut moral is a refreshing change.

There once was a frog who was getting ready to swim across the river. A scorpion came along and said, "Hey, frog, could you give me a ride? I've got some business on the other side of the river."

"You're out of your mind," said the frog. "If I let you anywhere near me, you'll sting me to death."

"Don't be ridiculous," said the scorpion. "If I sting you to death, how will I get to the other side?"

"Good point," admitted the frog.

And so the scorpion jumped on the frog's back, and the frog started to swim. But when they were halfway across—guess what? The scorpion stung the frog!

"Why did you do that?" asked the frog.

"I'm going to die—and you're going to drown!"

"I can't help it," said the scorpion. "It's my nature."

I'm sure you get my point. Eris is pretty much like the scorpion of the story. She just won't ever change.

(Voices are heard offstage.)

ATHENA *(offstage).* It's for me!

HERA *(offstage).* No, me!

APHRODITE *(offstage).* No, me!

CALLIOPE. But here comes trouble—right on schedule! If you don't mind, I'd rather not get more involved.

(CALLIOPE steps aside. HERMES enters, holding the apple, followed by ATHENA, HERA, and APHRODITE.)

ATHENA. Give me that apple, Hermes!

HERA. No, it's mine!

APHRODITE. It's mine, I tell you!

HERMES. Ladies, ladies, let's be civil! Surely we can come to some reasonable solution.

ATHENA. Give it to me. That's reasonable.

HERA. The fairest? You? I hardly think so!

APHRODITE. The apple *says* it's mine in plain writing!

151

HERMES. Maybe we could divide it in thirds.

ATHENA, HERA, and APHRODITE *(together).* Don't you dare!

ATHENA. Just hand it over, Hermes.

HERA. No, give it here.

APHRODITE. No, to me!

(ZEUS enters.)

ZEUS. What's all this ruckus?

HERA. Zeus, darling, thank goodness you've come! Somebody just rolled this apple into the banquet hall, *obviously* as a gift to me. And these two upstarts are claiming it for themselves!

ZEUS. But, Hera, my dear, how do you *know* it's for you?

HERA. It's written right there on the apple. Go on, take a look.

ZEUS *(reading).* "For the Fairest."

HERA. There. You see? Who could that mean except me?

ATHENA. Huh!

APHRODITE. The nerve!

ZEUS *(to* HERA, *uneasily).* Now, dear, of course you're the fairest in my eyes.

APHRODITE *(to ZEUS).* Well, of course!

ATHENA *(to ZEUS).* You're her husband!

HERMES. They've got a point, Zeus. You're not exactly impartial.

ATHENA. *Thank* you, Hermes. You're always the voice of reason.

APHRODITE. Hera has always got the ruler of the universe himself to tell her how beautiful she is. Why does she need a golden apple to say so?

ATHENA. So kindly give the apple to me.

APHRODITE. Stop it, Athena. This isn't worthy of you. You're the goddess of war and wisdom. Beauty isn't your area of expertise. You're not even looking for a lover—at least not the last I heard. So what do you want with an apple to say how fair you are?

ATHENA. Well, what do *you* want with it, Aphrodite? You're simply wallowing in beauty and romance and all that kind of mushy nonsense. What difference is a little golden apple going to make in *your* life?

ZEUS. Who do *you* think should get it, Hermes?

HERMES. Don't ask me. I'm just a lowly messenger god. You're the king. You make a decision.

ZEUS. Absolutely not. I've got to live with all of you.

HERA. Traitor!

APHRODITE. Coward!

ATHENA. Milksop!

ZEUS. And since none of the other gods are likely to accept the job, I suggest we find a mortal to do the judging.

HERA. A mortal?

APHRODITE. A *mere* mortal?

ATHENA. Whatever for?

ZEUS. Why ever not? Mortals can judge beauty as well as gods. Yes, I know just the man for the job. He lives on Mt. Ida, not far from Troy. His name is Paris, and he's a shepherd.

HERA. A sheep herder?

ZEUS. Don't be a snob dear. It's said that he's the handsomest man in the world, and he's got a marvelous eye for beauty. What's more, he won't be prejudiced.

HERA. I don't know.

APHRODITE. A simple shepherd?

ATHENA. It's rather demeaning.

ZEUS. Very well. Hermes can just keep the apple for himself.

HERMES. It looks tasty.

HERA (to HERMES). Don't eat it! It's golden!

APHRODITE. We'll go see Paris.

ATHENA. Yes, we'll go.

ZEUS. That's more like it. Hermes, escort the goddesses to Mt. Ida, won't you? You can referee the contest, make sure that everything's on the up and up.

HERMES. As you wish. Follow me, ladies.

(HERMES, HERA, ATHENA, *and* APHRODITE *exit.*)

CALLIOPE (stepping forward). Excuse me, O Lord of the Heavens.

ZEUS. Ah, Calliope! Good to see you! Are you going to recite an epic at the banquet?

CALLIOPE. I hadn't planned on it.

ZEUS. A pity. But what can I do for you?

CALLIOPE. I couldn't help overhearing—well, eavesdropping, actually. I just wondered, why did you pick Paris to be the judge—out of all the mortals in the world?

ZEUS. It's a simple matter of geography, Calliope. Mt. Ida is all the way across the Aegean Sea. Paris just happened to be the first mortal I could think of who lives *far away* from here. With some luck, I'll get twenty or thirty minutes of peace from those quarrelsome goddesses.

CALLIOPE. But Paris is—

ZEUS. Can we talk about it later? The banquet awaits, and I don't want to miss another minute of it.

CALLIOPE. But, sir—

ZEUS. And if you can think of an epic, we'd all love to hear it. (He exits.)

CALLIOPE (to the audience). Oh, I don't like this. I don't like it one bit. You see, I happen to know a little secret about Paris. Do you want to hear it? Don't worry, this story is short, too.

Well. King Priam of Troy and his wife Hecuba once had a baby. A seer told King Priam that if the baby grew up, he'd cause the destruction of Troy. The baby just *had* to be killed.

Well. Neither Priam nor Hecuba could bring themselves to kill their own little baby. So they handed him over to a shepherd and told *him* to do the job.

Well. The shepherd didn't have what it takes to kill a baby, either. So he raised the child as his own.

Well. That baby is all grown-up now. And do I need to spell out the rest? He just *happens* to be Paris. And he's a ticking historical time bomb— the walking, talking doom of the Trojan civilization itself.

Well. Don't ask me why, but somehow it makes me nervous that the three most powerful Olympian goddesses are on their way to pay him a visit. I think we'd better stay on top of this story. Let's head on over to Mt. Ida.

"But how do we get there?" you ask. Simple! This is a play. All we need is a change of scene.

(She snaps her fingers.)

There! See? Just a snap of my fingers, and we're in a meadow on the slopes of Mt. Ida—all the way across the Aegean Sea! Ah, the magic of theatrical storytelling!

(She looks around.)

And if I'm not mistaken, we've arrived ahead of Hermes and the goddesses. That's good. Maybe we can forestall a real disaster.

And look—here comes a shepherd. It's Paris, I'll bet.

(CALLIOPE steps aside as PARIS enters.)

PARIS. Oenone! Come quickly! Look!

OENONE *(offstage).* What is it?

PARIS. Come right away or you'll miss it!

(OENONE enters.)

OENONE. Well?

PARIS *(pointing).* Right there, on that bush—a sparrow!

OENONE. So?

PARIS. It's the first sparrow of spring!

OENONE *(amused, pointing elsewhere).* And what do you call that?

PARIS. Um . . . the *second* sparrow of spring?

OENONE *(pointing again).* And that?

PARIS. The third?

OENONE *(pointing again).* And in that tree over there—that must be the first *flock* of sparrows of spring. Paris, the sparrows have been back for a good while now. The fields are in bloom, and the trees are leafy green. Spring is here already. And you're just now noticing it?

PARIS *(with an embarrassed shrug).* I never claimed to be very observant.

OENONE. It's not that. You're always daydreaming. You're always off in a world of your own. What are you thinking about all the time? No, don't tell me. I'll guess. You're dreaming of your birthright. You're wondering what life would be like if you lived in Troy as a prince.

PARIS. No.

OENONE. I'm sure it's true. And why not? *I* often think about all the pomp and glory you're missing. And, oh— I'll bet you dream all the time of living in bliss with a beautiful princess instead of a simple shepherdess like me.

PARIS. You're not a simple shepherdess. You're the fairest and most beautiful creature alive.

OENONE *(laughing).* Paris, you've barely set foot out of this meadow since you were a baby. Who are you comparing me to? Your sheep?

PARIS. And you're a goddess, too.

OENONE. Just a lowly water nymph.

PARIS. There's nothing lowly about you.

Why would I dream of a mere mortal princess when I already have a beautiful goddess like you?

OENONE. Do you really mean that?

PARIS. Can you doubt it? And if I don't notice the coming of spring—well, it can only be because I'm always dazzled by the springtime in your face.

OENONE. Stop it.

PARIS. And why should I want to be a prince of Troy? Here, I'm prince of all I see. And unlike the prince of a great city, I have no enemies to hurt me, no wars to fight. I have everything I could need or want.

OENONE. So you never dream of leaving me?

PARIS. Never. I'd be crazy to. Why, we're perfect for each other. Look at what we've accomplished. We've gotten the flock through another winter together!

OENONE. It's true. We should celebrate. I've got an idea.

PARIS. What is it?

OENONE. A gift. You wait right here.

PARIS. But where are you going?

OENONE. Do you want to spoil the surprise? Just wait. And don't try to follow me.

(OENONE *exits.* CALLIOPE *steps forward.*)

CALLIOPE. Nice girl.

PARIS. She is, isn't she? I wonder what she's going to bring me. It'll be perfect, of course. Her gifts always are. I wish I knew of something to give her. Sometimes I feel—well, like I don't deserve her, like I don't bring anything special to her life. *(Pause)* But—who are you?

CALLIOPE. That doesn't matter. I'm here to warn you. Three goddesses are on their way here to see you.

PARIS. Goddesses?

CALLIOPE. And I think it might be a good idea for you to hide before they get here.

PARIS. Why? Do they mean to do me harm?

CALLIOPE. Not exactly. It's hard to explain. You see— *(Looking offstage)* Oh, no—too late!

(CALLIOPE *steps aside as* HERMES, ATHENA, HERA, *and* APHRODITE *enter.*)

HERMES. The shepherd Paris, I presume.

PARIS. The same.

HERMES. Greetings from Mt. Olympus. I am Hermes, messenger of the gods. Permit me to introduce you to the goddesses Athena, Hera, and Aphrodite.

PARIS. I'm honored.

ATHENA. Likewise.

HERA. The honor's mine.

APHRODITE. Enchanted.

PARIS. To what do I owe this pleasure?

HERMES. Our father Zeus, Lord of All the Heavens, wishes to entrust you with a sacred task. First of all, let me present you with this.

(HERMES *hands the golden apple to* PARIS.)

PARIS. A golden apple! How pretty! "For the Fairest," it says.

HERMES. Indeed. And because you are the handsomest man in the world and a keen judge and connoisseur of feminine beauty, Zeus has sent us to you. He wishes you to decide just who *the Fairest* is—the most beautiful woman in all creation.

PARIS. Really? Perfect! I know just who it should go to! *(Calling offstage)* Oenone! Come quick! I've got a gift for you!

ATHENA. Oenone?

HERA. Who on earth is Oenone?

PARIS. She's my beloved.

APHRODITE. And why are you calling her?

PARIS. Why, to give her the apple, of course. *(Calling again)* Oenone!

HERMES *(leading* PARIS *aside)*. Paris, perhaps we should have a little god-to-man talk. I understand that you're devoted to your girlfriend. And I respect that. It's commendable. But try to be objective. Can her beauty really compare with that of a true goddess?

PARIS. She *is* a goddess. Haven't any of you heard of Oenone the water nymph?

ATHENA. Oenone the water nymph?

HERA. Do you think we've heard of every water nymph on the planet?

APHRODITE. Nymphs are *so* common—next door to mortal!

PARIS. But I swear to you, she's the fairest, the most beautiful—

HERMES *(to* PARIS*)*. Ah, ah, ah! Think before you speak, son. There's a political issue that you seem to be overlooking. You happen to be in the presence of the three most powerful goddesses in the universe.

PARIS. So?

HERMES. So . . . you shouldn't jump to conclusions. You should take a really close look at these ladies before giving the apple to Oenone.

(Pause. PARIS *looks over the goddesses.)*

PARIS. I still think that Oenone's—

HERMES. *Don't say it*, Paris!

PARIS. Do you want me to lie?

HERMES. Why, no—not exactly. I just think you need to consider power and influence as part of your decision. Because, under certain circumstances, power and influence *might* amount to much the same thing as beauty.

*(*CALLIOPE *steps forward.)*

CALLIOPE *(to* HERMES*)*. Why not just let him give the apple to Oenone?

ATHENA. Calliope!

HERA. What are you doing here?

APHRODITE. Poor thing, weren't you invited to the banquet?

CALLIOPE *(to* HERMES*)*. He obviously believes Oenone is *the Fairest*.

HERMES. He's also rather prejudiced.

CALLIOPE. So? Who isn't when it comes to beauty? You won't find a really impartial judge anywhere in the world. And if he tries to choose between these three—well, there's no doubt that it will lead to trouble.

APHRODITE. Why don't you mind your own business?

HERA. This is none of your concern.

CALLIOPE. Listen, I'm just trying to save everybody a whole lot of grief.

ATHENA. Oh, it's not so hard to see what you're really up to. You'll persuade Paris not to give the apple to any of us, we'll all head back to the banquet, and *then* you'll wheedle Paris into giving it to *you.*

CALLIOPE. What?

APHRODITE. Of course! It's obvious!

CALLIOPE. It's not true!

HERA. We're all wasting words. As queen of the heavens, it's up to me to set a few matters straight. We live in an orderly universe where everyone has a place. Mortals rank lower than water nymphs, and water nymphs rank lower than Olympian goddesses. It is therefore a logical fact that no mortal can be as beautiful as a water nymph, and no water nymph as beautiful as an Olympian goddess. So it follows that Oenone is out of the running for the apple. She is not a viable candidate.

CALLIOPE. But, Hera—

HERA. Perhaps I forgot to mention— Olympian goddesses most emphatically outrank Muses.

CALLIOPE (to the audience). You can't say I didn't try.

ATHENA. Well. It seems that we've narrowed the field to three contestants.

APHRODITE. So it does.

HERA. And now, Paris, you must carry out your sacred task. Which of us is the most beautiful woman in all creation—Athena, Aphrodite, or myself?

PARIS. I must say, I'm overwhelmed—as well as honored. Do I have to decide right here and now?

HERA. Are you trying to shirk your duty?

PARIS. Oh, not at all. But you're *all* so extremely beautiful, it's going to be a difficult choice. Perhaps if I could— (He stops.)

HERA, ATHENA, and APHRODITE (together). What?

PARIS. Interview you individually, maybe.

HERA. Interview?

ATHENA. Whatever for?

APHRODITE. Can't you just look?

PARIS. It's just that . . . well, in my considerable experience as a judge and connoisseur of feminine beauty, I've learned that too much sheer loveliness in one place at one time can be distracting. I think I'd make a better decision if I could . . . observe you one at a time.

HERA. I see nothing wrong with that.

ATHENA. It suits me well.

APHRODITE. Me, too. Which of us should go first?

HERA. I will, of course.

(ATHENA *and* APHRODITE *protest at the same time.)*

ATHENA. Now wait just a minute—

APHRODITE. Shouldn't we draw straws or—?

HERA *(silencing them)*. Am I or am I not queen of the heavens? Now, clear off, the lot of you.

(ATHENA and APHRODITE exit, grumbling to each other.)

HERA *(to HERMES)*. Did I fail to make myself completely clear?

HERMES. But your husband asked me to referee.

HERA. Are you saying you don't trust me?

HERMES. Of course not, Your Highness, but—

HERA. And is my husband here at the moment?

HERMES. No, Your Highness, but—

HERA. And in his absence, who should you obey?

HERMES. You, Your Highness, but—

HERA. Then kindly make yourself scarce.

HERMES. Right away, Your Highness.

(HERMES exits. HERA turns and notices CALLIOPE.)

HERA. Calliope! Still here? Is my voice not carrying properly today?

CALLIOPE. I beg your pardon, Your Highness. But is there any harm in my hanging around? Just as an impartial observer?

HERA. Nobody is impartial when it comes to beauty. You said so yourself. Now—scat!

(CALLIOPE steps forward and speaks to the audience.)

CALLIOPE. I don't know about you, but I'm in no mood to miss all this. "But what choice do we have?" you ask. Don't forget, this is a play. As always, we have the magic of theatrical storytelling at our disposal. All I have to do is—*(snaps her fingers)*—and we're completely invisible! *(She steps aside.)*

HERA. How do we proceed?

PARIS. Kindly walk back and forth a bit.

(HERA does so.)

PARIS. Now turn around, please.

(HERA does so.)

HERA. Well? Am I or am I not beautiful?

PARIS. Very beautiful.

HERA. Then let's keep this whole thing short and simple, shall we? Just give me the apple now, and you'll save us all a lot of time and trouble.

PARIS. No. I'm sorry, but the other goddesses deserve proper viewings.

(Pause)

HERA. I happen to know a secret about you, Paris.

PARIS. Do you?

HERA. And I rather doubt that the other goddesses know it. You're more than a simple shepherd. You're actually a prince of Troy—or at least you ought to be. Tell me, don't you ever dream of your birthright?

PARIS. It sometimes crosses my mind.

HERA. And don't you feel that you've been done a terrible injustice?

PARIS. I'm happy here.

HERA. That doesn't answer my question. *(Pause)* What if I were to offer you all the glory you deserve?

PARIS. You mean, make me a prince again? I could do that for myself, I think. All I'd have to do is go back to Troy and present myself to my father. He couldn't very well turn me away. I suspect he'd be relieved to see me still alive.

HERA. But you choose not to.

PARIS. Yes.

HERA. And I believe I know why. After the lowly life you've lived, you think the world owes you more than even your princehood. You think you deserve much, much greater glory. I happen to agree with you. *(Pause)* I can make you mightier than the mere prince of a magnificent city. I can make you mightier than your father Priam or any other earthly ruler. I can place at your feet two-thirds of the known world. I can make you the king of all Europe and all Asia.

(PARIS laughs.)

HERA. Does that amuse you?

PARIS. Only two-thirds of the known world, Hera? Europe and Asia, nothing more? Surely, as queen of all the heavens, you can offer me the whole thing. Why not Africa, too?

HERA. You drive a hard bargain. I like that, I admit. Offhand, I'm not sure about Africa's availability. I promise to look into it, though.

PARIS. Our interview is over, I think.

HERA. Are you rejecting my offer?

PARIS. I didn't say that.

HERA. What are you up to, Paris? With mortals, it's usually easy to tell. But you're really quite mysterious.

PARIS. Send me the next goddess.

HERA. Of course. You want to find out what Athena and Aphrodite have to offer. A wise tactic, very wise. I'd be disappointed in you if you didn't explore all your possibilities. Still, I'm confident I'll win. Athena and Aphrodite can't give you anything like what I've offered.

PARIS. Another goddess, Hera. It doesn't matter which.

HERA. Certainly, certainly. You'll make an excellent ruler, Paris. *(HERA exits.)*

CALLIOPE *(to the audience).* Whoa! Two-thirds of the known world, she says! And with a little luck, maybe Africa, too! That's quite a step up from a simple herder of sheep. And yet, I wonder . . . just what *is* Paris thinking?

(ATHENA enters.)

ATHENA. It appears that I'm next in line.

PARIS. So it does, Athena.

ATHENA. What would you like me to do?

PARIS. Kindly walk back and forth a bit.

(ATHENA *does so.*)

PARIS. Now turn around, please.

(ATHENA *does so.*)

PARIS. Thank you, Athena. You may go now.

ATHENA. Is that all? But you talked rather longer with Hera. What about, I wonder?

PARIS. I'll see Aphrodite next.

ATHENA. Don't be evasive, Paris. I'm the goddess of wisdom and nobody's fool. Hera offered you something in return for the apple, didn't she?

PARIS. I'm not free to discuss it.

(*Pause*)

ATHENA. I know a little secret about you, Paris.

PARIS. You do?

ATHENA. You're more than just a shepherd. You're actually a prince of Troy.

PARIS. Interesting. Hera happens to know that little secret, too.

ATHENA. I suppose she would. As queen of the heavens, she stays very well-informed. I suppose she offered you to restore you to your rightful rank.

PARIS. If you must know, she offered me somewhat more than that.

ATHENA. Indeed?

PARIS. She said she'd make me ruler of all Europe and Asia.

ATHENA. What? And not Africa, too?

PARIS. Possibly. She couldn't make any promises.

ATHENA. And did you accept her offer?

PARIS. I'd rather not say.

ATHENA. You don't need to. I think I know. She underestimates you, Paris. She doesn't realize that you're the kind of man who wants to make his own way in life. To be *given* the whole world on a silver platter—that would bore you, I'm sure. I can offer you something much more to your liking.

PARIS. What's that?

ATHENA. The command of the mightiest army in the world. With it, you can achieve the greatest dream of Troy—to conquer Greece.

PARIS. Only Greece?

ATHENA. Just for starters. The rest is up to you. Europe, Asia, Africa—I'll leave all that to your own ambition. And if I'm not mistaken, you wouldn't want it any other way.

PARIS. I'd like to see Aphrodite now.

ATHENA. Of course, of course. You've made your decision, but you want to see the charade quite through, for appearance's sake. Shrewd, very shrewd. I understand you very well. I think we understand each other. We'll do great things together, Paris. (*She exits.*)

CALLIOPE (*to the audience*). A conquering warrior? Paris? Well, now that I think about it, maybe so. After all, a military leader and a shepherd are in pretty much the same line of work. The difference is, the sheep in an army have all got swords and spears and are ready and eager to kill other sheep. Still, does Paris have the stomach for that kind of thing?

(APHRODITE *enters.*)

APHRODITE. Here I am—last, but hopefully not least. What do you want me to do?

PARIS. Kindly walk back and forth a bit.

(APHRODITE *does so.*)

PARIS. Now turn around, please.

(APHRODITE *does so.*)

PARIS. Thank you. That will do.

APHRODITE. So I've won, then?

PARIS. I haven't decided. I need to mull it over. Perhaps you could leave me alone for a few minutes.

(*Pause*)

APHRODITE. I know a little secret about you, Paris.

PARIS. Let me guess. You know that I'm more than just a shepherd—that I'm really a prince of Troy. Hera and Athena both brought up that little matter, too.

APHRODITE. Ah, well. It's hard to keep a secret in this universe. Did they offer to restore you to your rightful rank?

PARIS. It wouldn't have mattered if they had.

APHRODITE. No, I don't suppose it would have. (*Pause*) It's true, what they say about you.

PARIS. What's that?

APHRODITE. That you're the handsomest man in the world.

PARIS. Flattery won't win you the apple.

APHRODITE. Oh, no, I'm sure it won't. You're immune to all kinds of temptations, aren't you? You're a man of great character. Why, I imagine Hera and Athena offered you—what? The earth and the heavens, perhaps?

PARIS. Hera did offer me Europe and Asia.

APHRODITE. Ah, power!

PARIS. And Athena would have made me the conqueror of Greece.

APHRODITE. Ah, glory! Most men's minds would have been turned—but not yours, I'm sure.

PARIS. No.

APHRODITE. No, indeed. Your values are too high, too noble for paltry power, for vulgar glory. What you really want is *love*.

PARIS. I already have love.

APHRODITE. Oh, yes, Oenone. I'd almost forgotten her. She *is* quite pretty, I'll admit. But what if I were to offer you the love of the most beautiful woman alive?

PARIS. You mean yourself?

APHRODITE. Why, Paris! You make it sound like I've already won the contest.

PARIS. I didn't say that.

APHRODITE. I'm going to tell you something, and I trust you not to tell it to anybody else. My beauty—

divine though it may be—is not exactly peerless. There is a woman in Greece who is at least my match.

PARIS. A mortal?

APHRODITE. Half mortal, half goddess.

PARIS. Oenone is all goddess.

APHRODITE. A water nymph, that's all. The woman I speak of is a daughter of Zeus himself.

PARIS (*laughing*). Oh, come now. All kinds of mortals claim that Zeus is their father. It means nothing without proof.

APHRODITE. She was born out of an egg, Paris. Zeus came to her mother in the form of a swan. And from an egg, the most beautiful woman in the world appeared. Have you ever heard of a mortal who was *hatched*? I can show you pieces of the shell, if you like. What more proof of her divinity do you need?

PARIS. I can't leave Oenone.

APHRODITE. Of course you can. She'll be fine without you. Do you think she really needs you?

PARIS. But she loves me.

APHRODITE. She feels sorry for you. And it's not hard to see why. I hope you don't mind my saying so, but you haven't got the makings of a shepherd. That's nothing to be ashamed of; it's just not in your blood. Anyone can see that she pretty much runs this meadow. And what do you have to offer *her* in life?

PARIS. Not much. But then, what do I have to offer a daughter of Zeus—the most beautiful woman in the world?

APHRODITE. Oh, a great deal, I think—if you go back to Troy and reclaim your birthright. You'll be a prince, and fully worthy of her hand—the perfect match for a royal demigoddess. As for Oenone—well, let's face it, you'll always be something of a dead weight to her. My guess is that she's always wondering whether or not to leave *you*.

PARIS. I suppose so.

APHRODITE. Why fight it, Paris? Anyone can see it's your destiny.

(*Pause*)

PARIS (*giving her the apple*). Here.

APHRODITE. Why, Paris, I'm so honored! And grateful! And touched!

PARIS. We should call the others.

APHRODITE. No! There will only be a lot of hard feelings and bad tempers. We don't need that. Come with me. I'll fly you directly to Greece—and to your new love.

CALLIOPE (*to the audience*). It looks like I'd better turn visible. (*Snaps her fingers*) Paris, don't go with her.

APHRODITE. Calliope! Still here, are you?

CALLIOPE (*to* PARIS). Let her have the apple if you must. But don't accept her bribe. And don't go with her.

APHRODITE. We'll both thank you to mind your own business.

THE APPLE OF DISCORD

CALLIOPE. Remember the prophecy, Paris. You'll be the ruin of Troy.

APHRODITE. If the prophecy is true, he'll be the ruin of Troy whether he goes back there or not. If it can't be helped, why should he waste his life in this puny little meadow?

CALLIOPE (to PARIS). But think of Oenone.

PARIS. I *am* thinking of Oenone.

CALLIOPE. She loves you.

PARIS. She doesn't need me.

APHRODITE. Wisely said, Paris. Let's go, before the others come snooping.

PARIS (to CALLIOPE). Say good-bye to her for me.

(PARIS *and* APHRODITE *exit.*)

CALLIOPE (to the audience). Why did I get myself mixed up in this? I *could* be reciting a long, tedious epic to a peacefully snoring audience. Right now, that sounds like a really great way to spend the afternoon.

(ATHENA, HERA, *and* HERMES *enter.*)

ATHENA. Paris, what have you decided?

HERA. Where *is* he?

CALLIOPE. He's gone.

HERA. Calliope! Are you still here?

HERMES. I don't see Aphrodite.

HERA. Oh, no! You don't think that Paris—?

ATHENA. He did! He gave the apple to Aphrodite!

HERA. What do you suppose she offered him as a bribe?

CALLIOPE. No more than you two offered him.

ATHENA. Were you eavesdropping this whole time?

HERMES. Bribes? You goddesses offered him bribes?

HERA. Oh, shut up, Hermes.

ATHENA (to CALLIOPE). What did she offer him?

CALLIOPE. The most beautiful woman in the world.

HERA. Is that all? When he could have had all of Europe and Asia?

ATHENA. A beautiful woman—when he could have been the conqueror of Greece!

HERA. The fool!

ATHENA. He deserves no better!

HERMES. Well, I guess it's settled then.

HERA. I guess it is. I hope Aphrodite enjoys her apple.

ATHENA. She certainly got it cheap.

HERA. In the meantime, we're missing the banquet.

ATHENA. I suppose we'd better get back.

HERMES. Are you coming with us, Calliope?

CALLIOPE. No. I've got something to take care of here.

ATHENA. You'll not be reciting an epic at the banquet then?

CALLIOPE. No.

HERA. A pity.

HERMES. Come on, ladies. Let's be off now.

(HERMES, ATHENA, *and* HERA *exit.*)

CALLIOPE *(to the audience).* A pity is right. I'd rather swallow nails than have to deal with what comes next. Oh, why didn't I stay back in Greece and mind my own business?

(OENONE enters, holding an apple.)

OENONE. Paris! I've got it! Come, have a look! Have a taste! *(She stops upon seeing CALLIOPE.)* Oh. Hello. Who are you?

CALLIOPE. Calliope.

OENONE. Calliope? You mean *the* Calliope? Calliope the Muse? You're kidding.

CALLIOPE. No.

OENONE. But aren't you in the epic business? And isn't this kind of setting a little—well, serene and bucolic for you? You must feel very out of place.

CALLIOPE. Yes, I suppose I do.

OENONE. Where's Paris?

CALLIOPE. He's gone.

OENONE. But where? This is just like him—always disappearing, even when there's a flock to be watched. And look—the sheep are wandering away in all directions! *(Calling out)* Paris, where are you? Come and see what I've got for you!

CALLIOPE. He's not coming back.

OENONE. Of course he is. You don't know him. He's got the attention span of a hummingbird, and he'd never go very far. Besides, he knows I've got a present for him. He wouldn't miss that!

CALLIOPE. What is it?

OENONE. An apple—from our very favorite apple tree.

CALLIOPE. Just an apple?

OENONE. Oh, this is no ordinary apple. This is the first truly perfect apple of spring. I had to climb far out onto the longest branch of the tree to get to it. I almost fell before I grabbed it. But here it is. Look at how red it is. And not the slightest bruise!

CALLIOPE. So I see.

OENONE *(calling out).* Paris!

CALLIOPE. Oenone, I wish I didn't have to be the one to tell you, but he's really *not* coming back. He left you for somebody else.

OENONE. I don't believe you.

CALLIOPE. It's true.

OENONE. A mortal?

CALLIOPE. Half mortal. But half divine, too.

OENONE. Well, isn't that perfectly silly? I'm *all* goddess. Why would he leave me for someone who's only half divine?

CALLIOPE. Please listen—

OENONE. No. You're lying. I don't even believe you're really Calliope. Why would the Muse of epic poetry come around telling lies to a simple water nymph? I don't know who you are, and I don't want to know. I don't believe a word you say.

CALLIOPE. He told me to tell you good-bye.

OENONE. I said I don't believe you.

CALLIOPE. All right then.

(OENONE *sniffs and wipes her eyes.*)

CALLIOPE. Do you want a handkerchief?

OENONE. I'm not crying. I'm angry, that's all. Where *is* he? He's got a lot of nerve, wandering off without telling me why or where. I've got half a mind to eat this apple all by myself. On second thought, you take it. (*She hands the apple to* CALLIOPE.)

CALLIOPE. But, Oenone—

OENONE. No, go right ahead. He'll feel guilty when I tell him, and it'll serve him right. Go on, eat it. Enjoy it. I've got to get the flock back together. (*She exits.*)

CALLIOPE. Poor thing! Such a shame.

(ERIS *enters.*)

ERIS. Hi, Calliope.

CALLIOPE. Eris!

ERIS. What do you think of my handiwork?

CALLIOPE. You mean breaking the heart of an innocent water nymph? What did Oenone ever do to you? She didn't even *know* about the banquet.

ERIS. Oh, she doesn't matter—not in the grand scheme of things. In another three or four thousand years, hardly anybody will remember her name. She just happened to get in the way of the *real* trouble I've caused. You still haven't figured it out, have you? Don't you know who the most

beautiful woman in the world is? It's Helen!

CALLIOPE. Helen—the queen of Sparta?

ERIS. Yes, *that* Helen. And when Paris meets her, he'll fall insanely in love with her and carry her off with him. He won't care in the least that she's already married!

CALLIOPE. To Menelaus—the most powerful king in Greece!

ERIS. That's right. And he's got a treaty with all the other kings in Greece. If anyone should ever steal Helen from him, they'll all join together and fight to get her back.

CALLIOPE. That will mean war with Troy!

ERIS. But not just any war. This will be the worst fighting the world has ever seen. And it's liable to go on for— oh, ten years I expect! And the gods of Olympus will get into it, too— quarreling and squabbling among themselves as they take one side or the other. It'll be a grand time for me!

CALLIOPE. Did you really *plan* all this?

ERIS. Oh, I'd love to say I did. But, no, you can't plan a true masterpiece of mayhem and destruction. It starts with a flicker of inspiration and ends with a bonfire of luck. Still, that apple *was* a stroke of genius, you'll have to admit. See you later, Calliope—but not at any banquets, at least not soon. The gods will have too much to worry about for feasting and partying. (*She exits.*)

THE APPLE OF DISCORD

CALLIOPE *(to the audience).* I'm reminded of another little story. There once was a butterfly that lived in the forest. One day, it flapped its wings and started a tiny breeze. The breeze grew and grew as it traveled far and wide. Finally, after a few weeks and hundreds of miles, the breeze turned into a terrible tornado. And all because of the flick of a butterfly's wing!

Life is like that sometimes, as you can see. In the years ahead, the city of Troy will be completely destroyed. And thousands upon thousands of the world's best, brightest, strongest, and bravest men will perish in battle. Women will be left widowed, children fatherless. Even the gods will wail with anguish and despair. It will be stupid, pointless, bloody, and heartbreaking. And all because of a beautiful woman—and a little golden apple.

Wouldn't it be splendid if I could change it all with a simple little—?

(She snaps her fingers.)

But you can't undo the course of history—not even through the magic of theatrical storytelling.

It will make for a great epic, anyway—maybe even two or three or four epics. I guess I'd better get back to work, follow this madness through to the end. Is it any wonder I sometimes hate my job?

(She bites into the apple.)

Hmm. Sweet—but also bitter. I'll bet Aphrodite's apple tastes much the same.

(She exits.)

PLAYWRIGHT'S POSTSCRIPT

Paris was eventually wounded in the Trojan War. Only Oenone could cure his wound. But remembering how Paris had betrayed her years earlier, she refused to help him, and he died.

Near the end of this play, Calliope tells the story of a butterfly flapping its wings and causing a tornado hundreds of miles away. This little parable does not come from myth or folklore. Instead, it comes from science.

Scientists working in a field called *chaos theory* are interested in how even very small actions can have very large consequences. These scientists have explained how a butterfly might, indeed, cause a tornado in much the way described by Calliope. So in this play, myth and science briefly meet. Chaos theorists would probably agree that a little golden apple could start the world's most terrible war.

Interestingly enough, the word *chaos* comes from classical mythology. According to the ancient Greeks and Romans, it was the confused mass that existed before anything else in the universe. And of course, we use the word loosely in everyday life to describe any great state of confusion.

CONNECTING TO OTHER CULTURES

Eris, the goddess of discord, resembles many mischievous deities in other cultures. Determined to cause trouble among the Norse gods, the troublemaker Loki killed the seemingly invincible god Balder with a sprig of mistletoe. And according to African legend, the trickster Legba deliberately provoked a quarrel between gods and mortals. This led to the gods moving away from the earth.

ODYSSEUS AND THE SIRENS

SETTING THE STAGE

As Eris predicted in the previous play, the Trojan War dragged on for ten terrible years. At last, the Greeks won it by sheer trickery—the Trojan Horse.

The shrewd Greek chieftain Odysseus came up with the idea of building a huge wooden horse in which he and other soldiers would hide. The Trojans unwittingly took the horse inside their city. The soldiers came out at night, opened the gates of Troy, and the city fell to the Greek army.

But even in victory, further troubles awaited the Greeks. When the Greek army sailed toward home, a terrible storm sank most of its ships. Only a few Greeks made it back, and those who did suffered frightful misfortunes. For example, the chieftain Agamemnon was murdered in his own palace by his wife and her lover.

As for Odysseus, his ships were blown off course, and he wound up wandering the world for ten years. Homer's epic poem *The Odyssey* tells the story of his travels. The following episode, in which Odysseus encounters the mysterious Sirens, is taken from *The Odyssey*. It is introduced by Terpsichore, the Muse of choral song and the mother of the Sirens.

MUSING ABOUT THE MYTH

The gods and goddesses often guided and protected mortals, especially those who pleased them. Sometimes, however, they seemed to take pleasure in tempting humans to act in self-destructive ways. As you read, think about temptations you have faced, how you responded, and what happened because of your actions.

ODYSSEUS AND THE SIRENS

CHARACTERS:

TERPSICHORE (turp sik′ ō rē), the Muse of choral dance and song

ATHENA (a thē′ na), the goddess of war and wisdom

THREE SAILORS

EURYLOCHUS (ū ril′ o kus), the helmsman of Odysseus' ship

ODYSSEUS (ō dis′ ē us), a Greek hero and adventurer, the ruler of Ithaca

THREE SIRENS, female, birdlike demons

OTHER NAMES MENTIONED IN THE PLAY:

CHARYBDIS (ka rib′ dis), a monster

CYCLOPS (sī′ klops), a one-eyed giant cannibal; the plural is CYCLOPES (sī klō′ pēz)

ITHACA (ith′ a ka), an island kingdom ruled by Odysseus

KORE (kō′ rē) (another name for PERSEPHONE per sef′ ō nē), a young goddess

ORPHEUS (or′ fē us), a singer and poet

PENELOPE (pē nel′ ō pē), Odysseus' wife

SCYLLA (sī′ luh), a monster

TARTARUS (tar′ ta rus)

TELEMACHUS (tē lem′ a kus), Odysseus' son

SETTING: *The Mediterranean Sea somewhere near Sicily*

TIME: *A year or two after the end of the Trojan War*

(The set sketchily represents ODYSSEUS' *ship. Center stage is the mast; from it hangs a coil of rope. Stage right is the tiller. Upstage is a row of three benches. Stage left is a raised platform upon which the* SIRENS *will appear.* TERPSICHORE *enters and speaks to the audience.)*

TERPSICHORE. They don't make ships like they used to. That's not necessarily bad, you understand. Ships in ancient times had an unfortunate way of sinking much more often than they do now. Still, the big metal hulks that plow the waves today lack some of the—how shall I put it?— the *panache* of ships of olden days.

(While TERPSICHORE *is speaking,* ATHENA *enters. She crosses stage left and poses as a sculpture, facing left. She will remain frozen until she speaks later in the play.)*

170

TERPSICHORE. For example, how many ships today have goddesses carved on their prows? Very few, I think. This one's a beauty, isn't she? All decked out in armor, warlike, very majestic. *(Wandering about as she shows off the ship)* Oh, and the rest of the ship is equally elegant. Her hull is long and graceful, built from smooth, finely hewed planks. She's painted with red and blue tar, bright and lively colors—or at least they used to be. The paint has long since dulled and chipped from age and wear. *(Pointing to the mast)* A single great, square sail is enough to carry her through the sea. The sail isn't raised just now, though. Our ship is pulling away from an island. And until she reaches the open sea and a fair wind, she'll need a crew of mighty oarsmen.

(THREE SAILORS have entered. They sit down on the benches and pantomime rowing.)

TERPSICHORE. Don't laugh, please. In your mind's eye, imagine that these three men are forty.

(The SAILORS grumble to each other as they row.)

1ST SAILOR. Where's he taking us next, do you suppose?

2ND SAILOR. Straight to damnation, I expect.

3RD SAILOR. We've already been there, don't you remember?

1ST SAILOR. That's right, we paid a visit to the dead themselves.

3RD SAILOR. Can't be any place in creation worse than that.

2ND SAILOR. Don't bet on it. If there is, the captain's sure to find it.

(As TERPSICHORE continues speaking, EURYLOCHUS enters, walks to the tiller, and begins to steer.)

TERPSICHORE. The helmsman steers the ship. As second in command, he's a man with great duties and responsibilities. And he doesn't let anybody forget his authority.

EURYLOCHUS *(to the SAILORS)*. Row, you lazy sea turtles, row! We'll lose the tide and end up stranded on the shoals. Row, I said! Hard to it, you vermin!

TERPSICHORE. And, oh, don't let me forget the captain—the hero of our story.

(As TERPSICHORE continues, ODYSSEUS enters and walks toward ATHENA. He stands behind her, staring at her wistfully.)

TERPSICHORE. They call him lots of things, this man. Long-enduring Odysseus; worldly Odysseus; storm-tossed great Odysseus; tactful, shrewd, and crafty Odysseus; Odysseus, master of tactics, born for exploits. And because he's a pirate, sometimes raider of cities. But one phrase fits him best, I think: Odysseus, man of twists and turns.

And who am I, you ask? My name is Terpsichore, the Muse of choral song. And why am I telling a tale of a shrewd but unlucky pirate-king? After all, it hardly seems the most musical of themes. You'll understand soon. For now, let's eavesdrop on a pirate's prayer.

ODYSSEUS AND THE SIRENS

(TERPSICHORE *steps aside to watch, and* ODYSSEUS *speaks to* ATHENA.)

ODYSSEUS. Oh, Athena, gray-eyed goddess of war and wisdom, why have you forgotten me? Why don't you answer when I call to you day and night? Too long, too long, you have left me alone amid the seas and islands.

Sometimes, the only sound I can hear is my own voice, weeping and desolate. For beneath the hollow bluster of the storm and surge, the winds and waves themselves are silent—silent and godless.

Oh, gray-eyed worker of wonders, do not stay so far away. Trouble surrounds me on all sides, and I have no one to help me. I am weak and worn to the very bone, and my mind and heart are empty.

(EURYLOCHUS *has been watching* ODYSSEUS *uneasily. He steps away from the tiller and walks toward* ODYSSEUS.)

ODYSSEUS (to ATHENA). Speak to me again, like you used to—just one word, one tiny syllable, the merest sigh. Don't let it be said among the living that you left your favorite mortal to die in misery.

EURYLOCHUS. You're talking to a piece of wood.

ODYSSEUS (to EURYLOCHUS). Leave me alone.

EURYLOCHUS. Gladly—once you give me my orders.

ODYSSEUS. You have your orders.

EURYLOCHUS. To set a course due east? That's no order. Empty words, that's all.

ODYSSEUS. That's the way home.

EURYLOCHUS. After all these endless, storm-tossed travels, how can you have any idea?

ODYSSEUS. I can tell by the stars and the sun.

EURYLOCHUS. Bilge. It's a guess, that's all.

ODYSSEUS. What do you want me to tell you, Helmsman?

EURYLOCHUS. After more than a year of wandering, something to give me and the men a scrap of hope.

ODYSSEUS. Get back to the tiller.

EURYLOCHUS. Aye, as you command. But first, may I speak freely, Captain?

ODYSSEUS. When have I ever stopped you?

EURYLOCHUS. We're pirates. Or we were pirates once, before that wretched war in Troy. Why don't we do what we do best? Find a town on the coast, raid it, rule it, become kings, make it our home.

ODYSSEUS. And what of Ithaca?

EURYLOCHUS. What *of* Ithaca? What kind of home awaits us there? How long have we been away, Captain? Eleven, twelve years? Will our children even know us? Have our wives been waiting all this time? Why wouldn't they give us up for dead? Why wouldn't they remarry?

ODYSSEUS AND THE SIRENS

ODYSSEUS. Worry about your own wife. My Penelope will never remarry.

EURYLOCHUS. How can you know that?

ODYSSEUS. Watch your tongue, Eurylochus.

EURYLOCHUS. Can we even *find* Ithaca?

ODYSSEUS. Due east, just like I told you.

EURYLOCHUS. And what dangers will we find on our way?

ODYSSEUS. I don't know.

EURYLOCHUS. You don't, eh? Well, I can't imagine that wooden goddess is going to tell you. But if she does, kindly share her tidings with the rest of us. Meanwhile, I won't hold my breath. Athena may have looked out for you in the old days, but not anymore. It's time you accepted that. *(Stepping away from* ODYSSEUS, *calling to the* SAILORS*)* Avast, put down your oars! We're clear of the island, and we've got a fair wind, so let's not lose it. Hoist the sail, and spread it full.

*(*EURYLOCHUS *returns to the tiller and steers. The* SAILORS *get to their feet and pantomime hoisting the sail.)*

ODYSSEUS *(to* ATHENA*).* Do you see? Do you hear? Men mock me, saying, "Let Athena help him, since he is her favorite!" Why don't you speak? Have I wronged you in some way? If so, I beg of you, please tell me so I can make amends.

EURYLOCHUS *(to the* SAILORS*).* Don't be dainty with the ropes! What's the matter, do you reckon they'll break?

Afraid of getting blisters on your fingers? Pull, pull!

(The SAILORS *and* EURYLOCHUS *freeze.)*

ODYSSEUS *(to* ATHENA*).* But it seems that you've truly forgotten me. Yes, I mean nothing to you anymore.

*(*ODYSSEUS *turns from* ATHENA *and starts to walk away. Still motionless,* ATHENA *speaks.)*

ATHENA. Odysseus. Wait.

ODYSSEUS *(turning toward her).* Goddess!

ATHENA. I am here. *(Coming to life and stepping toward him)* You just asked if you had wronged me. The question astounds me. *Of course* you wronged me—and most painfully.

ODYSSEUS. But how?

ATHENA. You know perfectly well.

ODYSSEUS. I don't.

ATHENA. When the war ended and you Greeks were victorious, a Trojan princess sought safety in a temple— *my* temple.

ODYSSEUS. Cassandra, yes. But what's this got to do with me?

ATHENA. Don't interrupt, Odysseus. Don't stir my anger anew. A Greek soldier snatched her from my statue, even as she knelt and prayed to me. He carried her off to be a general's unwilling mistress.

ODYSSEUS. Ajax did that. He gave her to General Agamemnon. I had nothing to do with it.

ATHENA. True. And that was your misdeed.

ODYSSEUS. I don't understand.

ATHENA. You Greeks—you let Ajax get away with it, all of you. You let Agamemnon claim Cassandra for his own. Not one of you stopped it from happening. Not one of you punished the evildoers when it was done. I was wronged by an entire army—the very army I had helped through ten long years of war. So I made your victory a bitter one. When you boarded your ships and sailed back to Greece—

ODYSSEUS. You sent the storm that broke our fleet apart.

ATHENA. That's right. You and your crew aren't the only Greeks who never made it home.

(Pause)

ODYSSEUS. How kind of you to tell me. *(He starts walking away from her.)*

ATHENA. Just what do you think you're doing?

ODYSSEUS. What does it look like I'm doing? I'm turning my back on you—just as you turned your back on me.

ATHENA. You are one impudent mortal.

ODYSSEUS. And you are one petty goddess. The very idea of punishing a whole army—nay, a whole civilization—for the misdeeds of two stupid men! Do you know what we've been through since we got hit by that storm of yours?

ATHENA. I have some idea, yes.

ODYSSEUS. Well, you're going to hear it anyway. We landed on the island of the Cyclopes—vicious, one-eyed, giant cannibals. I've never seen their like before. A bunch of my men got eaten there, and the rest of us barely escaped with our flesh on our bones. Then we landed on another island, and what do you guess we found? More cannibals! They sank my whole fleet—all my ships except this one. I can't tell you how many men I lost; I don't even know. And this island we're now sailing away from, it belongs to a witch who turned half of my crew into pigs—*pigs*! It took some fancy thinking on my part to get them turned back into men again.

And, oh, that isn't half of it. I've even paid a visit to the country of the dead—and sometimes I wonder why I didn't just stay there. It couldn't be much worse than my life here among the living.

And through it all, I never stopped praying to you, every hour of every day, begging you to come back to me. I never stopped searching my heart for some wrong I must have done you. And now, at last—at long, long last—I know what I did to deserve such sorrow. Nothing! Absolutely nothing!

ATHENA. Don't provoke me, Odysseus.

ODYSSEUS. Why not? If you're going to be angry with me anyway, it might as well be over *something*.

(Pause. ATHENA *laughs.)*

ODYSSEUS. What do you find so funny?

ODYSSEUS AND THE SIRENS

ATHENA. I'm not sure. Myself, I suppose. I ought to strike you dead here and now for such brazen insolence. But I'd quite forgotten how much I like you, O man of twists and turns. You really are an enigma.

ODYSSEUS. How nice that you're amused. And now—perhaps you'd be so kind as to turn back into a mute block of carved wood. I liked you better that way. And I think you were more of a help to me. *(He turns again to walk away.)*

ATHENA. Oh, don't go away mad, Odysseus.

ODYSSEUS. All right. I'll just go away.

ATHENA. Don't you want my help?

ODYSSEUS. I'll get along on my own, thank you.

ATHENA. You'll live by your wits, eh?

ODYSSEUS. I've managed for quite a while now.

ATHENA. Yes, you have—and admirably. And if you want to hold a grudge, that's fine. *I* certainly held one for long enough, so fair's fair.

ODYSSEUS. I'm glad we see things eye to eye.

ATHENA. I'll leave you alone, if you insist.

ODYSSEUS. I do.

ATHENA. Very well, then. *(Pause)* So—a course due east, is it?

ODYSSEUS. Isn't that the way to Ithaca?

ATHENA. I thought you didn't want my help.

ODYSSEUS. You're right. I don't.

ATHENA. How sad. I'll just have to let you and your men sail straight into certain death.

(Pause)

ODYSSEUS. What danger do you mean?

ATHENA. The Sirens.

ODYSSEUS. I thought they were only a myth.

ATHENA. A myth is as real as anything else—real enough to sink a fleet or burn a city.

ODYSSEUS. But aren't the Sirens supposed to be dead? I heard they killed themselves.

ATHENA. Where did you hear a story like that?

ODYSSEUS. It's an old one among seafaring folk. They say that Jason and his crew sailed past them on their way to win the Golden Fleece. The Sirens sang their song to them— the same song that lured so many other sailors to their deaths. But the singer Orpheus was aboard. He plucked his lyre and sang a song so beautiful that the Sirens never stood a chance. And so they killed themselves from despair.

ATHENA. A pretty tale—if only it were true. No, the Sirens are as alive as ever.

ODYSSEUS. Can't we keep away from Siren Land?

ATHENA. No. It's your only way back.

ODYSSEUS. Surely we can resist their song.

ATHENA. You can't. If you hear it, you'll throw yourself into the sea or beach your ship on their island. And there you will die.

ODYSSEUS. But what sort of song can be that deadly?

ATHENA. That's not for mortals to know.

ODYSSEUS. But—

ATHENA. I'm telling you the truth, Odysseus. Trust me.

ODYSSEUS. How can we hope to save ourselves?

(ATHENA *takes a ball of wax out of her robe.*)

ATHENA *(holding the wax toward him).* With this.

ODYSSEUS *(taking the wax).* Beeswax! Of course! We'll stop our ears with it! We won't hear a thing! Now why didn't I think of that on my own?

ATHENA. You would have, if you'd had time to think it through. You're very clever. But you must hurry. You'll be nearing Siren Land any moment now, and you've got to be ready. The wind will die, and your sail won't do you any good.

ODYSSEUS. We'll take to our oars, then.

ATHENA. Get to it. You've not a moment to lose. But remember— don't even *think* of listening to the Sirens.

ODYSSEUS. I'm not a fool.

ATHENA. I hope not. *(She walks toward the prow.)*

ODYSSEUS. Athena.

ATHENA. What?

ODYSSEUS. Thank you for coming back to me.

ATHENA. Save your gratitude. We've still got things to settle between us—after you get past the Sirens.

(ATHENA *freezes again into the prow sculpture.* ODYSSEUS *stares at her for a moment.* EURYLOCHUS *and the* SAILORS *come to life.*)

1ST SAILOR. The sail's gone slack.

2ND SAILOR. There's nary a swell.

3RD SAILOR. We're becalmed for sure.

ODYSSEUS. I expected as much. It means we're nearing the island of the Sirens.

2ND SAILOR. The Sirens?

3RD SAILOR. But aren't they dead?

1ST SAILOR. Or only a myth?

ODYSSEUS. They're alive and well—and as deadly as ever.

EURYLOCHUS. But how can you know that?

ODYSSEUS. I don't have time to explain. We've got to get moving, so be sprightly about it. First, lower the sail. Then muster again for further orders.

(The SAILORS *pantomime lowering the sail.)*

EURYLOCHUS. What's this all about, Captain?

ODYSSEUS. I just explained that, didn't I?

EURYLOCHUS. I don't understand. You just told me that you didn't know what dangers we'd be facing. But now—

ODYSSEUS. A piece of wood told me.

EURYLOCHUS. Athena?

ODYSSEUS AND THE SIRENS

ODYSSEUS. You said it, not me.

EURYLOCHUS. Have you really spoken with her?

ODYSSEUS. I don't expect you to believe me.

EURYLOCHUS. Forgive me for doubting you, Captain. But there *is* a fine line between talking to gods and being just plain barmy.

ODYSSEUS. So there is, so there is. And if you ever find out just where that line is drawn, kindly tell me. I'm as anxious to know as anybody.

(The SAILORS *have finished lowering the sail and have gathered around* ODYSSEUS *again.)*

1ST SAILOR. Further orders, Captain?

ODYSSEUS *(passing the wax among them).* We'll all put this in our ears. The Sirens' singing can't hurt us if we don't hear it.

3RD SAILOR. Aye, Captain.

2ND SAILOR. Good thinking, Captain.

ODYSSEUS. Now get back to your oars, men, and row hard and fast. And Eurylochus, get back to the tiller.

(The SAILORS *and* EURYLOCHUS *murmur in agreement and begin to walk away.)*

ODYSSEUS. Wait.

(The SAILORS *and* EURYLOCHUS *turn toward him again.)*

ODYSSEUS. Tie me to the mast.

3RD SAILOR. What?

ODYSSEUS. You heard me. Be quick, and use good, strong knots.

1ST SAILOR. But why?

ODYSSEUS. No questions, sailor. I gave you an order.

(The SAILORS *take the rope from the mast and tie* ODYSSEUS *to it. While they work,* EURYLOCHUS *speaks to* ODYSSEUS *worriedly.)*

EURYLOCHUS. What about the wax?

ODYSSEUS. I won't be needing it.

EURYLOCHUS. So you plan to listen to them?

ODYSSEUS. What do you think?

EURYLOCHUS. Did Athena put this idea into your head?

ODYSSEUS. No.

EURYLOCHUS. Why do you want to do it, then?

ODYSSEUS *(to the* SAILORS*).* Don't tie that knot there. I'll pick it apart with my fingers. *(To* EURYLOCHUS*)* Think about it, Helmsman—a song that men have heard but never lived to tell about. What might such a song be like?

EURYLOCHUS. Why didn't you just ask Athena?

ODYSSEUS *(to the* SAILORS*).* Tighter around the ankles, or I'll kick myself loose. *(To* EURYLOCHUS*)* I did ask her. And do you know what she told me? "That's not for mortals to know." Those were her exact words. Oh—and then she said, "Trust me."

EURYLOCHUS. Don't you think you should?

ODYSSEUS. I'm tired of trusting the gods. Look where it's gotten me. Look where it's gotten all of us. I've got a hunch, Eurylochus. Do you want to hear it? *(To the* SAILORS*)* Tighter, tighter! Don't worry about my circulation. *(To* EURYLOCHUS*)* I think the Sirens know a secret that we mortals aren't supposed to learn. That's what they sing about. And if a single man could hear it and live . . .

EURYLOCHUS. What?

ODYSSEUS. Maybe we could be free, we mortals—free of the waywardness of gods and goddesses.

EURYLOCHUS. I don't like this. You've got no business putting yourself at risk.

ODYSSEUS. What's the risk?

EURYLOCHUS. Death, of course.

ODYSSEUS. Not if I can't get away from this mast.

EURYLOCHUS. Madness, then.

ODYSSEUS. Have I ever struck you as perfectly sane? If I go completely mad, you'll probably never notice the difference.

EURYLOCHUS. Think of your wife and son. Think of how much you want to get home.

ODYSSEUS. This might be my only way home.

(The SAILORS *have finished tying* ODYSSEUS *and gather in front of him.)*

ODYSSEUS. Helmsman, steer us near the shore—as near as you can without running us aground. And men, row slowly, very slowly. It's my one chance to hear the Sirens, and I don't want to miss a word or a note. But,

Helmsman, watch me close and make sure I don't get loose. Tighten the ropes if you have to. I might rave a little, but just ignore me.

EURYLOCHUS. Shouldn't be hard, sir. I won't be able to hear you.

ODYSSEUS. True, true. Once we've cleared the island and you're sure we're out of earshot, then you can cut me loose—but only then. Have you got all that?

*(*EURYLOCHUS *and the* SAILORS *murmur their agreement.)*

ODYSSEUS. Good. Now get back to your posts. And stop your ears well.

*(*EURYLOCHUS *returns to the tiller and the* SAILORS *to their oars.* TERPSICHORE *steps forward to speak. As she does, the* SAILORS *row more and more slowly. Steering,* EURYLOCHUS *keeps a wary eye on* ODYSSEUS.*)*

TERPSICHORE. The Sirens—musical demons, singers of deadly sweet melodies. I'm sure you're starting to understand why I, the Muse of choral song, am interested in this tale. A bit of pride is mixed up in it, too. You see, the Sirens happen to be my daughters.

But how, you ask, can a song be so beautiful that it kills? Is such a thing even possible? I'd guess that Odysseus and his men are starting to believe it. For as they come in sight of the island, they can see that its beaches are strewn with the sunbaked bones of the dead.

*(*TERPSICHORE *steps aside to watch as* ODYSSEUS *calls out.)*

ODYSSEUS AND THE SIRENS

ODYSSEUS. Ahoy, you broken remnants of long-lost men! What brought you to this dreadful pass? A song, I'm told—but I hear no song. No, there's a ghastly hush about this place, as if the sea itself fears it might wake you. Not even the waves dare break against a shore made out of bones, not sand. The tide creeps cravenly about you like a worm. Huge birds caress the air so gently with their wings, they stir no breeze as they fly over you, and they hold their breath lest they utter the faintest cry.

So tell me, bones, since the rest of creation has lost its voice—what became of you? What sealed your doom? What, has eternity got your tongues? Won't you tell me? I think I understand. There is no song. There are no Sirens here. Only a silence that taunts and kills. Closer and closer you came to this island, hoping, like me, to hear—something! Anything! And death claimed you in this place, as I sometimes hope it will claim me.

But not this time. I'll sail on by. And when I'm freed from these ropes, I'll salute you. But, oh, how I wish we could have talked a little, swapped some sorrows, maybe even shared some melancholy laughter. I wish, at least, I could have learned your names.

(A pool of light rises on the stage left platform. The THREE SIRENS *step onto the platform. The following song can be sung to many different hymn, anthem, or ballad tunes.)*

SIRENS.
Hail! Our hero comes this way,
 The conqueror of Troy!
How many foemen did you slay,
 Or fortress walls destroy?

Odysseus, O mortal blessed,
 Graced by Athena's love!
You shall prevail in every quest.
 What mountains can't you move?

And yet—how strange, what we
 behold;
 Our eyes must be belied.
Odysseus, so proud and bold,
 Just like a slave is tied.

ODYSSEUS. Mockery, mockery—all is mockery. Go on and mock, you half-bird, half-woman creatures. I know I cut a comical figure, but at least I am wholly a man. You and you and you shall never be all woman.

(The SIRENS *now speak instead of sing.)*

1ST SIREN.
Oh, we don't mock—we're just
 surprised
To see your glory compromised.

2ND SIREN.
We knew that you were coming
 here,
But not tied up like this, we fear.

3RD SIREN.
Please tell us, for we have no clue—
What captor got the best of you?

ODYSSEUS. Myself—I'm my own captor, tied here at my own command and for my own safety. I don't care to add my bones to your grim shore.

ODYSSEUS AND THE SIRENS

SIRENS (*speaking together*).
> Then sail on by—yes, sail on by,
> If truly you don't wish to die.

ODYSSEUS. No. I want to hear you sing.
Sing to me as you did to all the others.

3RD SIREN.
> Very well, if that's your will.

1ST SIREN.
> We'll sing to you with all our skill.

2ND SIREN.
> We think you know, and know quite well,
> The risk of falling in our spell.

1ST SIREN.
> But first, we wish you'd make it clear
> What sort of song you wish to hear.

ODYSSEUS. To begin—perhaps something to satisfy my curiosity. What sort of creatures are you, and how did you come to be?

(*The* SIRENS *sing again. The following will fit the tune of "Londonderry Air," also called "Danny Boy."*)

SIRENS.
> When we were girls, throughout the woods we'd ramble—
> In days gone by, in days so long ago.
> We'd lightly dance through tangled brush and bramble
> And gather flowers wherever they did grow.
>
> We were companions to a youthful goddess,
> Our comrade dear, and Kore was her name—
> Just like a star, so radiant yet modest,
> A perfect creature, without fault and without blame.
>
> One dreadful day, when we went out a-roaming,
> Our precious Kore vanished into air.
> Though far and wide we searched and went a-combing,
> We could not find poor Kore anywhere.
>
> We asked the gods to give us wing and feather
> So we could fly and seek her high and low.
> But she is gone, we'll never be together;
> So on this island we now rest and sing our woe.

ODYSSEUS. A sad and bitter tale. Like me, you know what loss and sorrow are. But tell me, birdlike women, why do you have no wings?

(*The* SIRENS *speak again.*)

1ST SIREN.
> We lost our wings—alas, alack!
> And we will never get them back.

2ND SIREN.
> We've nothing but our pride to blame
> For bringing us disgrace and shame.

3RD SIREN.
> We thought our singing was the best,
> And dared the Muses to a test.

2ND SIREN.
> The Muses won this little match,
> And for a prize, our wings they snatched.

1ST SIREN.
> So on this island we must stay,

ODYSSEUS AND THE SIRENS

And never, ever fly away.

ODYSSEUS (*chuckling wryly*). Ah, pride goes before a fall! Poor fools, poor fools.

SIRENS (*speaking together*). Mockery, mockery—all is mockery.

ODYSSEUS. Oh, I'm not mocking you, ladies—at least not you in particular. We're *all* fools in the eyes of the gods, aren't we?

1ST SIREN.
So you say, and think you know;
But really, it need not be so.

ODYSSEUS. What do you mean by that?

3RD SIREN.
Patience, friend, and wait a bit.

2ND SIREN.
We'll presently get 'round to it.

3RD SIREN.
Of us, you now know everything.
But what of you? Oh, won't you sing?

1ST SIREN.
Yes, sing to us of your own life—
Your mirth and sorrow, joy and strife.

ODYSSEUS. I've neither the voice for song nor the knack for rhyme. A song from my gullet would curdle your blood. Besides, it seems that my life is already an open book to you.

1ST SIREN.
Only the details, not the whole;
We cannot see inside your soul.

ODYSSEUS. I am a man who has suffered much and has seen much suffering.

3RD SIREN.
Oh, man of luck—oh, happy man!

1ST SIREN.
How great your blessings are, how grand!

ODYSSEUS More mockery! Has a man ever been less happy, less blessed?

2ND SIREN.
Sorrows are teachers, sage and wise.

3RD SIREN.
You know more than you realize.

1ST SIREN.
So tell us, tell us what you've learned
While you've twisted, while you've turned.

ODYSSEUS. I've learned that men are sometimes loyal, sometimes treacherous. But the gods are neither—they act upon our lives without rhyme or reason. Who can know the will of the gods? Do they even have a will? And yet—who can escape their pointless power?

Mockery, mockery—all is mockery.

In Troy, I fought for ten long years. There I learned what war really is—a chess game without rules, in which we mortals are helpless pieces upon ever-shifting squares. All the martial virtues and frailties are but illusions. For what is courage but the whispered word of some god in one's ear? And what is cowardice but the sudden absence of that god? And what is skill in battle but a god directing one's arm, one's sword, one's spear?

Mockery, mockery—all is mockery.

ODYSSEUS AND THE SIRENS

2ND SIREN.

How much you've learned! You're wise indeed!

3RD SIREN.

What more knowledge can you need?

ODYSSEUS. My very knowledge is a mockery. I know nothing that can do me or anyone else the slightest good. I want wisdom to equal my suffering, wisdom that's worth the price I've paid for it. I want *true* understanding—the kind that makes one free. And I think . . .

3RD SIREN.

Think what, think what, oh, questing friend?

2ND SIREN.

Tell us, tell us, saddest of men.

ODYSSEUS. I think I can learn from you the greatest secret of all—a secret denied me by the gods.

2ND SIREN.

Oh, excellent Odysseus!

1ST SIREN.

How ready you are to learn from us!

ODYSSEUS. It's true, then! Oh, sing it to me, please!

(*The* SIRENS *sing again. The following will fit the tune of "Greensleeves."*)

SIRENS.

Not far from here there is a spring
    With waters still and gleaming.
Gaze in its crystal pool and learn
    What lies beyond all seeming.

Gaze, gaze in its pool and find

A sight to surely delight your
    mind.
See, see the truth sharp and bright
    By gazing in the clear water.

(*The* SIRENS *hum as* ODYSSEUS *speaks.*)

ODYSSEUS. My reflection, eh? Thank you, but no. I've seen my face in mirrors and waters all over the world too often to have a scrap of vanity left. I'm not a pretty sight, I know that better than anyone else. Still, I must admit, your song is strangely compelling—

(*The* SIRENS *sing to the same tune.*)

SIRENS.

The mirrors where you have looked
    have lied
        And kept the truth from you
        cruelly.
They've shown you nothing but a
man
        And not the god you are truly.

Yes, yes, you're a god, my friend,
    With might and power without
    end
Learn, learn who you really are
    By gazing in the clear water.

(*The* SIRENS *hum as* ODYSSEUS *speaks.*)

ODYSSEUS. To be a god! To see and know all! To wield unimaginable power! Now that's a thing devoutly to be wished. And yet—what of the men who came this way before? What of their bones on your beach? You promised them the same, I expect.

(*The* SIRENS *sing to the same tune.*)

ODYSSEUS AND THE SIRENS

SIRENS.
> Their brittle bones they did not
> need;
> > They left them without misgiving.
> For now they scale immortal heights,
> > And lives divine they are living.
>
> Be, be like those men divine,
> > And let your greatness gleam and
> > shine.
> Live, live for eternity
> > By sipping from the sweet water.

(ODYSSEUS *begins to struggle with his ropes.*
EURYLOCHUS *eyes him worriedly.*)

ODYSSEUS. Temptresses, cunning
temptresses! I feel your spell tighten
even as my ropes loosen. But I'm not
ready to shuffle off this mortal coil,
not yet. I still have human duties and
longings. What of friends, family, and
home?

(*The* SIRENS *speak instead of sing.*)

1ST SIREN.
> Now that's a thing to make one
> wonder.

2ND SIREN.
> But who can set a god asunder?

3RD SIREN.
> Who can keep him from his home,
> Forcing him to always roam?

2ND SIREN.
> When immortality is won,
> You'll find Telemachus, your son.

1ST SIREN.
> Come this way—yes, come to me—
> And find your wife Penelope.

ODYSSEUS. Telemachus! Penelope!
Home! At last, at last! Yes, yes! I'll
come there; I'll join you! I'll jump
over the side and swim right to
you!

(ODYSSEUS *loosens the ropes. The* SIRENS *sing
again—the same hymn, anthem, or ballad tune
as when they first appeared.*)

SIRENS.
> Hail! Our hero comes this way,
> > To claim his rightful power!
> He'll be immortal from this day,
> > A deity from this hour!

(*The* SIRENS *hum as* ODYSSEUS *struggles and
speaks.*)

ODYSSEUS. How near, how near is all
I've quested for! Oh, the happiness I
might know! But these ropes—these
infernal ropes!

(EURYLOCHUS *steps away from the tiller and
approaches* ODYSSEUS. *The* SIRENS *sing to the
same tune.*)

SIRENS.
> Although you fight with all your
> might
> > In hopes that you might flee,
> The spirit wills but ropes hold tight,
> > And flesh cannot break free.

(*The* SIRENS *hum.* ODYSSEUS *is almost free of
his ropes, but* EURYLOCHUS *ties him tight
again.*)

ODYSSEUS. Helmsman, what in the
name of Hades are you doing? Set
me free, curse and confound you!
Don't tie me tighter! I order you,
cut me loose, or you'll pay with
your life! And before I'm through,
you'll beg me for a quick and easy
death!

ODYSSEUS AND THE SIRENS

(But EURYLOCHUS *can't hear* ODYSSEUS. *He finishes tightening the ropes, then returns to the tiller. The* SIRENS *sing to the same tune.)*

SIRENS.
> We've failed, we Sirens of renown,
> To bring our hero home,
> And so we have no choice but drown
> Beneath the wave and foam.

ODYSSEUS. No! Stay! Wait for me! I'll come there! I promise!

(The SIRENS *leap off the platform, then dash offstage.)*

ODYSSEUS. Life, life, life—why do you still hold me in your cold and clammy grip? What use do you have for me, except to mock me? Can't anybody in this vast and lonely world please tell me if I have a wife, a son, a home? If only I knew! If only I knew!

*(*ODYSSEUS *hangs his head, unconscious. A silent moment passes. Then* EURYLOCHUS *walks in full view of the rowing* SAILORS *and removes the wax from his ears. The* SAILORS *stop rowing and do the same.)*

EURYLOCHUS. We're out of earshot of the Sirens, men. Let's look to the Captain.

(The SAILORS *rise to their feet.)*

3RD SAILOR. Great gods!

1ST SAILOR. Is he—?

2ND SAILOR. Dead?

EURYLOCHUS. Cut him loose.

(The SAILORS *cut the ropes with knives.* ODYSSEUS *collapses into their arms.)*

EURYLOCHUS. Captain, talk to us.

ODYSSEUS. I'll live. Blast it all, I'll live. Back to your oars, men. The sooner we're away from this cursed island, the better.

(The SAILORS *go back to their benches and row.* ODYSSEUS *remains crouched on the deck.)*

EURYLOCHUS. What happened? Tell me.

ODYSSEUS. In good time, Helmsman. Give me a moment or two to gather my wits. Get back to the tiller.

EURYLOCHUS. Aye, Captain.

*(*EURYLOCHUS *goes to the tiller and steers.* ATHENA *comes to life and approaches* ODYSSEUS.*)*

ATHENA. Well, well, well. Behold, valiant Odysseus, master of tactics, born for exploits, raider of cities.

ODYSSEUS. Go on and taunt me. I can't blame you. I did disobey you.

ATHENA. I wouldn't call it disobedience. It was something worse. A betrayal between friends.

ODYSSEUS. How can we be friends— you a goddess, me a mortal? Go on, be angry.

ATHENA. I have no words for what I feel.

ODYSSEUS. I suppose you gods and goddesses have feelings that we mortals know nothing about.

ATHENA. Oh, yes. Whole worlds and skies full of pain, whole aching oceans unfathomably deeper than mere heartbreak.

ODYSSEUS. I won't say I'm sorry.

ODYSSEUS AND THE SIRENS

ATHENA. Nor would it help if you did. I must leave you now. I'll warn you of one danger, though. Soon, you'll be faced with Charybdis—a huge monster who lives under the waves. She's always drinking or belching up water. When she drinks, she creates a terrible whirlpool that will pull your ship down to its doom. When she belches, she makes great waves that will scuttle you. Either way, you'll be lost.

ODYSSEUS. We'll sail past her.

ATHENA. The only way is near Scylla, a monster who lives in a cave on a cliff. She has six heads with long, spindly necks. When you sail past her, she'll dive down and devour as many of your men as she can.

ODYSSEUS. We'll escape her.

ATHENA. You can't—not if you hope to stay clear of Charybdis. You'll lose six men at least, and that's if you're lucky and fast on your oars.

ODYSSEUS. Is that the worst of it?

ATHENA. Not even nearly the worst. But I've told you too much already. I'll be back someday, Odysseus. I can't tell you when. Farewell.

(ATHENA *freezes into the prow sculpture again. For a moment,* ODYSSEUS *stands staring at her pensively. Then he walks toward* EURYLOCHUS.)

EURYLOCHUS (*still steering*). Must have been quite some song they sang, Captain. Did you learn the secret you hoped for?

ODYSSEUS. No.

EURYLOCHUS. What did they sing then?

ODYSSEUS. That they'd kill themselves because I didn't go to them.

EURYLOCHUS. Think they did?

ODYSSEUS. Not likely. After all, they did sing the same to Jason and his men. There will always be Sirens—if not on that island, in some mad part of our hearts.

EURYLOCHUS. You sure fought like a devil to get away. Ropes or no ropes, I was afraid we'd lost you.

ODYSSEUS. Maybe you did. Maybe it's only Odysseus' hollow, weather-beaten husk that's on this deck, walking and talking as if it were a man. Maybe his bones are bleaching themselves white in the sun on that beach—his bones and his soul.

EURYLOCHUS. I don't follow you, sir.

ODYSSEUS. Oh, yes, you do. The question is, should you?

EURYLOCHUS. Eh?

ODYSSEUS. Do you ever think of mutiny? Answer me squarely, Helmsman.

EURYLOCHUS. Every day, sir.

ODYSSEUS. And every hour of every day?

EURYLOCHUS. Pretty nearly.

ODYSSEUS. I'm glad to hear it.

EURYLOCHUS. Are you all right, Captain?

ODYSSEUS. I'm fine, Eurylochus. I was just looking our goddess over a bit. She's more than a little worse for wear. The teak grain is starting to split. There's a crack from the top of her helmet all the way down to her brow. The paint on her cheeks is chipping away. Her gray eyes have faded almost white in the sun. And her gown is encrusted with barnacles. We'll have to take her in for repairs when we get back to Ithaca.

EURYLOCHUS. But what of the *real* goddess? Isn't she with you again?

ODYSSEUS. She's just a piece of wood. Due east, Helmsman. Due east.

EURYLOCHUS. Yes, Captain.

(EURYLOCHUS *calls out to the* SAILORS.)

EURYLOCHUS. Backs into it, men. Row sprightly. It's a foul wind coming up, and we'll have no use for the sail, so spare no muscle. Don't doze, confound you!

(EURYLOCHUS *steers, the* SAILORS *row, and* ODYSSEUS *stares longingly out to sea.* TERPSICHORE *steps forward to speak to the audience.*)

TERPSICHORE. Athena will be back to help him someday. He's her favorite, whether she wants him to be or not. Gods and goddesses can't choose their loved ones, any more than we mortals can. But it will be years before she returns. During that time, Odysseus' troubles will bloom like crazed flowers.

He and his crew will skirt the awful whirlpool mouth of Charybdis, but at a deadly price. Six men will be slain and eaten by Scylla—one man for each of the monster's heads. And soon afterwards the ship will sink, and all aboard will drown except the captain himself. By the time Odysseus, man of twists and turns, gets home to Ithaca, he will be all alone.

And what will he find there? What of his wife Penelope and his son Telemachus? And what of himself? When he enters his house again, who will greet him when he looks into the mysterious pool of his own heart? We'll save that story for another day.

(*The curtain falls.*)

PLAYWRIGHT'S POSTSCRIPT

I have taken one great liberty with Homer's version of this story. According to *The Odyssey*, it wasn't Athena who warned Odysseus of the Sirens. It was Circe, the witch who turned many of Odysseus' men into pigs.

I wrote Athena into this episode because I was fascinated by Odysseus' troubled relationship with the Olympian deities. In his world, heroes normally received constant help from the gods. But during his travels, poor Odysseus was mostly ignored by them for years. It was only near the end of his wanderings that Athena finally came to his aid.

How did Odysseus feel about his abandonment by the gods? Athena's presence in this story allowed me to explore his feelings in dialogue with her.

Classical storytellers described the Sirens in many different ways and disagreed on how many there were. According to Homer, there were only two. Other sources said that there were three or four. I decided that three would make a good number for this play.

CONNECTING TO OTHER CULTURES

Over the ages, there have been many stories of mysterious creatures who lure sailors and travelers to their deaths. Such stories have been told about mermaids, beautiful women with the tails of fish.

In swamps and marshes, mysterious lights sometimes appear by night. These are often called *will-o'-the-wisps*, and they are a natural phenomenon produced by gases. People have been known to drown while trying to follow them. This has led to Siren-like folktales in which will-o'-the-wisps are spirits luring people to their deaths.

PROTEUS

SETTING THE STAGE

At the end of the Trojan War, the Greek chieftain Menelaus set sail for home. But like Odysseus in the previous play, he was blown off course in a storm and wandered for years before he arrived in his home city of Sparta. Along the way, he had an extraordinary encounter with Proteus, the magical, shape-shifting Old Man of the Sea.

The story of Menelaus' adventure with Proteus was told by Homer in his epic poem *The Odyssey*. It was also the subject of a lost play by Aeschylus, an Athenian dramatist of the 5th century B.C. Aeschylus' *Proteus* was a satyr play—a comedy that included a chorus of satyrs. In classical mythology, satyrs were minor gods with the upper bodies of men but the legs, feet, and horns of goats.

The play that follows is a bit like a satyr play. But instead of a chorus of satyrs, the chorus here is a group of rowdy sea nymphs. Appropriately enough, this play is introduced by Thalia, the Muse of comedy.

MUSING ABOUT THE MYTH

In classical myths, mortals who are tested by the gods—and pass the test—often become heroes. As you read, think about the kinds of trials and challenges that modern heroes face.

PROTEUS

(The curtain rises on a beach on the island of Pharos. The stage can actually be completely bare, except for a single flat or screen upstage, behind which PROTEUS *will make his transformations.* MENELAUS, *apparently unconscious, lies faceup on the ground.* THALIA enters, carrying a cloth handbag. She does not see MENELAUS at first. Considering that she is the Muse of comedy, she is surprisingly serious—even dour. In fact, she will not so much as crack a smile until the very end of the play. She speaks to the audience.)*

THALIA. Oh, what I wouldn't give for a good laugh. A riotous, unbridled, out-of-control belly laugh—that's what I've got in mind. The kind of laugh that makes you cry out "Stop it, you're killing me!"—and really mean it. The kind of laugh that busts your gut, then your lungs, then your heart, then explodes all your veins and arteries and snaps your bones into pieces and grinds them up into powder.

It's been a long time since I laughed like that—a millennium or more. I guess it's been several hundred years since I even cracked a smile. Even a titter or a giggle or a smirk would be welcome. But I wouldn't say no to the laugh that kills—not that I *can* be killed. I'm immortal, you see. I've survived the kind of laughter that cripples creeds and dogmas, topples tyrants and idols, wipes out whole armies, destroys great civilizations, sinks entire continents beneath the waves. I've survived it—and loved it. But it's been way too long.

I know what you're wondering. "If she wants a good laugh, what's she doing here, on some uninhabited island in the middle of nowhere?" Well, this island isn't quite as dismal as it looks, nor quite as uninhabited. A god lives here—a trickster god. Not one of your tragic tricksters, chained to a rock high in the mountains for stealing fire from Olympus, but a good old-fashioned low-down prankster, on the loose and up to no good. He's an old friend of mine, and he's usually able to make me laugh in a pinch.

(Noticing MENELAUS*)*

But what have we here? A drowned corpse, I believe. Yes, it's not hard to guess this poor devil's story. His ship went down in a tempest with all on board. He thrashed and flailed through the wind and waves for hours and hours, struggling for strength and air, until at last the surf hurled him against this beach, and he crept weakly to this spot. And then—ah, one last, sweet gasp of hope! But too late, his lungs were saturated by the salty brine. He gave up the ghost and perished.

Well.

This isn't very funny, is it?

(Kneeling beside MENELAUS *and looking at his neck)*

But what do I see? His carotid artery—it's throbbing. This corpse has a pulse. Strictly speaking, that means it's not a corpse at all—at least not yet. I guess I'd better do something to revive this fellow. If he dies on me, it'll really put me in a foul mood. I'm liable not to snap out of it for centuries.

But what to do? When was the last time I studied life-saving? Well, never, actually. I guess I'll have to improvise.

(Repeatedly pushing on MENELAUS' *chest)*

Out with the bad air, in with the good.

Out with the bad air, in with the good.

Out with the bad air, in with the—

MENELAUS *(opening his eyes)*. Madam, would you mind telling me exactly what you're doing?

THALIA. Ah, excellent. I've saved you.

MENELAUS. From what?

THALIA. From drowning, of course.

MENELAUS. I wasn't drowned.

THALIA. What were you, then?

MENELAUS. Asleep.

THALIA. Oh. *(Pause)* Well. This is rather embarrassing. Do pardon me for disturbing you. Please—go back to sleep. And pleasant dreams.

(THALIA turns to go.)

MENELAUS. Wait a minute. Who are you? I was under the impression this island was uninhabited.

THALIA. It is—at least by mortals.

MENELAUS. So you're a goddess?

THALIA. Of sorts.

MENELAUS. What's your name?

THALIA. Not so fast. It's my divine prerogative to ask you first. Just who are *you*? And what gave you the right to lie on this beach pretending to be drowned?

MENELAUS. I'm an adventurer, a warrior, and a king.

THALIA. That's what they all say.

MENELAUS. It's true. My name is Menelaus.

THALIA. The king of Sparta?

MENELAUS. My reputation precedes me, then.

THALIA. I've heard of you, yes. But what are you doing on this island?

MENELAUS. Oh, it's a long, terrible story. Suffice it to say I'm in an awful predicament. But who are you?

THALIA. Thalia, the Muse of comedy.

MENELAUS. I'm dreaming.

THALIA. No.

MENELAUS. Yes, I'm dreaming that I'm in a play.

THALIA. You're not dreaming—but you *are* in a play.

MENELAUS *(looking around)*. Really? Where's the audience?

THALIA. You can't see them. That's one of the rules of being a fictional character.

MENELAUS. I wonder if anyone I know is watching.

THALIA. Don't get vain. Just be yourself. And stay focused. Being in a play doesn't make your predicament less real.

MENELAUS. But if you're the Muse of comedy, surely you can make my story end happily.

THALIA. Comedies don't always end happily, any more than tragedies always end unhappily.

MENELAUS. Most of the comedies I've seen end in marriage.

THALIA. Which I think proves my point.

MENELAUS. Oh. I suppose it does, now that you mention it.

(The CHORUS OF NYMPHS *is heard shouting offstage.)*

CHORUS.

Head 'em up,

Move 'em out!

MENELAUS. But what have we here?

(The SEALS *and the* CHORUS OF NYMPHS *enter, followed by* IDOTHEA. *The* NYMPHS *and* IDOTHEA *all carry cloth bags.* IDOTHEA *stands and watches as the* NYMPHS, *chanting and dancing, herd the* SEALS. *The* SEALS *keep rhythm by clapping their fins and barking.)*

CHORUS.

The nymphs are singing—each to

each,

So move it, you seals, and get up on

the beach.

You'd better get moving—get

moving, you all,

Or we'll sell you to a circus where

you'll balance a ball.

Head 'em up,

Move 'em out!

Yes, a big, bright ball on your little

black nose—

And they might make you wear

some cute little clothes,

Like a sailor's suit with a sailor's cap,

And you'll work day and night and

never get a nap.

Head 'em up,

Move 'em out!

You'll get a fish for your pains—a

measly fish,

And just for doing tricks, not

whenever you wish.

You'll bark for your breakfast and

juggle for your lunch.

You'll not much like it—at least that's

my hunch.

Head 'em up,

Move 'em out!

So be grateful, you seals, for all

you've got.

You've got room to swim, got room

to trot—

And last but not least, you've got

plenty to eat.

To prove it, right now I'll give you a

treat!

Whoa,

Doggies!

(The chanting and dancing end. The NYMPHS *take fish out of their bags and throw them to the seals. The seals seize the fish and turn away from the audience. During the following dialogue, munching sounds are heard. When the seals turn toward the audience again, the fish are gone.)*

THALIA *(approaching* IDOTHEA*).* Good morning, dear.

IDOTHEA *(embracing* THALIA*).* Thalia! How wonderful to see you!

THALIA. It's good to see you, too. *(Turning to the* CHORUS*)* And good morning, girls.

CHORUS LEADER *(embracing* THALIA*).* Good morning to you, Thalia.

IDOTHEA. It's been an awfully long time.

THALIA. Yes, it has, hasn't it?

IDOTHEA. I imagine you've dropped by to get your funny bone tickled a bit.

THALIA. Exactly.

IDOTHEA. You look like you could use it. Forgive me for saying so, dear, but you look so cross.

THALIA. Don't I know it. But where's your father?

IDOTHEA. Oh, Daddy's running a little late. Off causing trouble somewhere. He'll be here presently.

MENELAUS (*to* THALIA). Would you be so kind as to introduce us?

THALIA (*to* MENELAUS, *indicating the* CHORUS). These lovely ladies are sea nymphs.

MENELAUS (*to the* CHORUS LEADER). Charmed.

THALIA (*to* MENELAUS). And this is Idothea, daughter of the sea-god Proteus.

MENELAUS (*to* IDOTHEA). Delighted.

THALIA (*to* IDOTHEA). And this is Menelaus. Surely you've heard of him.

IDOTHEA. I can't say I have.

THALIA. Oh, Idothea, when*ever* are you going to start keeping up with current events?

MENELAUS. I happen to be the king of Sparta.

IDOTHEA. That's nice. Where's Sparta?

MENELAUS. In Greece, of course.

IDOTHEA. Must be landlocked, or I'd have heard of it.

THALIA (*to* IDOTHEA). Does the Trojan War happen to ring a bell?

IDOTHEA. No. Was it something important?

THALIA. Only the direst catastrophe to ever strike human civilization. And it was pretty tough on the gods, too.

IDOTHEA. I must have missed it, somehow.

THALIA. Honestly, Idothea. Your ignorance sometimes approaches the encyclopedic. Menelaus here married Helen, the daughter of Zeus, the most beautiful woman in the world. Then one day, the Trojan prince Paris came to Sparta and snatched Helen away without so much as a by-your-leave and carried her off to Troy. Well, Menelaus isn't a fellow to take that sort of thing lying down. So he summoned all the chieftains and soldiers of Greece, and they set sail for Troy—

MENELAUS. And there we fought a terrible, ten-year war. Thousands died, the best and brightest among them, in a prolonged and senseless butchery. Ah, the futility of it, the agony, the waste, the horror! And all for a beautiful face. If only I'd known, if only I'd known.

THALIA. Come on, buck up. You Greeks won, didn't you? That's what counts.

CHORUS LEADER. But what are you doing here?

MENELAUS. When the slaughter ended, we Greeks loaded up our ships with Trojan treasure—Helen included. We set sail for Greece, expecting a glorious homecoming. But a storm struck our fleet. A frightful night passed, with waves as high as mountains, winds as mighty as gods. Then in the morning arrived a calm—a calm as dreadful as the storm. I scanned the sea far and wide, but saw not a ship other than my own. The water was strewn with wreckage and the bodies of drowned men.

THALIA. I must say, this is not the least bit amusing.

MENELAUS. You don't believe me?

THALIA. Unfortunately, I do. You were funnier when I thought you were dead.

MENELAUS. Well, it wasn't *all* bad. I still had my own ship—and my own skin. And I had my wife again, too. And we went on some very interesting wanderings for several years— *profitable* wanderings, if I may say so. We landed on the island of Cyprus, then sailed along the Mediterranean coast to Phoenicia, Libya, Egypt, all those places. Went down the Nile as far as Ethiopia. Visited every king and ruler along the way. Some treated us hospitably, gave us gifts. When they didn't, we robbed and pillaged. Gathered goblets, bowls, rings, and necklaces without number. And, ah, the rubies, amethysts, beryls, emeralds, diamonds, pearls—

IDOTHEA. Oh, I *do* love pearls!

MENELAUS. —to say nothing of the gold and silver.

CHORUS LEADER. Gold and silver aren't so bad, either.

MENELAUS. Filled up the ship's hold eventually, and it got dangerous to try to sail with more. So I set a course for Sparta. I reckoned I'd be the richest man in the world—if only I could get home.

IDOTHEA. That sounds like a big "if only."

MENELAUS. Indeed. A calm befell us on the way, stranding us on this wretched island. There's been no wind for 20 days now, and our provisions are running short. If we don't get away from here, we'll all starve or die from thirst. A god must be angry with me about something. I wish I knew what.

CHORUS LEADER. But where's your ship?

MENELAUS *(pointing).* Anchored around that cape, there. You can just see the prow.

THALIA. And Helen? And your crew?

MENELAUS. All aboard, except me. I had to get away for the night, had to clear my head, think of some way out of this mess.

THALIA. Wait a minute. Something rings a little false, here. The most beautiful woman in the world is on board your ship—and you had to get away for the night?

MENELAUS. Let me tell you something. Being married to the most beautiful woman in the world isn't quite as blissful as you might expect.

IDOTHEA. Really?

CHORUS LEADER. I don't believe it.

MENELAUS. Well, *do* believe it. Ten years in Troy hasn't worked wonders for her disposition.

(HELEN silently enters. Everyone on stage can see her—except MENELAUS.)

MENELAUS. To tell the truth, Paris and his family spoiled her something terrible. They made over her too much, catered to her every whim. And now—well, she's awfully demanding.

THALIA. Uh, Menelaus—

MENELAUS *(ignoring her).* And of course, it went rather to her head to have the world's greatest war fought over her. Now she's as vain as can be, thinks she's the center of the universe.

IDOTHEA. Uh, Menelaus—

MENELAUS *(ignoring her).* Nothing's good enough for her these days. I can't do anything to make her happy. Why, I've accumulated the greatest stash of treasure in the world, and she acts like it's a pile of junk.

CHORUS LEADER. Uh, Menelaus—

MENELAUS. I know, I know, you're all women, and you feel like you've got to defend her. But you haven't spent years sailing the seas with her. If you had—oh, you'd sing a different tune, I promise you.

THALIA, IDOTHEA, and CHORUS LEADER *(together).* But, Menelaus—

MENELAUS. "When are we going back to Sparta, Menelaus?" "Why can't you make my life as nice as it was in Troy, Menelaus?" "When can I buy some new outfits, Menelaus?" "When are we going to get some slaves, Menelaus?" "Don't you think the daughter of a god deserves better, Menelaus?" Oh, it goes on and on and on! Beautiful? Certainly. But a holy terror to live with. She's shrill, carping, and impossible to please—a shrew, a nag, a fury, a vixen.

HELEN. Don't forget a harpy. *(Long pause as she steps in front of* MENELAUS*)* Good morning, dear.

MENELAUS. Good morning, my pet. Uh, about what I just said—

HELEN. Not now, dear. Later. Let's not make a scene in front of our new friends. And what lovely friends they are! To find one's husband surrounded by a gaggle of gorgeous women—it might make the average wife jealous. Of course, he *did* fight a ten-year war over me in which thousands of men were killed and an entire civilization was destroyed, so I feel fairly secure. Menelaus, would you care to introduce me?

MENELAUS. Certainly, darling. *(Indicating the* CHORUS*)* These lovely ladies are sea nymphs.

HELEN. Charmed.

CHORUS LEADER. Likewise.

MENELAUS *(indicating* IDOTHEA*).* And this is Idothea, daughter of the sea-god Proteus.

HELEN *(to* IDOTHEA*).* Proteus. The name doesn't ring a bell. Strange, because I'm intimately acquainted with a great many gods and goddesses. Still, I'm sure your father is quite influential. Even minor deities have their place in the grand scheme of things. I'm Helen—Zeus' daughter.

IDOTHEA. Strange—*your* name doesn't ring a bell.

HELEN. No?

IDOTHEA. Still—charmed.

HELEN. Likewise.

MENELAUS *(to* HELEN*).* And this is Thalia, the Muse of comedy.

HELEN *(to* THALIA*).* Oh, comedy! So we're all in a play, are we?

THALIA. Indeed, we are.

HELEN *(looking all around).* What fun! Where's the audience?

MENELAUS. You can't see them, dear. That's one of the rules.

HELEN *(preening a little).* But they can see me.

MENELAUS. Indeed, they can.

HELEN *(to* THALIA*).* The Muse of comedy, are you? So you can give our story a happy ending.

THALIA. That remains to be seen.

HELEN. Oh, I'm sure you can manage it. *(A stage whisper to* MENELAUS*)* Slip her something nice, dear—a ring or a bracelet. Even Muses have their price.

*(*THALIA*'s expression—even sourer than before—shows that she has heard this.)*

HELEN *(turning to the seals).* And, oh, what adorable creatures! What on earth are they?

MENELAUS. Seals, of course.

HELEN. Really! I've heard of seals, but I've never seen one. Oh, they're so cute, with their sleek black fur and their big floppy fins and their pointy little noses! *(Approaching one of the seals)* And you're the cutest of them all, aren't you? Yes, you're positively irresistible. *(Tugging on the seal's whiskers—to the seal's annoyance)* And what's your name, widdle sealie-weelie? What a pwecious widdle baby-waby you are! *(To* MENELAUS*)* Oh, darling, she'd make a wonderful pet! I've just got to have her!

MENELAUS. How do you know it's a "her"?

HELEN. She has to be. Look at her soft, gentle, docile expression. *(To the seal)* Won't you come home with me, widdle sealie-weelie?

IDOTHEA. I'm afraid that's not possible.

HELEN. Why ever not?

THALIA. These seals belong to the god Poseidon. They're sacred to him.

IDOTHEA. It's my father's job to watch over them.

CHORUS LEADER. And it's our job to herd them.

HELEN *(to* MENELAUS*).* Well, you'll just have to talk to Poseidon, won't you, darling? I'm sure he can spare his sacred seals for the richest king on earth—and the most beautiful queen in the universe.

MENELAUS. If you insist, dear.

HELEN *(to* IDOTHEA*).* What's its name?

IDOTHEA. He—she doesn't have one.

HELEN. Sacred seals, and they don't even have names? Tut-tut-tut. What would Poseidon say to that? *(To the seal)* Well. Something about you reminds me of my own dear sister. So I'll name you after her. Yes, Clytemnestra! That's what I'll call you.

IDOTHEA. Cly—?

CHORUS LEADER. Clytem—?

THALIA (to HELEN). Doesn't exactly flow trippingly on the tongue.

HELEN. *I* can say it. And I like it. That's all that matters. *(To* MENELAUS) As for the rest of them—kill them and skin them. They'll make lovely gowns.

(The SEALS *bark and huddle together with alarm.)*

MENELAUS. But what are you doing ashore, dear?

HELEN. You sound as if you wish I hadn't come.

MENELAUS. Oh, no, not at all. But this island might be dangerous.

HELEN. It doesn't *look* very dangerous. You didn't think I was going to stay on that cramped and smelly ship while you were out having adventures, did you? So I ordered your helmsman to put me ashore.

MENELAUS. You gave orders to my helmsman?

HELEN. Of course. When the captain's away, the wife takes command. Isn't that one of the rules of sailing?

MENELAUS. No.

HELEN. Well, it should be. Anyway, he was more than happy to oblige. If I didn't know better, I'd have thought he was happy to be rid of me.

MENELAUS. Perish the thought.

HELEN. I've spent the whole morning looking for you—and exploring. This island isn't half bad, as godforsaken wastelands go. I do believe we could set up housekeeping here.

MENELAUS. You mean *live* here?

HELEN. Well, what choice do we have— at least for the time being? You're not enough of a sailor to get us away from here without a good wind. And I'm so tired of living on that ship. Being seasick all the time will give me wrinkles before you know it— and we can't have that, can we?

As it happens, I've found a nice cave we can live in until the wind picks up. Oh, it needs a bit of work, but it's got possibilities. And it's quite spacious. We'll need to put in a few windows. And a chimney.

MENELAUS. Put windows and a chimney in a *cave*?

HELEN. Of course, darling. I've got every confidence in your architectural skills. I'm going back there right now, start planning where to put all our treasure. *(Another stage whisper to* MENELAUS) And dear—it would be a good idea to make slaves of these women.

MENELAUS. What?

HELEN. Well, not Thalia, of course. She's the Muse of comedy, so she's very important. We don't want to put her out. But all the others, certainly.

MENELAUS. But they're goddesses.

HELEN. Just barely. I've never heard of this Proteus fellow, so his daughter means nothing to me. And as for the nymphs—well, nymphs hardly even count. They're certainly not as divine as I am.

(From their outraged expressions, it is apparent that the NYMPHS, IDOTHEA, *and* THALIA *have all heard every word of this.)*

HELEN *(full voice again).* Anyway, I'm off to the cave. Won't you come and take a look for yourself?

MENELAUS. I'll be along shortly, dear.

HELEN *(pointing).* Just follow that ravine. You can't miss it. And don't be long.

MENELAUS. I won't, dear.

(HELEN exits.)

MENELAUS.

> I can't abide her constant
>   preening;
> Enduring it is so demeaning.
> I'm weary of her pretty face,
> Revolted by her style and grace.

(The NYMPHS *chant and dance, accompanied by the barking and clapping of the* SEALS.*)*

CHORUS.

> So *this* is the face that launched
>   thousands of ships
> And plunged civilization in a total
>   eclipse.
> It's a pretty face, I'll give her that
>   much—
> But if you ask me, she's isn't worth
>   such
>> A big to-do,
>> A big to-do,
>> A big to-do,
>> A big to-do.
>
> She's got beauty to spare, got beauty
>   by the batch;
> She just hasn't got personality to
>   match.

> She's got herself a mouth, and that's a
>   fact—
> And I'd be half-tempted to give it a
>   smack
>> If I were you,
>> If I were you,
>> It I were you,
>> If I were you.

(The chanting and dancing end.)

MENELAUS *(to the* CHORUS). Well, you're *not* me—and I'm not the kind of man to slap his wife around. *(Pause)* As for abandoning her on a desert island . . . hmmm.

CHORUS LEADER. Don't you *dare* leave us stuck with her!

MENELAUS. Don't worry, I was just indulging a passing fantasy. But I've really got to get us off this island. You're goddesses. Surely you can help me.

THALIA. Just possibly. I've got an idea that might get you home.

MENELAUS. Really?

THALIA. If not, the outcome should at least be funny.

MENELAUS. For you, maybe. But what have you got in mind?

THALIA. First, let me consult with my friend.

(THALIA begins whispering to IDOTHEA.)

IDOTHEA *(listening to* THALIA). Oh, that is a thought. . . . Yes, it *would* be amusing. . . . *(Starting to laugh)* True, true, it would serve Daddy right, the old rogue! . . . He's had it coming for years. . . . I can see it all now! . . . But do you really think this Menelaus fellow can actually—? . . . Yes, you're right, even if he can't, it'll be . . . (*Laughing hysterically*) Oh, stop it, Thalia, you're killing me!

THALIA (*aloud, to* IDOTHEA—*and still deadly serious*). So should we do it, then?

IDOTHEA (*still laughing*). By all means! It'll be too, too funny!

MENELAUS (*to* THALIA *and* IDOTHEA). Would you two care to share the source of your amusement with the rest of us?

CHORUS LEADER. Yes, please do.

IDOTHEA (*to* MENELAUS). It's like this. My father is a wonderful sea-god. He sees all and knows all—or *almost* all, anyway—about the past, present, and future. And whenever he speaks, he tells the truth.

MENELAUS. Ah, a soothsayer!

IDOTHEA. What's a soothsayer?

MENELAUS. Oh, it's a type of character we've got back in Greece. Someone who always tells the truth—about the past, present, and future.

IDOTHEA. Shouldn't you call him a *truth*sayer, then? What does *sooth* mean, anyway?

MENELAUS. Well, I—I don't exactly know. Pretty much the same thing as *truth*, I guess. Anyway, if your father's a soothsayer, I'm in luck. He'll be able to tell me how to get away from here.

THALIA. Proteus isn't so much a sooth*sayer* as a sooth*laugher*.

MENELAUS. Who cares if he says the sooth or laughs the sooth? The sooth is the sooth—er, the truth is the truth, I mean. And the truth is what I need to get off this island. (*To* IDOTHEA) So—when do I get to meet your father?

IDOTHEA. He'll be here very soon.

MENELAUS. And how do I get him to tell me the, uh, truth?

THALIA. Well, that's where things get a little sticky.

(IDOTHEA *starts laughing again.*)

THALIA (*to* IDOTHEA). Control yourself, dear. (*To* MENELAUS) You have to grab hold of him. Then you have to hold him tight until *he* starts asking *you* questions. Then you let him go—and he'll tell you anything you want.

MENELAUS. So I wrestle him, then.

IDOTHEA (*sputtering*). Yes!

THALIA (*to* IDOTHEA). Please!

IDOTHEA (*bringing herself under control*). Sorry.

MENELAUS. This is almost too easy! Why, I'm probably the greatest wrestler in the known world. Couldn't have pinned Achilles or Big Ajax, I don't suppose, but they're both dead. I don't guess there's anyone alive who can beat me. (*Rolling up his sleeves*) So where is this Proteus fellow? What's he look like? How strong is he? A big bruiser, I expect.

IDOTHEA. They call him the Old Man of the Sea.

MENELAUS. An old man, you say? Well, I'll go easy on the codger. I'll be careful not to hurt him.

THALIA. Before you get too confident, there's something you should know about him.

MENELAUS. Well?

THALIA. He's a shape-shifter.

MENELAUS. What's a shape-shifter?

CHORUS LEADER. He's able to change shape at will.

IDOTHEA. He can become a rock, a weasel, a bear, a dolphin, a cloud—anything he wants to be, whenever he wants.

CHORUS LEADER. Makes him devilishly difficult to hang on to.

THALIA. Tell me, have you got that type of character back in Greece?

MENELAUS. I can't say we have.

THALIA. Sounds daunting, doesn't it?

MENELAUS. Daunting or not—bring him on, I'm ready.

IDOTHEA. That's the spirit. But he mustn't see you as you are. He'll just turn around and run back into the waves. You need a disguise. *(Rummages around in her sack)* Got just the thing in here somewhere. Where is it? Ah, here it is.

(IDOTHEA pulls out a sealskin.)

MENELAUS. A sealskin?

IDOTHEA. Don't worry, we didn't club it to death. We don't do that kind of thing. This skin belonged to one who got sick and died.

MENELAUS. I'm supposed to *wear* it?

IDOTHEA. Right. When he comes along, he'll think you're just another seal. Then he'll stretch out on the beach and go to sleep. When he does, you pounce.

MENELAUS. I don't know . . .

IDOTHEA. What's the problem?

MENELAUS. It's pretty undignified.

IDOTHEA. Do you want him to answer your questions or don't you?

MENELAUS. Oh, all right. Help me into it.

IDOTHEA *(draping the sealskin over* MENELAUS). Here you go.

MENELAUS. Phew! This thing reeks to high Olympus! Get it off me!

IDOTHEA. What are you talking about? Seals have a lovely smell.

THALIA *(taking an atomizer out of her pouch)*. Maybe this will help.

(THALIA sprays the sealskin with the atomizer.)

MENELAUS. Hey, *that's* better. In fact, that's just about the sweetest smell I've ever sniffed. What is it, anyway?

THALIA. Essence of ambrosia.

MENELAUS. Ambrosia? Isn't that supposed to make you—?

THALIA. Immortal, yes. But only if you eat it. And I'm not feeding any to you. Whatever your virtues may be—and I'm not convinced you've got any—you don't strike me as god material. It'll be just as well for you to crawl inside some hole and die properly when your time comes.

MENELAUS. Thanks for that sentiment.

PROTEUS (*offstage*). Ahoy! I'm home!

IDOTHEA (*to* MENELAUS). Here comes Daddy now. Quick, down on all fours. And whatever you do, don't talk!

(MENELAUS *gets down on all fours among the other seals.*)

CHORUS LEADER. Although a little barking and flipper-clapping might be appropriate.

THALIA. To say nothing of comical.

IDOTHEA (*laughing again*). Oh, Thalia, you do know how to make me laugh!

THALIA (*who still hasn't cracked a smile*). I wish I could say you did the same for me. And control yourself. You'll spoil the whole thing.

(*The* CHORUS *begins to giggle.*)

THALIA (*to the* CHORUS). Oh, really— not you, too.

CHORUS LEADER. We'll keep ourselves under control. Promise.

THALIA. You'd better. Honestly, I wish *I* was as vulnerable to a cheap laugh as the rest of you. It would save me a world of trouble.

(PROTEUS, *a decrepit and thoroughly grouchy old man, enters wearing a tattered cloak. The* CHORUS *starts chanting and dancing, accompanied by the* SEALS' *clapping and barking.*)

CHORUS.
Hello, Old Man—you're running late.
You're usually back by seven or eight.
It's not like you to make us wait.

But now that you're here, let's celebrate.
What stories have you got, what tales to relate?
Come on, tell us—and tell us straight!

PROTEUS.
I had to tease some mortals, and I had to tease some gods,
And play pranks by the dozens and do mischief by the wads.
A trickster's got a lot to do, a lot of obligation
To fill the world up to the brim with laughter and elation.

CHORUS.
And elation.
And elation.
And elation.

PROTEUS.
I know what's going on out there, I know the past and future,
And if I tell your fortune, what I say will really suit you.
The trick is getting hold of me and getting me to say it.
But I won't make it easy; I don't like to give away it.

CHORUS.
Give away it.
Give away it.
Give away it.

PROTEUS.
Folks think I will come out with it; they think I will tell all,
And I don't tell them otherwise, I get them in my thrall.
But when they grab a hold of me, a

new shape I disclose—
And just before I run away, I turn
  and thumb my nose.

CHORUS.
Thumbs his nose.
Thumbs his nose.
Thumbs his nose.

PROTEUS.
I do a good night's trickery; I cause a
  good night's trouble,
And when I'm done with all of that,
  I rush here on the double.
It's hard to be the orneriest; it's hard
  to be the best—
And now that I am home again, I'm
  ready for a rest.

CHORUS.
Ready for rest.
Ready for rest.
Ready for rest.

(The chanting and dancing end.)

IDOTHEA *(kissing* PROTEUS *on the cheek).*
Good morning, Daddy.

PROTEUS. Hmmph!

THALIA. Hail Proteus, O fabled Old
Man of the Sea, O King of the Low-
Down No-Good Pranksters!

PROTEUS *(crossly, to* THALIA*).* You again!
Off with you!

THALIA. Is that how you greet me after
hundreds of years?

PROTEUS. Seems like only yesterday.

THALIA. I'd almost think you weren't
happy to see me.

PROTEUS. I'm not. Can't you see I'm up
to my neck in females as it is? What
do you want from me, anyway?

THALIA. What does everybody want
from you? A good joke.

PROTEUS. You tell *me* a joke.

THALIA. Oh, but I'm just a humble
Muse. I'm not worthy to tell a joke
to such an exalted comedian as
yourself.

PROTEUS. Flattery isn't funny. Knock it
off. And go away.

IDOTHEA *(to* THALIA*).* Daddy will feel
better after his nap.

THALIA *(to* IDOTHEA*).* Oh, I hope not.
He's not the least bit amusing when
he's in good spirits.

PROTEUS *(to the* CHORUS*).* So did you
round up all the critters?

CHORUS LEADER. All here and
counted, sir.

PROTEUS. I'd better count 'em myself.
You girls don't exactly have a way
with numbers. *(Counting the seals)* One,
two, three . . . *(Coming to* MENELAUS*)*
Wait a minute. Here's a newcomer.

IDOTHEA. The god Poseidon, in his
infinite bounty, has given us another
sacred seal to look after.

PROTEUS. He's generous, that Poseidon
is. Always ready and willing to stick
us with another mouth to feed. This
one sure is an ugly cuss.

CHORUS LEADER. I think he's cute.

PROTEUS. Your taste in seals sometimes
scares me. Well, we'd better welcome
him to the pack. Give me a fish.

(The CHORUS LEADER *reaches into her sack
and gives* PROTEUS *a fish.* PROTEUS *shoves
the fish into* MENELAUS' *mouth.)*

PROTEUS. There you go, you toad-faced mutt. Eat hearty.

(When PROTEUS *turns away, a disgusted* MENELAUS *spits out the fish and hides it behind him.*)

PROTEUS (*to* THALIA). What? Still here, are you?

THALIA. You didn't really expect me to go away, did you?

PROTEUS. That's what you'd better do, if you know what's good for you.

THALIA. Is that a threat?

PROTEUS. It sure is.

THALIA. Do your worst. It takes a lot to make me laugh.

IDOTHEA. Oh, Daddy—

PROTEUS. What is it, girl?

IDOTHEA (*pointing to* MENELAUS, *barely restraining a giggle*). Our newcomer seems pretty hungry.

PROTEUS (*to* MENELAUS). You sure went through that fish in a hurry. As ravenous as you are ugly, eh? Liable to eat me out of a week's catch, you are. (*To the* CHORUS LEADER) Give me another.

(The CHORUS LEADER *gives* PROTEUS *another fish.* PROTEUS *sticks it in* MENELAUS' *mouth.*)

PROTEUS (*to the* CHORUS LEADER). Keep stuffing fish down his gullet. Maybe he'll die of gluttony.

CHORUS LEADER. I'll be sure to do that, sir.

(As before, MENELAUS *spits out the fish and hides it.*)

PROTEUS. And now I'm going to take my morning nap. Until I get up, I'm not in for visitors. (*To* THALIA) Especially you.

THALIA. Right.

PROTEUS. I mean it. If you're still here when I wake up, there'll be trouble, I promise.

THALIA. That's just what I'm hoping.

(As the dialogue continues, the CHORUS LEADER *tries to shove another fish into* MENELAUS' *mouth.* MENELAUS *growls at her, and she puts the fish back in her bag.*)

PROTEUS (*not noticing this activity, to* THALIA). Careful what you wish for. When it comes true, you'll wish it hadn't.

THALIA. I'll probably laugh till I vomit.

PROTEUS. May you strangle on it.

THALIA. To laugh myself to death—now *that's* a consummation to be devoutly wished. If only it were possible.

PROTEUS. Anything's possible. (*Taking off his cloak and lying down among the seals*) Oh, my weary bones! Oh, what a world, what a world! It's truly a vale of tears, that much is sure. It's no place for a charming and delightful sprite like myself. A trickster's lot is not an easy one. Sometimes I wish I'd never been born! (*Covering himself up with the cloak, becoming drowsy*) Maybe I'll wake up, and this whole life of mine will have been just a dream. But fat chance of that. For all my days are sorrows, and my travail grief. Now *there's* a line to really get a laugh . . .

PROTEUS

(Fast asleep now, PROTEUS *snores loudly. The* CHORUS *gathers around* MENELAUS. *They chant to him in hushed voices.)*

CHORUS.
> He's fast asleep!
> So it's time to leap!
> Grab him hard and hold him tight
> and make him weep!
> Get up and prance!
> Take a fighting stance!
> With this old boy, you'll never get a
> second chance!

*(*MENELAUS *leaps to his feet. Still wearing the sealskin, he calls out to* PROTEUS *in a dramatic voice.)*

MENELAUS. On your feet, trickster—and face your challenger!

*(*PROTEUS *sits up with surprise.* THALIA, IDOTHEA, *and the* CHORUS *all groan with dismay.)*

PROTEUS. What the—?

THALIA. Oh, Lord Zeus!

IDOTHEA *(to* MENELAUS*).* You weren't supposed to *challenge* him.

CHORUS LEADER *(to* MENELAUS*).* You were supposed to *pounce* while he was still asleep!

MENELAUS. It's not a warrior's way to pounce on an old man unawares.

THALIA. You'll never catch him now.

MENELAUS. We'll see about that.

PROTEUS. A talking seal!

MENELAUS. Not a seal, old man.
> *(Throwing the sealskin aside with a flourish)* I'm Menelaus, king of Sparta, conqueror of Troy! The greatest

warrior alive—and the greatest wrestler!

PROTEUS. I should have known! I've never seen a seal with an appetite like yours!

MENELAUS. Prepare to tell the sooth—er, truth!

PROTEUS. And prepare to meet your match, great wrestler that you are—for I am greater! Why, I've defeated Achilles and Big Ajax in my time! Even the mighty Heracles is afraid to tangle with me!

MENELAUS. Achilles? Big Ajax? Heracles? I don't believe it!

PROTEUS. I always tell the truth. Or haven't you heard?

*(*MENELAUS *lunges at* PROTEUS. *With surprising athletic ease,* PROTEUS *rolls out of his way.* MENELAUS *lunges again and again, but* PROTEUS *repeatedly and deftly escapes him. At last,* PROTEUS *disappears behind the upstage screen, leaving* MENELAUS *dazed.)*

MENELAUS. As slippery as a greased seal, that rascal! What have I gotten myself into?

THALIA. I think you're about to find out.

(A loud roar is heard behind the screen. An actor comes out from behind the screen wearing a huge TIGER *mask, growling and stalking* MENELAUS.*)*

MENELAUS. Great Olympus! What beast is this?

(The CHORUS *divides into halves on each side of the stage; one half will taunt* MENELAUS, *the other half will root for him. The* CHORUS

LEADER *can join with either side. The* SEALS *bark and clap throughout the following wrestling match.*)

FIRST HALF-CHORUS.
> Tiger, tiger, burning bright,
> Liable to put up quite a fight.
> With teeth in his mouth and claws
>   on his feet,
> He just might be pretty hard to beat!

MENELAUS. A tiger! I had no idea there were giant carnivores on this island!

IDOTHEA. It's only Daddy.

THALIA. Don't tell me you're afraid of a helpless old man.

MENELAUS (*hiding behind* IDOTHEA).
> Talk to him! Tell him not to kill me!

THALIA. Is this Menelaus, the conqueror of Troy, the greatest wrestler alive? Hiding behind a woman?

SECOND HALF-CHORUS.
> Fight him, Menelaus!
> Don't let him get you down!
> He's not a *real* tiger,
> Just a trickster clown!

(MENELAUS *gathers his nerve and leaps at the* TIGER. *But the* TIGER *swiftly disappears behind the screen.*)

MENELAUS. Where—where is he?

THALIA. Off changing shape again, I imagine.

(*A terrible hiss is heard behind the screen. Several actors emerge, carrying a huge* SNAKE *puppet.*)

FIRST HALF-CHORUS.
> Ooh, it's a snake! I *do* hate snakes!
> A critter like this sure raises the
>   stakes!

> He'll bite you with his fangs, if that's
>   your fate,
> Or he'll squeeze you tight till you
>   suffocate.

(*The* SNAKE *slithers and hisses around the stage.* MENELAUS *dashes all about, dodging it.*)

MENELAUS. Oh, Lord Zeus! It's huge!

IDOTHEA. It's only Daddy.

MENELAUS. Is it venomous?

THALIA. Doesn't much matter, does it? He can swallow you like a hamster.

SECOND HALF-CHORUS.
> Don't be scared
> Of that hissing sound!
> He's not a *real* snake,
> Just a trickster clown!

(MENELAUS *lunges at the* SNAKE, *which swiftly disappears behind the screen.*)

MENELAUS. What's this? He's turned himself into thin air!

THALIA. You're not that lucky, I'm afraid.

(*A hideous grunting and snorting is heard behind the screen. An* ACTOR *comes out wearing the mask of a huge* BOAR, *stalking* MENELAUS *around the stage.*)

MENELAUS. Shades of Hades!

FIRST HALF-CHORUS.
> A big, wild boar with tusks in his
>   head!
> You'd better watch out, or he'll make
>   you quite dead!
> Here's a challenge; here's some
>   sport—
> With an oink and a grunt and a
>   snort-snort-snort.

MENELAUS. It's the biggest boar alive!

IDOTHEA. It's only Daddy.

MENELAUS. A sword, a sword! Somebody give me a sword!

THALIA. Do we look like armed warriors? Besides, this is supposed to be a hand-to-hand contest.

MENELAUS. But look at those tusks! It's not fair!

SECOND HALF-CHORUS.
Fight him, Menelaus!
Don't let him get you down!
He's not a *real* boar,
Just a trickster clown!

(MENELAUS *lunges at the* BOAR, *which swiftly disappears behind the screen.*)

MENELAUS. He's gone—again! Oh, what next, what next?

THALIA. The worst, I expect.

(*A rumbling sound is heard behind the screen. Two actors come out carrying a blue sheet, making it billow and swell as they chase* MENELAUS. *This represents a gigantic* WAVE.)

MENELAUS. An ocean wave!

FIRST HALF-CHORUS.
Surf's up, and it's coming right over dry land!
A wave is crashing down onto the sand!
Better run, better hide, don't try to swim!
Your chances of survival are looking quite dim!

MENELAUS. It's a regular tsunami!

IDOTHEA. It's only Daddy.

MENELAUS. It'll drown me for sure!

THALIA. If it doesn't crush you to a pulp.

SECOND HALF-CHORUS.
Don't be scared,
You're not going to drown.
It's not a *real* wave,
Just a trickster clown!

MENELAUS. It's no use. If I try to attack, he'll change shape again— and next time, he'll be something even worse.

THALIA (*rummaging in her bag*). Not necessarily. I might be able to help.

MENELAUS. How?

(THALIA *takes a corked bottle out of her bag and hands it to* MENELAUS.)

THALIA. Catch him in this.

MENELAUS. A bottle? He'll never fit.

THALIA. Sure, he will. This bottle contains a vacuum. Just pop the cork, and it'll suck him right up.

MENELAUS. You're kidding.

THALIA. Maybe I am, maybe I'm not. Find out for yourself.

(MENELAUS *opens the bottle. The actors playing the* WAVE *wrap themselves up in the sheet and disappear behind the screen.*)

THALIA. There! You've got him!

IDOTHEA. Quick—cork him up!

(MENELAUS *puts the cork back in the bottle.*)

MENELAUS (*to the bottle*). Aha! Now I've got you! I beat you fair and square! And now, you'd better talk! Do you hear me? Talk! (*Shaking the bottle*) Hey, what's this? This bottle feels— (*Removing the cork*) —empty!

(PROTEUS comes out from behind the screen— in his original form. Not noticing PROTEUS, MENELAUS peers inside the bottle.)

MENELAUS. There's nothing in here!

PROTEUS *(tapping on MENELAUS' shoulder).* Mind if I have a sip? I'm awfully thirsty.

MENELAUS *(dazedly, unaware of whom he's talking to).* It's no use. It's empty.

PROTEUS. Could I have the bottle, then? It might come in handy. Maybe I can find a spring nearby.

MENELAUS. Off with you, old fellow.

FIRST HALF-CHORUS.
Why begrudge the old boy a bottle?
Poor old geezer can barely waddle!
Don't be a skinflint, don't be greedy.
Anyone can see he's really needy!

MENELAUS *(giving the bottle to PROTEUS).* Oh, all right, it's no good to me.

PROTEUS *(taking a long swallow from the bottle).* Mmm, delicious. I thought you said it was empty. *(PROTEUS starts to walk away.)*

SECOND HALF-CHORUS.
Don't be a fool,
A moron all-around.
He's not just an old geezer—
He's a trickster clown!

(Realizing his mistake, MENELAUS rushes after PROTEUS and grabs hold of him.)

MENELAUS. Now I've got you, you old rascal—for real, this time!

PROTEUS. Just who do you think you are, young whippersnapper? What gives you the right? What make you so high-and-mighty?

MENELAUS. You already know that, old man. I'm Menelaus, king of Sparta, conqueror of Troy, and the greatest—

THALIA *(interrupting).* Um, Menelaus.

MENELAUS *(to THALIA).* What?

THALIA. He's asking you questions.

MENELAUS. So?

THALIA. That's your cue.

IDOTHEA. You're supposed to let him go now.

MENELAUS. This a joke, right?

THALIA. Exactly.

IDOTHEA. Even so, you've got to let him go.

MENELAUS. What'll he do if he gets loose?

THALIA. He'll answer your questions.

MENELAUS. And if I don't let him loose?

PROTEUS. What do you *think* I'll do, you big, ignorant bully?

THALIA. He'll keep on asking rhetorical questions.

IDOTHEA. And he'll never stop.

(MENELAUS lets go of PROTEUS, who indignantly shuffles to the opposite side of the stage.)

PROTEUS. It's a fine day when a god can't take a little nap on his own private desert island! And when his own daughter conspires to play tricks on him!

IDOTHEA *(giggling).* You have to admit, it was pretty funny.

PROTEUS *(to THALIA).* Did *you* think it was funny?

CHORUS LEADER (giggling). Oh, don't ask Thalia. She doesn't think *anything's* funny.

PROTEUS. That makes two of us.

MENELAUS. Come on, old man. Tell me what you know.

PROTEUS. About what?

MENELAUS. About why I'm stuck on this island and how I can get home.

PROTEUS. Let me tell you something, boy. You've got yourself a *god* mad at you. And not just any god, but the big boss of all the gods.

MENELAUS. Lord Zeus?

PROTEUS. The very one. How long has it been since you made a sacrifice to him?

MENELAUS. Well—since before I sailed to Troy, I suppose.

PROTEUS. And what's that? Seventeen, eighteen years?

MENELAUS (shrugging). I've been busy.

PROTEUS. Then get unbusy.

MENELAUS. I'll do that. I'll make a sacrifice right now, right on this very beach.

PROTEUS. That won't do.

MENELAUS. Why not?

PROTEUS. Look around you. What'll you sacrifice? Do you see any heifers? Do you see any bulls?

MENELAUS (looking at the seals). Hmmm . . .

CHORUS LEADER. Don't even think of it.

PROTEUS. If you want smooth sailing back to Greece, what you've got to do is sail over to Egypt, then down the Nile a hundred, two hundred miles or so. Then build a pretty little shrine and make a really nice sacrifice.

MENELAUS. But I just *came* from the Nile.

PROTEUS. It's not my call, son. And Zeus doesn't care about your convenience.

MENELAUS. How can I sail anywhere in this dead calm?

PROTEUS. What dead calm?

(Pause. MENELAUS raises his finger in the air.)

MENELAUS. Why, there's a good strong breeze! And it's coming from the north—perfect for taking me straight to the Nile Delta! Thanks for the advice, old man. I'll be on my way.

PROTEUS. Not so fast. I've got something else to tell you.

MENELAUS. Well?

PROTEUS. I don't quite know how to say it. There's no way to break it gently. Truth is, I wish I didn't have to be the one to tell you.

MENELAUS. Bad news, eh?

PROTEUS. Naw, it's good news. That's why I wish I didn't have to tell you. (Pause) You're going to die someday.

MENELAUS. That's good news?

PROTEUS. And when you do . . . you'll go to the Elysian Fields.

MENELAUS. You mean—the Isles of the Blest? Eternal paradise?

PROTEUS. What other Elysian Fields are there?

MENELAUS. I'm—I'm overwhelmed. It's more than I ever dared to hope for—more than I thought I deserved.

PROTEUS. You don't deserve it. Don't get the idea it's because of anything good you've done in life. It's just that you *are* Zeus' son-in-law. And as mad as he is at you, you're family. That counts for something—I wish I knew what.

MENELAUS. Have you got anything else to tell me?

(PROTEUS *starts tapping his foot. The seals begin clapping to his beat.*)

PROTEUS. As a matter of fact, I do.

MENELAUS. What is it, then?

PROTEUS. You might not like it.

MENELAUS. Try me.

PROTEUS.
You think you got the best of me;
  you think you're pretty smart.
You think you've got a handle on the
  trickster's tricky art.
And now you think you know the
  truth, but is that just a dream?
You haven't figured out that things
  aren't always what they seem.

MENELAUS.
What do you mean?
What do you mean?
What do you mean?

PROTEUS.
I always tell the truth, they say—they
  say I cannot lie.
Others will tell brazen fibs and
  falsehoods—but not I.
It's not my nature to deceive; it's
  simply not my way.
I'm honest as a god can be—at least
  that's what they say.

CHORUS.
That's what they say.
That's what they say.
That's what they say.

PROTEUS.
I take whatever shape there's been
  since all the world began.
So how can you be quite so sure I'm
  really an old man?
It might be just another shape to add
  to your confusion.
Mightn't every shape I take be
  nothing but illusion?

MENELAUS.
Just illusion?
Just illusion?
Just illusion?

PROTEUS.
If every shape I take's a lie, how
  honest can I be?
And what about the shapes of
  words—not just the shapes you see?
People say a lot of things of less and
  greater worth.
Maybe *truth* is nothing but a grand
  disguise for mirth.

MENELAUS.
Nothing but mirth!
Nothing but mirth!
Nothing but mirth!

PROTEUS.
But anyway, I've done my best—or
  maybe done my worst.
And maybe you are blessed, my
  friend, or maybe you are cursed.
So now I'm going to flee from here,

away from all this riot,
And dive into the sea—I hope I'll
   find some peace and quiet.

CHORUS.
   Peace and quiet.
   Peace and quiet.
   Peace and quiet.

(PROTEUS *exits, and the* SEALS *stop clapping.*
MENELAUS *is laughing uproariously.*)

THALIA (*sternly, to* MENELAUS). And just
   what do you find so funny?

MENELAUS. That old man—he really *did*
   win our wrestling match! He's got
   me pinned even now!

IDOTHEA. I don't understand.

MENELAUS (*still laughing*). How can I
   know what's going to happen next?
   How can anyone know anything at
   all? A soothlaugher, you called him—
   but you were wrong. He's a
   laughsayer. And what he says is greater
   than truth. Because in this vale of
   lunacy, what can possibly be greater
   than laughter?

THALIA. How nice that you're amused.

MENELAUS. And now—I'll be on my
   way.

CHORUS LEADER. Where?

MENELAUS. To Egypt, of course. I'm still
   in Proteus' grip, and I've got to do
   just what he says—whatever it may
   lead to. I'm not afraid, in any case.
   For I am Menelaus, king of Sparta,
   conqueror of Troy, the greatest
   warrior alive—and the greatest
   wrestler, next to Proteus! Farewell,
   ladies. It's been a pleasure.

(MENELAUS *starts to leave—in the opposite
direction from* HELEN's *exit.*)

CHORUS LEADER. Aren't you forgetting
   something?

MENELAUS (*stopping*). What?

IDOTHEA. Helen.

MENELAUS. Helen . . . Hmmm.

CHORUS LEADER. Don't even think of
   it.

MENELAUS. Don't worry, just indulging
   a passing fantasy.

(MENELAUS *crosses in the direction of* HELEN's
exit. On his way, he waves to THALIA.)

MENELAUS. Do cheer up, Thalia. You take
   life much too seriously. (*Calling offstage*)
   Oh, Helen, dear! We're setting sail!

(MENELAUS *exits. The* CHORUS *starts chanting and dancing, accompanied by the* SEALS
clapping and barking. The CHORUS *is divided
into halves, although the* CHORUS LEADER
now chants separately.)

FIRST HALF-CHORUS.
   Come on, Thalia, and laugh just a
      little!
   A laugh will fix you up as fit as a
      fiddle.
   Gonna leave in a snit, gonna leave in
      a huff?

THALIA.
   I guess I was expecting some funnier
      stuff.

SECOND HALF-CHORUS.
   Thalia, dearie, don't frown like that.
   It makes you look old, it makes you
      look fat.
   It's bad for your skin, it's bad for your
      face.

THALIA.

What can I say? I'm a hopeless case.

CHORUS LEADER.

It's no use, girls—it's not going to happen.

IDOTHEA.

Might as well hope to hear one hand clappin'.

CHORUS LEADER.

She's not going to laugh, she's not going to smile.

IDOTHEA.

It's not her way, it's not her style.

FIRST HALF-CHORUS.

All right, Thalia—be that way! We're not going to hang around here all day.

SECOND HALF-CHORUS.

Let's go catch up with Menelaus. Maybe he'll do something that'll really slay us.

(The TWO HALF-CHORUSES *join together as one again, and* IDOTHEA *joins in this last verse.)*

CHORUS.

Now *there's* an idea—it sounds like a plan.
I like this Menelaus. I'm becoming a fan.
Hanging 'round him is as sweet as honey.
He's cute as a button, as cute as a bunny.

(Everybody exits except THALIA, *who finally breaks into a smile and a chuckle.)*

THALIA.

He thinks he's so great, and that makes him funny.

*(*THALIA'*s laughter grows as she exits. Her laughter resounds from offstage.)*

PLAYWRIGHT'S POSTSCRIPT

Menelaus went on his errand to Egypt and returned home to Sparta, where he lived the rest of his life quite happily with Helen. After his death, he really did spend eternity in the Elysian fields. There are, indeed, great advantages to being Zeus' son-in-law.

Shape-shifters are very popular today. Computer graphics techniques have made them extremely easy to portray in movies and on television. When a character digitally transforms from one shape to another before our eyes, it is called *morphing*. Shape-shifters have appeared in numerous movies including *Terminator 2: Judgment Day* and television shows such as *Star Trek: Deep Space Nine* and *Roswell*.

CONNECTING TO OTHER CULTURES

Stories of shape-shifters like Proteus are extremely common throughout the world. They are usually mischievous characters. The Native American trickster Iktome was known to change shape, as was the African trickster Anansi; both of these tricksters were spiders. The troublesome Norse god Loki once turned into a salmon while attempting to escape the wrath of the other gods. And when he took the shape of a mare, he actually gave birth to the magical, eight-legged horse Sleipner.

PROMETHEUS UNBOUND

SETTING THE STAGE

When we last saw the Titan Prometheus in the play *Pandora*, he was being led away to a terrible punishment. He was to be chained to a rock high in the mountains. How long did poor Prometheus spend chained to that rock? Accounts vary between 30 and 30,000 years.

Sometime during the 5th century B.C., the Athenian playwright Aeschylus wrote a trilogy of plays about Prometheus. Only the first, *Prometheus Bound*, survives. It begins with Prometheus being chained to the rock by Might, Violence, and the forge-god Hephaestus. As Aeschylus told the story, Prometheus knew the secret of Zeus' possible downfall. If only Prometheus had told this secret, Zeus would have released him. But Prometheus stubbornly refused.

Aeschylus' *Prometheus Bound* was followed by a second play, now lost, called *Prometheus Unbound*. It told the story of Prometheus' release by the hero Heracles. The play that follows relates this episode. Because it deals with the trials and sufferings of a deity, it is introduced by Polyhymnia, the Muse of songs to the gods.

MUSING ABOUT THE MYTH

Myths, legends, and history often tell of individuals who make great sacrifices for the benefit of others. As you read, think about whether Prometheus' actions are heroic or merely foolish.

PROMETHEUS UNBOUND

CHARACTERS:

PROMETHEUS (prō mē′ thē us), a Titan

POLYHYMNIA (pol i him′ ni a), the Muse of songs to the gods

MIGHT

VIOLENCE

CHIRON (kī′ rän), a wise Centaur

RHODEA (rō dē′ a), a nymph, daughter of the Titan Oceanus

EUDORA (ū dor′ a), a nymph, Rhodea's sister

VULTURE, a monster, Prometheus' tormentor

HERACLES (her′ a klēz), a hero and demigod

OTHER NAMES MENTIONED IN THE PLAY:

MT. CAUCASUS (kä′ ka sus)

ZEUS (züs), the king of the Olympian gods

ALCMENA (alk mē′ na), the mortal mother of Heracles

HEPHAESTUS (he fes′ tus), the god of the forge

HERA (hir′ a), the queen of the Olympian gods

APOLLO (a pol′ ō), the god of light and wisdom

SETTING: *A ledge near the peak of Mt. Caucasus; an unnamed forest far from Mt. Caucasus*

TIME: *30,000 years ago and the mythical present*

(The stage has a turntable upstage center. The turntable is divided by flats. At rise, the flats facing the audience represent a cliff side; the four manacles that will hold PROMETHEUS *are fastened to it. Stage right of the turntable is a large rock upon which the* VULTURE *will perch. A set of steps leads down from the stage apron into the audience.* PROMETHEUS *enters from the back of the house and dashes down the aisle of the theatre, looking young and strong. He climbs the steps to the stage, speaking to the audience in a hushed, confidential, but exhilarated tone.* POLYHYMNIA *enters from the wings. She stands to one side and watches and listens.)*

PROMETHEUS *(his hands cupped together as if holding something small).* I've got it, my children—the greatest gift of all! I promised to bring it to you, and I did! *(Chuckling)* You didn't believe me. "You've given us so much already," you said. "What can be greater than an upright posture? Or godlike minds? Or letters and numbers? Or the wheel?" Well, here it is—something more wonderful than all those things put together.

(PROMETHEUS *kneels and opens his hands over the floor. A small spot of warm light appears before him.*)

Beautiful, don't you think? It's called fire—a hot, golden wind. More than that, it's the power of the sun itself, the greatest force in the universe. With it, you can transform your lives, transform your world. With it, you can be as great as gods.

And how did I get it? I stole it. I snatched it from the chariot of the sun and brought it here.

Oh, don't be shocked. And don't fear punishment. This was my deed, not yours. I'm solely responsible. I'll suffer for it, not you. And believe me, there was no other way. Lord Zeus didn't want you to have it. In fact, he wanted to destroy you—still wants to, I believe. He senses your power, your potential, and he fears it—fears it desperately. But now that you have fire, your destiny is in your own hands.

And now—let me show you all the things you can do with fire.

(PROMETHEUS *freezes.* POLYHYMNIA *steps forward and speaks to the audience.*)

POLYHYMNIA. "No good deed goes unpunished." I'm sure you've heard that old saying. It was first said of Prometheus—that Titan who created you mortals and gave you the greatest gifts to be imagined. I'm Polyhymnia, the Muse of songs to the gods—and he's a god who deserves a song. Perhaps soon he'll get one.

(MIGHT *and* VIOLENCE *enter as* POLYHYM-NIA *continues speaking.* VIOLENCE *is carrying*

a hammer and walks to the cliff face. MIGHT *walks to* PROMETHEUS' *side.* MIGHT *and* VIOLENCE *freeze.*)

POLYHYMNIA. It was long ago when he gave you fire—and long ago that he was punished for it. Soon after the theft, Zeus sent his agents Might and Violence to arrest him. They carried him away to the most desolate place on earth—the peak of Mt. Caucasus.

(*The spot of light vanishes.* POLYHYMNIA *steps aside to watch as* MIGHT, VIOLENCE, *and* PROMETHEUS *come to life.* VIOLENCE *is pounding the last of the chains into the cliff face with his hammer.*)

MIGHT. Here we are, Titan. We've reached the world's edge at last.

PROMETHEUS (*still on his knees*). The world has no edge.

MIGHT. No? This mountain peak certainly seems like it. I'd hate to think of what might lie beyond it.

VIOLENCE (*finishing his work*). On your feet, Prometheus.

PROMETHEUS. Why?

VIOLENCE. Why do you think? So we can chain you to this rock.

PROMETHEUS. No.

MIGHT. But, Prometheus—

PROMETHEUS. I came this far willingly. If you want me to go the rest of the way, you'll have to drag me.

VIOLENCE (*approaching* PROMETHEUS *menacingly*). As you wish.

MIGHT (*to* VIOLENCE). Stop.

VIOLENCE. But, Might—

MIGHT. Let me handle this. (*To*

PROMETHEUS) Don't be like this—for your own good. My partner doesn't know how to control himself. He's just itching for a chance to cause you injury.

PROMETHEUS. Is that so, Violence?

VIOLENCE (cracking his knuckles). Just try me. If I had my way, I'd tear you limb from limb, then scatter your pieces all over the earth.

PROMETHEUS. Go on and do it. Zeus wants me to suffer in torment forever. I'd like to hear you explain to him how you spoiled his plans.

VIOLENCE. A few broken bones won't spoil anything.

PROMETHEUS. I don't care.

MIGHT. But I do. Come along.

PROMETHEUS. Where is Justice?

MIGHT. Not here.

VIOLENCE. If she were, she'd call a theft a theft. She wouldn't take your side, that's for sure.

PROMETHEUS. You know that for a fact, do you? (To MIGHT) And you, too? Might makes right, I suppose.

MIGHT. That's not the way I see it. I'm just following orders. Come along. Don't make this harder than it needs to be.

(Pause. PROMETHEUS rises to his feet and allows MIGHT and VIOLENCE to lead him to the cliff face.)

PROMETHEUS (looking at the chains and manacles). I've never heard of any steel that could hold a Titan.

MIGHT. This steel is special, tempered by Hephaestus.

PROMETHEUS. The forge god made these manacles just for me, did he? What an honor.

VIOLENCE. They've got magic words engraved on them.

MIGHT. New words—words no one has ever spoken or heard before. They give these chains the power to hold anything that lives—mortal or god. (Holding one of the manacles before PROMETHEUS) Tyranny.

(MIGHT claps the manacle around PROMETHEUS' right wrist.)

VIOLENCE (holding another manacle before PROMETHEUS). Poverty.

(VIOLENCE claps the manacle around PROMETHEUS' left wrist.)

MIGHT (holding another manacle before PROMETHEUS). Ignorance.

(MIGHT claps the manacle around PROMETHEUS' right ankle.)

VIOLENCE (holding another manacle before PROMETHEUS). Inequity.

(VIOLENCE claps the manacle around PROMETHEUS' left ankle. PROMETHEUS is now bound hand and foot, his back against the cliff face.)

PROMETHEUS. These words may be new, but I know their meanings well.

MIGHT. We'll leave you now to the dreadful elements of these heights—bitter cold by night, blistering heat by day, fierce winds that never stop. But before we go, I must ask you a question, at Zeus' command.

PROMETHEUS. And what is that?

MIGHT. Do you repent?

PROMETHEUS. And if I say yes? Will Zeus release me?

MIGHT. I'm not at liberty to say.

PROMETHEUS. You don't need to. I know. My repentance would do me no good.

MIGHT. It might do good for your soul.

PROMETHEUS. My soul is at peace.

MIGHT. You don't even feel guilt for your crime?

PROMETHEUS. What crime?

VIOLENCE. Stealing from the gods—can there be any crime worse than that?

PROMETHEUS. Yes. Always letting the gods have their way.

VIOLENCE (*stepping toward* PROMETHEUS). Why, I ought to—

MIGHT (*to* VIOLENCE). Get back. Enough of that.

PROMETHEUS. Tell Lord Zeus that I *do* repent. I repent not having the strength to break these chains. I repent not having greater gifts than fire to offer humankind. I repent not hurling Zeus from his throne and casting him into oblivion.

VIOLENCE (*to* MIGHT). We don't have to listen to this!

MIGHT (*to* PROMETHEUS). Say no more.

PROMETHEUS. Oh, I'll say much, much more. You'll never hear the last of my defiance. I'll make the world echo with my hatred of Zeus.

MIGHT. You'll waste your breath. Zeus will stop his ears and command all of creation to do the same. And all of creation will obey.

PROMETHEUS. For how long?

MIGHT. He means for you to stay here for untold thousands of years.

PROMETHEUS. Not forever?

MIGHT. You'll not live forever. Without the food and drink of the gods, you'll slowly become mortal. And you'll die—forgotten and alone.

(*The sound of beating wings is heard.*)

VIOLENCE (*with a smirk*). Not *quite* alone.

(*The* VULTURE *appears, perching on the rock.*)

VULTURE (*with a hideous shriek*). Vengeance! Vengeance! Vengeance for Zeus!

PROMETHEUS. What bloody beast is that?

MIGHT. A monster sent by Zeus to torment you.

PROMETHEUS. Away with you, scavenger! Go feed on the dead!

VIOLENCE. You'll do, I think. It's your liver he wants.

PROMETHEUS (*to the* VULTURE). Tear it out, then, and kill me!

VULTURE. Vengeance!

MIGHT. Zeus won't let you die that easily. This monster will devour your liver when the sun reaches its fullest height in the sky—but you'll heal by night. And tomorrow he'll be back for another feast. And so it will go for the rest of your days.

VIOLENCE (*looking skyward*). It's just about noon now.

VULTURE. The sun! The sun!

MIGHT (*to* VIOLENCE). Our work is done. Go on ahead. I'll be right along.

VIOLENCE. But I want to see this.

VULTURE. The sun! The sun!

MIGHT (*to* VIOLENCE). It's not for us to see.

VULTURE. But, Might—

MIGHT. I outrank you. And I order you. Go.

(VIOLENCE *reluctantly exits.*)

MIGHT. Do you have a message I can take back to Lord Zeus?

PROMETHEUS. Tell him that I don't fear him, I don't fear his monster, and I don't fear his cruelty. For I know a secret.

MIGHT. What's that?

PROMETHEUS. I'll be freed someday.

MIGHT. I know that you're a prophet, Titan. You know many things of the past, present, and future. But even so, I think—

PROMETHEUS. Think what?

MIGHT. I think you're only dreaming.

PROMETHEUS. It's the truth.

MIGHT. I wish it were.

VULTURE. The sun! The sun!

MIGHT. I am sorry, Titan.

(MIGHT *exits, leaving the* VULTURE *and* PROMETHEUS *alone. The* VULTURE *spreads his wings, ready to dive at* PROMETHEUS.)

VULTURE. Vengeance!

PROMETHEUS. Justice!

(*The* VULTURE *and* PROMETHEUS *freeze.* POLYHYMNIA *steps forward and speaks to the audience.*)

POLYHYMNIA. All this happened many thousands of years ago. Prometheus is still up there on his rock, although the world no longer resounds with his cries of rage and defiance. Has he stopped shouting? Perhaps. Or perhaps, at Zeus' command, we've learned not to hear him.

(*The* VULTURE *exits.*)

POLYHYMNIA. Today we live in a different time—a smaller, shabbier time, they say. The Golden Age of justice, equality, and happiness is long since over. Now we live in the Iron Age—a time of rust and decay, treachery and mistrust. And yet, this age of ours is not without its heroes.

(HERACLES *enters. He is draped in a lion skin and carries a bow and quiver on his back. A gourd is slung over his shoulder.*)

POLYHYMNIA. You've heard of this fellow, I'm sure. Perhaps you even know him personally. There are few mortals whose lives he hasn't touched, whom he hasn't helped in some way.

(*While* POLYHYMNIA *keeps speaking,* HERACLES *comes to life. He takes an imaginary arrow out of his quiver and places it in his bow. He draws the string tightly, pointing off into the distance.*)

POLYHYMNIA. He's a big brute of a man, strong as a whole herd of oxen—been killing monsters since he was a baby. He's not terribly bright, but has a heart as big as a mountain. He's made quite a name for himself, doing good things throughout the world. He's a demigod—the son of Zeus and a mortal woman, Alcmena. His name is Heracles. Yes, I was sure you'd heard of him.

(HERACLES *shoots the imaginary arrow.* CHIRON *is heard offstage, crying with pain.* HERACLES *freezes with a look of alarm. The turntable starts revolving, carrying* PROMETHEUS *out of sight.*)

POLYHYMNIA. But did you hear that? A cry of agony! And it's not Prometheus, up on his mountain, but someone very close by. Who could it be? What could have happened?

(*On the other side of the turntable is revealed* CHIRON, *a creature with the head and torso of a man and the body of a horse. His body is immobile, and an arrow is stuck in one of his front knees. He clutches the arrow in pain.*)

POLYHYMNIA. It's the Centaur Chiron! You've heard of him, too, I'm sure—a magnificent fellow, with the head and torso of a god and the body of a stallion. He's full of knowledge and understanding, the wisest creature that ever lived—next to Prometheus. He's been the childhood tutor to the world's greatest heroes, and even to gods. He taught Heracles himself, I believe. And now he's been shot—by Heracles' arrow!

(POLYHYMNIA *steps aside to watch as* HERACLES *comes to life. He approaches* CHIRON.)

HERACLES. Chiron! Oh, great Olympus! You're wounded!

CHIRON. Heracles! What luck! You've come just in the nick of time! Some assassin is trying to kill me. Look— an arrow in my knee. Hmmph! It hurts like the very devil. He's still out there stalking me, I'm sure. His next arrow

is liable to do worse. Quick, find him before he can shoot again!

HERACLES. Oh, Chiron, beloved teacher—I've already found your assailant.

CHIRON. Who is he? Bring him to me.

HERACLES. He's here, teacher.

CHIRON. You?

(HERACLES *nods.*)

CHIRON. But why? We've not seen each other for years—not since you were a lad. And I thought we parted on the best of terms. Are you still angry that I made your lessons so difficult? You really did hate mathematics. And I know I could be something of a taskmaster.

HERACLES. I didn't mean to do it. I swear.

CHIRON. Why, then?

HERACLES. I was fighting your brother Centaurs.

CHIRON. Oh, don't call them my brothers—the savages!

HERACLES. They were determined to kill me, and I was determined not to be killed. I slew two or three of the scoundrels and put the rest to rout. They ran and ran, more like rabbits than horses, seeking refuge far away. I should have left them to their disgrace and shame, the cowards. But I was determined to kill just one more. So I shot an arrow after them, and . . .

CHIRON. It struck me.

HERACLES. The only Centaur who never harmed a living soul. Oh, forgive me, teacher. But what were you doing among them?

CHIRON. They always come to me when they're in trouble. It's the only time they pay any heed to me, the villains. But, rash Heracles! How many times did I tell you to take better care where you aim your arrows?

HERACLES (holding his gourd to CHIRON). Here. Drink this.

(CHIRON drinks from the gourd.)

HERACLES. Tell me how to heal you. You know so much of medicines and herbs. I'll fetch whatever you need.

CHIRON. Foolish fellow! Your arrows are magical. They make wounds that have no cure. You know that better than I do.

HERACLES. Then will you die?

CHIRON. Alas, no! Of all the Centaurs, only I am immortal. And immortality gets to be a habit one can't break. I was already weary of life—weary of watching this world grow smaller and meaner beneath Zeus' heel. The world was once filled with song, alive with melody and magic. But no more. I've longed to die for a long, long time. But I can't, I can't. And now I must live on in pain. Unless—

HERACLES. Unless?

CHIRON. Unless a dying god accepts my burden of immortality.

HERACLES. A dying god? Is such a thing possible?

CHIRON. It doesn't seem likely, does it?

HERACLES (taking an arrow out of his quiver). I can't live with having done this to you.

CHIRON. What are you going to do? Wound yourself? What do you think will happen if you do?

HERACLES. I'll die, of course.

CHIRON. Are you so sure? You're half god, you know. Perhaps you'll keep living.

HERACLES. Then at least I'll be able to share your pain.

CHIRON. Pain isn't something you can share. You can make more if it, yes, but what good is that? Your pain won't help relieve mine any. Put that thing away. Act like the hero you are.

HERACLES (putting the arrow back in his quiver). What can I do, then?

CHIRON. Talk to me awhile, before I go mad with pain, before I'm unable to ever talk again. That would give me some comfort. What have you been up to since I saw you last?

HERACLES. You wouldn't be proud of me.

CHIRON. Oh, I'm sure I would be. I've already heard wonderful stories of your kindness and heroism.

HERACLES. You've not heard of my failures.

CHIRON. Everybody has their failures.

HERACLES. Not like mine. I am strong like a god, but rash and foolish like a man.

CHIRON. Rashness and foolishness are the failings of gods, too. You're more godlike than you think. I've always been able to see into your heart. It's a good heart.

HERACLES. My heart is flawed.

CHIRON. Tell me.

(*Pause*)

HERACLES. I slew my own wife and children.

CHIRON. Why?

HERACLES. Pure madness. You know how Queen Hera hates me because I'm her husband's son by a mortal. She drove me mad. She made me kill my family. I don't remember doing it. But when I came to my senses, I saw their bodies . . .

CHIRON. No man is responsible for what he does in madness.

HERACLES. So they tell me. Still, my hands are stained with blood. I've undertaken many labors to make up for it. It's called *expiating*.

CHIRON. Yes, I've heard of it.

HERACLES. I've slain monsters, done impossible tasks, unheard-of deeds. My hands are cleaner now, I think. But my heart . . .

CHIRON. Your heart still aches.

HERACLES. My heart is flawed.

CHIRON. I say again, your heart is good.

HERACLES. That flaw in my heart—that rift between god and man—was my undoing. Hera put her madness there. Teacher, tell me—can it ever be healed?

CHIRON. Don't wish it to be healed. Only the cruelest hearts are perfect.

Your father has a perfect heart. Don't wish for a heart like his. You do good throughout the world. And wherever you go, you're loved for it. What more can you want?

HERACLES. I do good until I fall into rashness again—as I've done just now.

(CHIRON *groans with pain.*)

HERACLES. Oh, poor Chiron. However can I forgive myself for this? And here I've gone on babbling about my pointless life while you—

CHIRON. Heracles, I told you to babble.

HERACLES. Oh. That's right.

CHIRON. Now please—babble some more.

HERACLES. Well, I—

CHIRON. Wait! Listen! (*Pause*) Do you hear that?

HERACLES. Hear what?

CHIRON. Music. The world is singing.

HERACLES. I don't hear it.

CHIRON. The world is changing. It's becoming magical again. Zeus' stranglehold is loosening.

HERACLES. I don't understand.

CHIRON. Nor do I. But you must go— right now! A great adventure awaits you.

HERACLES. Where?

CHIRON (*pointing*). There.

HERACLES. Where are you pointing?

CHIRON. What did I always tell you was the most important truth in the world?

HERACLES. That the shortest distance between two points is a straight line.

CHIRON. Very good. You were a better pupil than I thought. (*Pointing again in the same direction*) Start walking that way. Follow a straight line the whole way. Don't stop walking until you find it.

HERACLES. Find what?

CHIRON. I don't know. You'll know when you get there. Will you go?

HERACLES. I'll go until I reach the world's edge, if you say so.

CHIRON. The world has no edge.

HERACLES. Then I could be walking a long time.

CHIRON. Perhaps. But you'll find what you're looking for. I promise.

HERACLES. But how can I just leave you here?

CHIRON. You have no choice. Go!

(CHIRON *and* HERACLES *freeze as* POLYHYMNIA *steps forward to speak to the audience.*)

POLYHYMNIA. That song Chiron mentioned—*I* certainly hear it. Listen! Can't you? (*Pause*) No? Perhaps it's not easily heard by mortal ears. Whenever there's a melody anywhere in the universe, I hear it as clear as a bell. Keep listening. I'm sure you'll hear this one, too, if you really try. It's lovely and strange.

(*The turntable begins to revolve, carrying* CHIRON *and* HERACLES *out of sight.*)

POLYHYMNIA. So Heracles sets out on his travels—walking in a straight line, just as his teacher commanded. He walks and walks through forests and rivers, over hills and mountains, never wavering, never turning, as straight as straight can be, for hundreds upon hundreds of miles. After weeks and months of walking without finding his goal, you'd think he'd get discouraged, vary his course, perhaps even turn back. But not Heracles. He's the most dogged and determined of heroes.

(*The turntable stops, revealing* PROMETHEUS *again, still chained to his rock. His body is draped with a blanket. He is now bearded, feeble, and old, and appears to be unconscious. As* POLYHYMNIA *continues speaking, the nymphs* EUDORA *and* RHODEA *enter and approach* PROMETHEUS. EUDORA *is carrying a small cloth sack and a gourd.*)

POLYHYMNIA. But here's Prometheus again, still chained to his rock. How wretched he looks, poor Titan! And yet, he hasn't been left alone all these thousands of years. Two sea nymphs have been climbing to this height daily, bringing him food and comfort.

(POLYHYMNIA *steps aside to watch.*)

RHODEA (*to* EUDORA). Is he dead?

EUDORA. No.

RHODEA. He looks dead.

EUDORA (*to* PROMETHEUS). We're here. We've brought your morning food and drink.

RHODEA. He's not answering. He's dead.

EUDORA. He can't die. He's immortal. (*To* PROMETHEUS) Are you asleep?

PROMETHEUS (*opening his eyes*). I never sleep.

EUDORA (*to* RHODEA). There. You see? (*To* PROMETHEUS) It's time to eat.

PROMETHEUS. What have you brought?

EUDORA (*holding the sack toward him*). What we always bring. A mix of nuts and dried apricots and figs.

PROMETHEUS. I won't eat it.

EUDORA. Why not?

PROMETHEUS. I'll not eat my children anymore.

EUDORA. Nuts and fruit aren't your children. They're not the flesh of the animals that you molded from clay.

PROMETHEUS. They live. All living things are my children.

RHODEA. Foolish Titan. You stopped eating anything but nuts and fruit ages ago. What will you eat now? Stones?

PROMETHEUS. Even stones contain the promise of life.

RHODEA. In the old days, maybe. The world isn't as magical as it used to be. The tyranny of Zeus has made everything more dead.

EUDORA (*holding the gourd toward him*). Some wine, then.

RHODEA. He won't drink it. Didn't you hear what he just said? Wine is made from grapes. Grapes are his children, too.

EUDORA. But what *will* you eat, then?

RHODEA. Nothing, isn't it obvious? And so our work is done. We needn't come around here anymore.

EUDORA. We can't just leave him to die.

RHODEA. So you admit it—he *can* die. More than that, he wants to die. He's given up on life—at long, long last. Show him some kindness. Leave him be.

EUDORA. He doesn't deserve to die alone.

RHODEA. Sister, listen to me. We've climbed up to this awful place every morning for 30,000 years. Even nymphs don't live forever. I want to get on with what life I've got left.

EUDORA. Go, then. When did I ask for your help? (*Touching* PROMETHEUS' *forehead*) You're sweating. Let's get this blanket off you.

PROMETHEUS. I need it for the cold.

EUDORA. At night you do, when the frost comes. But the sun is rising in the sky, and the air is getting hot. Soon you'll be roasting. Poor creature, you've lost all sense of the weather.

(EUDORA *removes the blanket from* PROMETHEUS. *His torso is bare, and a long scar stretches across his abdomen.*)

RHODEA. I'll fold the blanket.

EUDORA. No, it's soaked through with sweat. Drape it over a rock so it'll dry in the sun.

(EUDORA *hands the blanket to* RHODEA. *As* RHODEA *drapes it over the rock,* EUDORA *examines the scar.*)

EUDORA. Your wound healed well last night.

RHODEA (*leaving the blanket on the rock*). Small good it will do him. Come noon, it'll be as bloody as ever.

(The sound of beating wings is heard.)

POLYHYMNIA *(to the audience)*. Another creature has been steadfast in his duty, visiting Prometheus every day—his tormentor. Has the Vulture changed over all the millennia, I wonder?

(The VULTURE *appears, perching on the rock.)*

EUDORA *(to the* VULTURE*)*. Off with you, filthy beast! You're not welcome here!

RHODEA. You won't get rid of him. You ought to know that by now.

VULTURE. Good morning, Titan. I trust you passed the night tolerably well.

EUDORA *(to the* VULTURE*)*. Don't talk to him like that.

VULTURE. Like what?

EUDORA. Like you're his friend.

VULTURE. But I *am* his friend.

EUDORA. How dare you! You, whose beak and talons are forever stained with his blood, whose feathers are forever clumped with pieces of his flesh!

PROMETHEUS. Leave him alone. I'll not rail against him, nor should you.

EUDORA. But Prometheus—

PROMETHEUS. Or would you rather I made these mountains and valleys echo anew with my bellowings of rage, like they did for so many centuries?

EUDORA. Yes. You should hate him. You should cry out against him.

PROMETHEUS. I don't hate him anymore. Hatred dies when it has no purpose.

VULTURE. So does cruelty. I may be his tormentor, but my heart means him well.

EUDORA *(to the* VULTURE*)*. If you're his friend, help him. Talk sense to him. Get him to eat something, anything.

VULTURE *(to* PROMETHEUS*)*. What are you up to, then? Starving yourself to death?

PROMETHEUS. I'll eat nothing that lives, or that ever had life.

EUDORA *(to the* VULTURE*)*. He won't even touch nuts and fruit or drink any wine. He can't last long this way. Talk to him, tell him what he's got to live for.

VULTURE. I'd be glad to, nymph. But what *does* he have to live for?

EUDORA. His release from this rock.

VULTURE. Pah! Do you still believe that fairy tale?

EUDORA. The world needs him.

VULTURE. No doubt it does. The world's in a bad way. Alas, the world can't *have* him, thanks to Zeus. And he's not doing *himself* any good, chained up like this. We'd be kind to wish him a quiet, painless death.

RHODEA. The beast is right this once.

VULTURE *(to* PROMETHEUS*)*. I wish I could help you. You know I do. If it were in my power to slay you quickly with my beak or talons, I'd do it.

PROMETHEUS. I know you would. And I thank you for it.

EUDORA. Thank him! For wishing you dead?

PROMETHEUS (to EUDORA). It's a generous wish. The moment I die, he'll die, too. He has no purpose in the world except to wound me.

VULTURE. It's a purpose I loathe.

PROMETHEUS. I know, my friend. But I have much to thank you for. You do me great kindnesses. If it weren't for you, how would I know what was going on in the world? Come on, let's talk, it's not noon yet. What have you seen in your sky circlings since we spoke last? What news do you bring? There are wars, I suppose— and rumors of wars.

VULTURE. Oh, yes. And nation rising against nation, and kingdom against kingdom. And famines, pestilences, and earthquakes wherever you look. But that's not the really *interesting* news. A young hero is on his way here. He's climbing the cliff face even as we speak. He'll be here any moment.

EUDORA. A hero?

RHODEA. What on earth—?

PROMETHEUS. Does this hero have a name?

VULTURE. Yes. Heracles.

PROMETHEUS. Heracles!

VULTURE. Heard of him, have you?

PROMETHEUS. I'd almost forgotten how to hope.

EUDORA. Prometheus, who is this man? What does this mean?

POLYHYMNIA (to the audience). They'll know soon enough. Here comes our hero now—a mighty man-god with scant respect for obstacles.

(HERACLES lumbers onstage, dressed exactly as earlier. He is panting with exertion.)

HERACLES. Ooof! Huff! Thought you had the best of me, didn't you, mountain? Not a chance! I've climbed 'em higher and steeper—although I can't remember when. Well, mountain, maybe next time you won't stand in my way. You'll have the good sense to move. (Noticing EUDORA, RHODEA, and PROMETHEUS) But what's this? Living creatures—intelligent-looking bipeds, no less. Arrived here before me, did you? A pity. I figured I'd be the first fellow to scale these heights. Well, there are other mountains.

PROMETHEUS. The hero Heracles, I presume.

HERACLES. My reputation precedes me, then. It's the same everywhere. But none of this *hero* stuff, please. I can't stand much more of that. If I hear another ballad about myself, I'm liable to explode. A common adventurer—that's all I am. (Wiping sweat off his brow) It's hotter than a forge up here. Who'd have thought it'd be so hot at this altitude?

EUDORA. That's just by day.

RHODEA. You should feel the cold at night.

HERACLES. It's a regular hell on earth.

PROMETHEUS. Yes, that's exactly what it is.

HERACLES (*to* PROMETHEUS). But you're in a rough spot, aren't you? Judging from the rust on those chains, I'd say you've been here a good while.

PROMETHEUS. Quite a while, yes.

HERACLES. Poor devil! Don't tell me— you ran afoul of some penny-ante tyrant of some backwoods kingdom, a common thug who fancies he's lord of the whole universe. And he hung you up here to dry.

PROMETHEUS. How did you know?

HERACLES. Oh, it's an easy guess. I see tyranny everywhere I look, everywhere I go. Makes me sick to my heart. So how long have you been here? Two, three years, I expect.

PROMETHEUS. Thirty thousand.

HERACLES (*chuckling*). No, really? Well, I'm sure it seems so to you. (*Gazing far away*) You've got a fine view, anyway. On a clear day, I'll bet you can see the edge of the world.

PROMETHEUS. The world has no edge.

HERACLES (*chuckling again*). So I've heard. I don't quite have the brains to grasp that idea. (*Holding out a gourd*) But you look parched. How about something to drink?

PROMETHEUS. I'll not drink wine.

HERACLES. This isn't wine. I've learned better than to carry wine while climbing. Makes me light-headed and dizzy. Had some nasty falls on account of it. Pure spring water, that's what this is.

PROMETHEUS. Even the purest water is teeming with life.

HERACLES. Not this. No bugs or pollywogs, I assure you.

PROMETHEUS. It's full of creatures too small for the eye to see.

HERACLES. That's not very appetizing.

PROMETHEUS. I'll eat or drink nothing that lives.

HERACLES. Oh, really, now. I've got as much respect for life as the next man. But you're carrying it a little far.

EUDORA (*to* HERACLES). *Make* him drink it. He'll die if he doesn't.

HERACLES (*to* PROMETHEUS). Given up on life, have you? Yes, I can see it in your eyes. Well, somebody's got to make you see reason. (*Shoving the gourd at* PROMETHEUS' *face*) Drink it, I say.

PROMETHEUS. No.

HERACLES. Drink it, or I'll slap you good. And it'll hurt, I promise.

PROMETHEUS (*chuckling weakly*). Very well, then. Under the threat of violence, I'll drink.

(*As* PROMETHEUS *drinks,* HERACLES *turns his attention to* EUDORA *and* RHODEA.)

HERACLES. I take it you ladies look after him. Live on this ledge, do you?

EUDORA. No, we climb up here every day.

HERACLES. What devotion! True angels of mercy, you are. (*Noticing the* VULTURE) But what have we here? String me up by my toes if it's not the biggest bird in the world. A scavenger, too. Shoo, be off! This fellow's not dead yet. And when he is, there'll not be enough meat on his carcass to fill up your belly. Go feed on something your own size.

RHODEA. It's no use, he won't leave.

HERACLES. But what sort of vulture is he? A breed of these mountains?

VULTURE. Not at all. I'm one of a kind.

HERACLES. A talking vulture!

VULTURE. Much more than that. A monster.

HERACLES. Are you, now? I'm known for killing monsters. But I'll try to make an exception in your case.

RHODEA (to HERACLES). Where have you come from?

HERACLES. I'd rather not say.

EUDORA. Where are you headed, then?

HERACLES. My next adventure. This mountain happened to be in my path.

VULTURE. Whatever possessed you to climb it? Wouldn't it have been easier to pass through the surrounding valleys?

HERACLES. A wise fellow told me that the shortest distance between two points is a straight line.

PROMETHEUS. Yes, a wise fellow told me that, too. But these slopes, cliffs, and ridges are hardly a straight line.

HERACLES. Hadn't thought of it that way. Thinking's not my strong suit. Doesn't matter, though. Climbing's good exercise. Can't get enough exercise, that's what I always say. (Sipping water from his gourd) I'd love to stay and chat, but I've got to keep moving. My next adventure awaits—whatever it is. But before I go, I've got half a mind to break you loose. I'd better hear your story first, though—just to make sure you're not chained up here for some good reason.

PROMETHEUS. I'm the Titan Prometheus.

HERACLES (laughing heartily). That's good. Tell me another one.

(HERACLES' laughter dies away as he studies the serious faces around him. Long pause.)

VULTURE (to HERACLES). He's telling the truth, friend.

HERACLES. No.

EUDORA. Oh, yes.

HERACLES. I thought Prometheus was only a legend.

PROMETHEUS. Not a legend. A myth.

HERACLES. There's a difference?

PROMETHEUS. A legend is something that *was*. A myth always *is*.

HERACLES. But you're so small and weak—and old.

VULTURE. A god must eat ambrosia and drink nectar to stay great and immortal. He's had nothing but mortal food for 30,000 years. He's less god than man, now—and less alive than dead.

HERACLES. Then it's true?

EUDORA. Of course it's true.

VULTURE. Would a winged monster watch over any ordinary captive?

EUDORA. And why would anyone bind a mortal at such a height?

RHODEA. With chains that even a god can't break?

VULTURE. He is the Titan. Believe it, friend.

HERACLES. But how can I be sure?

PROMETHEUS. Because I know your heart. It's good—and it's flawed.

(HERACLES *falls on his knees before* PROMETHEUS.)

HERACLES. Then it *is* true! Forgive me for doubting you, O trickster, friend of humankind! Please help me in my unbelief.

PROMETHEUS. Your unbelief is nothing to forgive. I scarcely believe my own story anymore.

HERACLES. So is this is my destination! But what is my task?

PROMETHEUS. To set me free.

HERACLES. But even a god can't break your chains.

PROMETHEUS. No god with a cruel and perfect heart, like Zeus. But *you* have the heart to do it.

(The VULTURE *screeches horribly.*)

POLYHYMNIA (*to the audience*). Oh, what a shriek! Our monster is his old self again!

EUDORA. It's noon!

RHODEA (*covering her eyes and rushing to the edge of the stage*). I can't look.

VULTURE. The sun! The sun!

HERACLES (*to* PROMETHEUS). What's this? What's happening?

PROMETHEUS. Close your eyes and step aside. It's best that you not see.

HERACLES. See what?

VULTURE. The sun! The sun!

EUDORA (*to* HERACLES). He's maddened by the noon sun.

PROMETHEUS (*to* HERACLES). My friend has one last duty to perform before I'm freed. Let it happen.

HERACLES. I don't understand.

EUDORA (*to* HERACLES). Get an arrow ready! He's about to strike.

HERACLES. But vultures only feed on the dead.

EUDORA. Not this one.

VULTURE. The sun! The sun!

HERACLES (*taking the bow from his back*). It's high time this stopped.

PROMETHEUS. Don't kill him. He only does what he was created to do. He doesn't deserve to die.

HERACLES. You don't deserve to suffer.

VULTURE (*with trembling wings*). The sun! The sun!

EUDORA (*to* HERACLES). Quick! He's about to dive!

(HERACLES *has taken an imaginary arrow out of his quiver and placed it in his bow. He draws the string tightly, pointing directly at the* VULTURE.)

POLYHYMNIA. Pray, Heracles. Don't trust to your arms alone.

HERACLES (*calling to the heavens*). O Apollo, god of archers, you taught me how to use this bow. Guide my aim, now when I most need your aid.

Don't let me fail in this, my greatest task.

(The VULTURE *spreads his wings wide and lets out a terrible shriek.*)

EUDORA. Now!

(HERACLES *releases his imaginary arrow. Stricken, the* VULTURE *tumbles from his perch to the stage.*)

RHODEA (*with her eyes still covered*). Is it over?

EUDORA. You can look.

(RHODEA *uncovers her eyes.*)

VULTURE (*lying on the stage*). Your fame for archery is deserved, Heracles. Your aim was true.

PROMETHEUS (*to the* VULTURE). Oh, tell me it's not a mortal wound, my friend.

VULTURE. As mortal as can be—straight through the heart. I wish I had received it 30,000 years ago. (*To* HERACLES) Thank you.

HERACLES. Give your thanks to Apollo.

PROMETHEUS (*to* HERACLES). Break my manacles! Break them now!

HERACLES (*seizing one of* PROMETHEUS' *manacles*). There's a word engraved here.

PROMETHEUS. Tyranny.

HERACLES. This manacle holds me, too—and all mortal men and women. (*Breaking the manacle*) So much for Tyranny! (*Seizing another manacle*) And this one also has a name.

PROMETHEUS. Poverty.

HERACLES (*breaking the manacle*). So much for Poverty! (*Seizing another manacle*) And this one—

PROMETHEUS. Ignorance.

HERACLES (*breaking the manacle*). I feel smarter already. (*Seizing the last manacle*) And the last—

PROMETHEUS. Inequity.

HERACLES. Oh, yes. I know this one well.

PROMETHEUS. Quickly—before my friend gives up the ghost!

HERACLES. So a flawed heart is of some use, after all. (*Breaking the other manacle*) It gives me the strength to break Inequity!

(*Freed but feeble,* PROMETHEUS *staggers toward the* VULTURE *and crouches next to him.*)

PROMETHEUS (*to the* VULTURE). Your heart—

VULTURE. It's broken.

PROMETHEUS. Is there much pain?

VULTURE. None at all, only joy.

PROMETHEUS. Oh, if only I had a fraction of the power I once possessed! I'd heal you in an instant.

VULTURE. Don't wish me healed. I've lived to see you free. What more can I want from life? (*Chuckling hoarsely*) The fairy tale came true, after all!

PROMETHEUS. We'll carry you down from these heights. We'll put you in an honored grave, I promise.

VULTURE. No. Leave me here in the sky, where I belong. But—look at you, poor Titan! How weak you are, how gaunt. You'll die soon. Oh, if only I could make one last flight to heaven, steal you a dish of ambrosia, a draught of nectar. Yes, just that much more life . . . that's all I want . . . that's all I ask . . .

(*The* VULTURE *dies.*)

PROMETHEUS. Fly wherever you like, old friend. You're free.

HERACLES (*to* PROMETHEUS). Come on, old fellow. It's time we got you away from this awful place.

PROMETHEUS. Yes, it's time.

(PROMETHEUS *tries to rise to his feet, but collapses from weakness.*)

EUDORA. Oh, it's too late for him. He'll never make it down the mountain.

HERACLES. I'll carry him.

RHODEA (*to* EUDORA). Don't give up. Not now.

EUDORA. But if he survives the descent, what then? He's not a god anymore—just a frail and broken old man. Soon he'll die.

HERACLES. He won't die—not ever. (*Pulling* PROMETHEUS' *arm over his shoulder and helping him to his feet*) Up you go, trickster. Muster your strength, it's a long way down this mountain. And from there, it's much farther to where we have to go. You have some idea where that is, I imagine.

PROMETHEUS. Yes. I hope we're not too late.

HERACLES. If there's one thing I've learned, it's never to hope. Just keep on moving. It may not sound like much, but it's all the wisdom I've got.

PROMETHEUS. You're wiser than you know.

(*As* POLYHYMNIA *steps forward to speak to the audience,* HERACLES *leads* PROMETHEUS *away, followed by* EUDORA *and* RHODEA. *When* HERACLES, PROMETHEUS, EUDORA, *and* RHODEA *are off the turntable, they freeze. The turntable begins to turn, carrying away the* VULTURE's *body.*)

POLYHYMNIA (*to the audience*). Listen. That song is growing. You can hear it now, can't you? The very crags and crevasses are singing. It's still soft and low, but it will grow louder and clearer. No? You'll hear it soon. All the world will hear it soon. Meanwhile, more weeks and months pass as our travelers return to where Chiron lies wounded. What will they find there? Will the old Centaur's mind still be his own? Or will pain have left him nothing more than a crazed animal?

(*The turntable stops, revealing* CHIRON, *as before.* POLYHYMNIA *steps away to watch as* HERACLES, PROMETHEUS, EUDORA, *and* RHODEA *come to life.*)

EUDORA. Look!

RHODEA. A Centaur!

EUDORA. But aren't Centaurs supposed to be horribly fierce?

RHODEA. To say nothing of villainous?

HERACLES. Not *this* Centaur.

PROMETHEUS (*approaching* CHIRON). Greetings, honored teacher.

CHIRON. Ah, my two most memorable pupils—my best and my worst!

PROMETHEUS. But which of us is which?

CHIRON. Each of you is both. You are wise and foolish in equal measure, the two of you.

HERACLES (*to* PROMETHEUS). He was your teacher, too?

PROMETHEUS (*kneeling beside* CHIRON *and taking his hand*). Oh, yes. He's as old as the world. (*To* CHIRON) What times we had when I was young, eh? You'd carry me on your back through forests and meadows far and wide. And the whole while, you'd sing to me, recite fine poetry, lecture me about science, mathematics, history, and medicine.

HERACLES (*to* PROMETHEUS). You liked that stuff, did you?

PROMETHEUS. Very much.

CHIRON. I'm afraid Heracles may have been a bit too clever for all that sort of thing.

PROMETHEUS. I don't doubt it. He's a very bright fellow.

CHIRON. You don't look any the better for wear.

PROMETHEUS. Nor you. How's your wound?

CHIRON. 'Tis not so deep as a well, nor so wide as a church door—but 'tis enough, 'twill serve.

PROMETHEUS. And the pain?

CHIRON. Worse and worse by the minute. But all this time, I've had this lovely melody to comfort me.

RHODEA. Melody?

CHIRON. Yes. The world is filled with it. Can't you hear it?

EUDORA. No.

PROMETHEUS. How can I help you? What can I give you?

CHIRON. Death.

PROMETHEUS. As you wish.

CHIRON. I have nothing to offer you in return—except my immortality.

PROMETHEUS. I'll relieve you of your immortality. And I'll accept your pain, as well.

CHIRON. Oh, you needn't take my pain. My pain will die with me. That's the good thing about pain. But alas, you'll find more pain when you become immortal again—an infinite supply of it.

PROMETHEUS. We'll give you a fine burial.

CHIRON. I'll tend to my own burial, thank you. Instead, I ask a promise.

PROMETHEUS. Tell me.

(CHIRON *weakens during the following dialogue.* PROMETHEUS *cradles his head and torso in his arms.*)

CHIRON. Always defy Zeus. Always hate him.

PROMETHEUS. I can't promise that. I've outlived my own defiance. And hatred dies when it has no purpose.

CHIRON. Then promise to make all thrones empty, all crowns broken.

PROMETHEUS. I promise.

CHIRON. Make courts and prisons fall to ruins.

PROMETHEUS. I promise.

CHIRON. Make knowledge and wisdom thrive.

PROMETHEUS. I promise.

CHIRON. Make envy, greed, and cruelty vanish from every heart.

PROMETHEUS. I promise.

CHIRON. Make love and goodwill grow in every heart.

PROMETHEUS. I promise.

CHIRON. Make all mortals equal—and greater than gods.

PROMETHEUS. I promise.

CHIRON. And last—promise always to be Prometheus.

PROMETHEUS. I've promised you that already.

CHIRON. So you have . . . So you have . . .

(CHIRON *dies.* POLYHYMNIA *wordlessly sings a melody—the "Ode to Joy" from Beethoven's Ninth Symphony.*)

PROMETHEUS. Farewell, teacher.

HERACLES. Farewell, taskmaster.

EUDORA (*hearing* POLYHYMNIA). Listen! A song!

RHODEA (*laughing*). The Centaur was right! The world is becoming magical again!

EUDORA. Strange. I'm sure I've never heard that melody before—and yet I know it, somehow.

RHODEA. So do I.

(EUDORA *and* RHODEA *begin to sing wordlessly along with* POLYHYMNIA. PROMETHEUS *gently lowers* CHIRON's *head and torso to the ground. He rises to his feet with renewed strength.*)

PROMETHEUS. Let's go, young adventurer.

HERACLES. But where?

PROMETHEUS. Wherever a straight line leads us.

HERACLES. To adventures, then?

PROMETHEUS. To a whole new world.

(HERACLES *and* PROMETHEUS *slowly begin to walk down the steps leading from the stage into the audience. They are followed by* EUDORA *and* RHODEA. POLYHYMNIA, EUDORA, *and* RHODEA *begin to sing the following words to the same tune as before.* POLYHYMNIA *follows the others down the steps and through the audience.*)

POLYHYMNIA, EUDORA, and RHODEA
(*together*).
Let the weary world awaken,
    For the trickster now is free!
He who was so long forsaken
    Shall unshackled always be!
What comes now that he's
    resurrected,
    And a Trickster Age is here?
Greet the strange, the unexpected;
    Greet it without dread or fear.

(*The little procession leaves the theatre as the lights slowly fade on* CHIRON's *body.*)

PLAYWRIGHT'S POSTSCRIPT

In this play, I have not dealt with Prometheus' secret. Prometheus knew that Zeus might eventually remarry and have a son who would overthrow him. According to classical stories, Prometheus eventually made peace with Zeus and told him this secret. Zeus was thus able to prevent his own downfall.

In 1820, the romantic poet Percy Bysshe Shelley wrote his own version of *Prometheus Unbound*. In his verse drama, Zeus did, indeed, fall from power around the time of Prometheus' release. Shelley lived in a time of great social and political change—the *Age of Revolution* many have called it. To Shelley, Zeus symbolized a kind of tyranny that he thought was dying in the world. And Prometheus' liberation symbolized a whole new world of human possibilities.

Today, we live in a time of even greater change. What does Prometheus' liberation symbolize to us?

CONNECTING TO OTHER CULTURES

Prometheus is a great trickster—a god who often breaks the rules. Countless trickster stories have been told throughout the world. The trickster has many faces. Sometimes he or she is a comic buffoon, trying to get away with some lowly theft and prank. Other times, the trickster is portrayed as a "culture hero," acting out of kindness toward human beings. Many tricksters, including Raven and Coyote in Native American stories, stole fire for humankind. Like Prometheus, they were usually punished bitterly for their kindness.

THUMBNAIL MYTHS: SELECTED SUMMARIES OF GREEK AND ROMAN STORIES

ACTAEON (ăk tē′ an)

Actaeon was a skilled young hunter. One day, he wandered away from his hunting companions and stumbled across a fountain where the goddess Artemis was bathing. Artemis was outraged to be seen naked, so she turned Actaeon into a stag. The hunter was then slain by his own hounds.

The Awakening of Adonis, 1899, John William Waterhouse

ADONIS (u dä′ nus)

Adonis was a beautiful young man, much loved by the goddess Aphrodite. One day while hunting, he was gored by a boar. Aphrodite rushed to his aid, but too late—he died in her arms. In memory of her love for him, she turned Adonis' spilt blood into a new kind of blood-red flower called the *anemone*.

Today, a classically handsome young man is often referred to as an *Adonis*.

ALCESTIS (al ses′ tis)

Alcestis was the devoted wife of King Admetus. When a prophecy revealed that Admetus would soon die unless someone died in his place, Alcestis willingly died to save him. But the hero Heracles (often known by his Roman name *Hercules*) rescued her from death and returned her to her grateful husband.

ANDROMEDA (ăn drä' ma da)

Andromeda was the daughter of King Cepheus and Queen Cassiopia of Ethiopia. Cassiopia boasted so much of her own beauty that she angered the gods, and a sea monster was sent to lay waste to the kingdom. An oracle said that the only way to get rid of the monster was by sacrificing Andromeda to it. So Cepheus and Cassiopia chained Andromeda to a rock by the sea, where the monster was expected to kill her. But when the monster arrived, the hero Perseus showed it Medusa's head [see MEDUSA], which turned the creature into stone. Perseus and Andromeda were then married.

ARACHNE (a rak' nē)

Arachne was so skilled in weaving and embroidery that she dared to challenge Athena to a weaving match. Enraged by Arachne's perfect work, Athena tore it to pieces in a rage. Stunned by this insult, Arachne hanged herself. Athena would not let her die and turned her into a spider, which goes on weaving its web as long as it lives.

The class to which spiders belong—Arachnida—is named after Arachne.

ASCLEPIUS (a sklē' pē us)

A son of Apollo, Asclepius was the god of medicine. As a child, Asclepius was tutored by the wise centaur Chiron, who taught him to cure any wound or disease. Asclepius made Zeus angry by raising a mortal from the dead, so Zeus killed him with a thunderbolt. But even death did not diminish Asclepius' power. For centuries after he died, his spirit healed those who visited his temple.

ATALANTA (ă tul an' ta)

Atalanta was a beautiful warrior, huntress, and athlete. She swore that she would marry no man unless he could defeat her in a foot race. Moreover, any man who took up this challenge and lost was put to death. Many suitors died before Hippomenes raced her. During the race, Hippomenes threw three golden apples in Atalanta's path. Atalanta stopped to pick up each apple, lost the race, and married Hippomenes.

ATLANTIS (ăt lăn' tas)

According to the Greek philosopher Plato, Atlantis was an island kingdom in what is now called the Atlantic Ocean. Many thousands of years ago, Atlantis conquered much of the Mediterranean region until it was finally defeated by Athens. The Atlanteans were wise and virtuous at first, but later became wicked and cruel. The island was eventually swallowed up into the sea by an earthquake.

This legend has led many people to wonder if such a kingdom might have really existed. The story may have been inspired by a gigantic volcanic eruption that took place in the Aegean Sea around 1500 B.C. Much of the island of Thera was then plunged beneath the sea.

BAUCIS AND PHILEMON (bo' sas *and* fa lē' man)

To test human hospitality, Zeus and Hermes once wandered through Phrygia disguised as poor travelers. Whenever they knocked on a door asking for food or shelter, they were turned away, even by the rich. Only the poor peasant Philemon and his wife Baucis took them in and treated them kindly.

Zeus and Hermes sent a huge storm which destroyed all the homes in Phrygia—except for that of Philemon and Baucis, which they turned into a temple. The couple served the rest of their days there as priest and priestess. They asked Zeus and Hermes to be allowed to die at the same moment, and the gods granted their wish. They were turned into two trees standing on either side of the temple.

CADMUS (kăd' mus)

Cadmus was the legendary founder of Thebes. On the site of that future city, he killed a dragon and sowed its teeth in the ground like seeds. An army of men sprang up, and Cadmus stopped them from killing him by tossing a stone among them. This confused the soldiers, who slew one another—all except five, who helped Cadmus found the city. He married Harmonia, a daughter of Aphrodite, and they ruled Thebes together for many years.

CALLISTO (ka lis' tō)

Callisto was a huntress who followed Artemis. Like all of Artemis' followers, Callisto vowed always to remain a virgin. But she became one of Zeus' many unwitting mortal lovers and gave birth to a son named Arcas. Out of jealousy, Hera turned Callisto into a bear. Arcas, himself a hunter, unknowingly tried to kill his mother before Zeus rescued her, turning her into the constellation Ursa Major (Great Bear). Arcas became the constellation Ursa Minor (Little Bear).

CASTOR AND POLLUX (kăs′ tar *and* pä′ luks)

Castor and Pollux were the sons of Leda (*see* LEDA AND THE SWAN). Although Castor was the mortal son of Leda's husband, Tyndareus, and Pollux was the immortal son of Zeus, they were considered twins and called the Dioscuri. They were inseparable companions and shared many adventures together. When Castor was killed, Pollux did not want to be immortal anymore. Touched by this devotion, Zeus allowed the brothers to remain together, living half of their days in the Underworld, the other half on Olympus. Eventually, they became the constellation Gemini.

Head of Leda, 16th century, Leonardo da Vinci

CEYX AND ALCYONE (sē′ iks *and* al sī′ uh nē)

King Ceyx and Queen Alcyone were as happy a couple as ever lived. When Ceyx died in a shipwreck, Alcyone grieved bitterly and tried to throw herself into the sea. But at that moment, the gods pitied her and turned her into a bird—the halcyon. They also restored her husband to life and turned him into another bird—the diver.

According to legend, the halcyon nests at sea for seven days, and during this time the weather is calm. Sailors call these *halcyon days*. The word *halcyon* has come to mean peaceful, calm, or happy.

CLYTIE (kli′ tē)

Clytie was a young woman who fell in love with the sun god Helios. When Helios neglected her, she pined away until she became a heliotrope, a flower that always turns its face toward the sun. She is also sometimes associated with the sunflower, which moves with the sun as well.

DAEDALUS AND ICARUS (de′ dul us *and* i′ ku rus)

The skilled craftsman and inventor Daedalus was once held prisoner by Minos, king of the island of Crete. This was Daedalus' punishment for helping the Athenian hero Theseus kill the Minotaur [see THESEUS AND THE MINOTAUR]. Determined to escape with his son, Icarus, Daedalus made two pairs of wings from wax and feathers. When he and Icarus put on the wings, Daedalus warned his son not to fly too close to the sun. But when they took to the air, Icarus disobeyed his father, and the wax of his wings melted in the sun's heat. Icarus plunged into the sea and drowned, but Daedalus escaped.

DAPHNE AND APOLLO (dăf' nē *and* a pol' ō)

Daphne was a nymph, the daughter of the river god Ladron. Apollo fell in love with her, but she fled from him. Just as Apollo was about to catch her, Daphne prayed to her father for help. So Ladron turned her into a laurel tree. In honor of Daphne, Apollo crowned poets and heroes with laurel leaves.

THE DEATH OF ACHILLES (a kil' ēz)

Achilles was the son of Peleus, a mortal, and Thetis, a sea nymph. When Achilles was a baby, Thetis bathed him in the river Styx. This made Achilles invulnerable, except for the heel that Thetis had held him by. When Achilles grew up, he became Greece's greatest soldier. But he was finally slain by the Trojan prince Paris, whose arrow was guided by Apollo to Achilles' heel.

Today, an *Achilles heel* refers to a point of weakness in an otherwise strong person.

Chroniques de France: The Death of Orpheus, 15th-century manuscript illumination

THE DEATH OF ORPHEUS (or' fē us)

After losing his wife Eurydice in the Underworld [see the play ORPHEUS AND EURYDICE], Orpheus mourned for the rest of his life, neglecting all other women. He also infuriated the god Dionysus by worshipping Apollo too devoutly. So Dionysus commanded his female followers, the Maenads, to tear Orpheus limb from limb. Orpheus' head, still singing, floated away to the island of Lesbos, where his oracle was founded. The rest of his body was buried by the Muses, and his lyre was turned into the constellation Lyra.

DEUCALION AND PYRRHA (dū kāl' yun *and* pir' a)

Deucalion was the son of the Titan Prometheus; his wife, Pyrrha, was the daughter of Epimetheus and Pandora [*see the plays* PANDORA *and* PROMETHEUS UNBOUND]. Zeus decided to destroy the human race in a great flood—all except for Deucalion and Pyrrha, the only virtuous people in the world. He instructed the couple to take shelter in a huge trunk, which bore them on the waves for nine days and nights. At last, they landed safely on a mountaintop.

Zeus then instructed Deucalion and Pyrrha to throw their mother's bones over their shoulders. At first, they were puzzled by his command, but they soon understood. By their *mother*, Zeus meant Mother Earth, the mother of all; by her *bones*, he meant stones. Deucalion and Pyrrha threw stones over their shoulders, which turned into men and women—the first in a new race of people.

Many other stories from all over the world tell of a flood destroying humankind. These include the biblical story of Noah and the ark.

DIDO AND AENEAS (dī' do *and* i nē' us)

According to Roman legend, the Trojan hero Aeneas escaped the destruction of Troy and sailed through the Mediterranean on many adventures. A storm brought him to Carthage, where Dido was queen. Dido fell in love with Aeneas, and he with her. But Jupiter (the Roman *Zeus*) knew that Aeneas was destined to help found the Roman civilization. So he sent Mercury (the Roman *Hermes*) to urge Aeneas on his way to Italy. Reluctantly, Aeneas left Dido, who committed suicide.

DIONYSUS AND THE PIRATES (dī uh nī' sus)

Not knowing Dionysus to be a god, a band of pirates once captured him and took him aboard their ship, hoping to sell him as a slave. The helmsman quickly realized that their captive was divine and begged the others to release Dionysus, but to no avail. Then a series of wonders took place. Wine flowed over the decks, vines grew on the masts and sails, and strange music filled the air. Dionysus took the shape of a lion, and the pirates began jumping overboard in terror. Dionysus stopped the helmsman from jumping, then turned the rest of the pirates into dolphins.

ECHO AND NARCISSUS (e' kō *and* när si' sus)

When Narcissus was born, a prophecy said that he would live a long life if he never saw his own reflection. He grew up to be a very beautiful young man, but he cared nothing for love.

A nymph named Echo fell in love with him. She had already been cursed by Hera and could not speak except to repeat the words of others. When Narcissus ignored her, Echo pined away until nothing was left of her but her voice.

The gods punished Narcissus by leading him to a pool, where he fell in love with his own reflection. Unable to tear himself away, he died of hunger. A flower named after him grew in the spot where he perished.

Today, there is a flower called the *narcissus*. Also, a person who is unhealthily self-centered is said to be a *narcissist*. And of course, an *echo* is a repeated noise caused by reflected sound waves.

HERO AND LEANDER (hē' rō *and* lē ăn' dur)

The Hellespont (now called the Dardanelles) is a strait separating Asia Minor from Europe. According to legend, a young man named Leander lived on one side of the strait, and a priestess of Aphrodite named Hero lived on the other. Leander used to swim the strait nightly to visit Hero, guided by a light in her tower. One stormy night, the light was blown out, and Leander drowned. Upon finding his body on the beach, Hero drowned herself.

IO (ī' ō)

Io, a priestess of the goddess Hera, had the misfortune of being loved by Zeus. To protect her from Hera's jealousy, Zeus turned Io into a cow. But Hera seized the cow and placed it under the guard of Argus, a creature with a hundred eyes. Zeus ordered Hermes to rescue Io, and Hermes killed Argus. But then Hera sent a gadfly, a type of fly that bothers livestock, to torment Io. Still in the shape of a cow, Io was pursued by the gadfly all over the earth. At last she arrived in Egypt, where she gave birth to Zeus' son, resumed her human shape, and was worshipped as a goddess.

The tail of the peacock, a bird sacred to Hera, is said to be marked with

Argus' eyes. And a person who causes continual annoyance to someone is often described as a *gadfly*.

JASON AND THE GOLDEN FLEECE

Jason was the son of Aeson, the king of Iolcos. When Aeson's half-brother Pelias seized the throne, young Jason was sent away to be raised and educated by the wise centaur Chiron [*see* ASCLEPIUS]. When Jason grew to manhood, he returned to Iolcos. Pelias agreed to restore Jason's birthright, but only if the young hero brought him a Golden Fleece that had once belonged to a sacred flying ram. Pelias was certain that Jason would perish in the attempt.

With a crew of the world's greatest heroes, Jason set sail in a ship called the *Argo* in quest of the Golden Fleece. He and his companions had many amazing adventures before they arrived in Colchis, which was ruled by the tyrant Aeetes. The Golden Fleece was in Aeetes' care, guarded by a fierce serpent.

Jason asked Aeetes for the Fleece, and the tyrant agreed to give it to him—provided he could pass several seemingly impossible trials and tests. Jason would certainly have failed without the assistance of Medea, Aeetes' beautiful daughter, who was a great sorceress. Medea had fallen in love with Jason and offered to help him with her magic. At last, she made it possible for him to get the Fleece.

Medea sailed with Jason to back to Iolcos, where Jason gave the Fleece to Pelias. Then Medea used her magic to trick Pelias' own daughters into murdering their father.

THE LABORS OF HERACLES (her' a klēz)

Heracles (often known by his Roman name *Hercules*) was Zeus' son by Alcmena, a mortal woman, so he was much hated by Zeus' wife, Hera. She drove Heracles mad, and he unwittingly killed his wife and children. As penance for this awful act, Heracles undertook 12 superhuman labors.

He began by slaying two monsters—a seemingly invincible lion and a nine-headed monster called the Hydra. Then he captured a sacred stag and a fierce wild boar. Afterwards, he cleaned the filthy stables of King Augeas by diverting two rivers through them.

With his bow and arrows, he killed an entire flock of man-eating birds. He also captured a mad bull that had been terrorizing Crete, then captured a herd of man-eating mares. He took a girdle from the Amazon warrior Hippolyta and seized a herd of oxen belonging to the three-bodied giant Geryon.

Finally, he went to the very ends of the earth to bring back some famous golden apples, then descended into the Underworld to get the three-headed dog Cerberus [*see the play* EROS AND PSYCHE].

When Heracles had accomplished all these deeds, he was forgiven for the killings he had committed in his madness. After he died, he was allowed to live in Olympus as a god.

LEDA AND THE SWAN (lē' duh)

Leda was the wife of Tyndareus, a king of Sparta, to whom she bore two children—Castor and Clytemnestra. She was also loved by Zeus, who came to her in the form of a swan. She laid an egg, from which hatched two children of Zeus—Pollux and Helen (*see* CASTOR AND POLLUX). Helen eventually became the cause of the Trojan War [*see the play* THE APPLE OF DISCORD].

MEDUSA (mi dū' suh)

Medusa was one of three sisters known as Gorgons. They had tusks, wings, scaly skin, and snaky hair, and anyone who looked at them turned instantly to stone. Of the three, only Medusa was mortal, and she was slain by the hero Perseus. Perseus took great care not to see her  directly. Instead, he looked at her reflection on his shield. So he was able to approach her closely enough to behead her. Athena eventually put Medusa's head on her shield, which she used to paralyze her enemies.

MIDAS (mī' dus)

King Midas was a great worshipper of the god Dionysus, who offered to grant a wish for him. Foolishly, Midas wished that everything he touched turned to gold. When the wish came true, even the food and wine he touched turned to gold. Faced with starvation, Midas begged Dionysus to undo his wish. The god ordered Midas to bathe in the river Pactolus. Midas did so, and the spell ended. But ever since, grains of gold have been found in the river.

Today, someone who has an uncanny ability with money is said to have a *Midas touch*.

NIOBE (nī′ uh bē)

Niobe was the proud mother of 14 children—seven sons and seven daughters. She boasted that she was an even greater mother than the Titan Leto, who only bore two children to Zeus—Apollo and Artemis. To punish Niobe for her pride, Apollo killed all her sons and Artemis killed all her daughters. Niobe turned into stone from grief. But even as a statue, she wept forever.

In literature and art, a grieving mother is often described as a *Niobe figure*.

Niobe's children are killed by Apollo and Artemis in this 1731 engraving by B. Picart.

ODYSSEUS AND THE CYCLOPES (ō dis′ ē us *and the* sī klō′ pēz)

During his long travels (*see the play* ODYSSEUS AND THE SIRENS), Odysseus and his sailors landed upon the land of the Cyclopes, who were giant, one-eyed cannibals. The Cyclops Polyphemus held Odysseus and his men prisoner in his cave, feasting on several of them. Odysseus managed to get Polyphemus drunk, and when Polyphemus asked what his name was, Odysseus said "Nobody." Polyphemus fell asleep, and Odysseus and his men shoved the sharp, red-hot point of a timber into his eye. Blinded, Polyphemus screamed to his fellow Cyclopes for help. They asked who was attacking him, and Polyphemus replied, "Nobody!" So the other Cyclopes ignored Polyphemus, and Odysseus and his men narrowly escaped.

ODYSSEUS' HOMECOMING (ō dis′ ē us)

After many long years of wandering (*see the play* ODYSSEUS AND THE SIRENS), Odysseus at last reached Ithaca, where he was rightfully king. He was disguised as a beggar, and the only creature that recognized him was his old dog Argus, who died upon seeing his master again.

Odysseus was horrified at what he found in his palace. It was full of barbarous men who were courting his wife Penelope. For years, Penelope had remained faithful to Odysseus, cleverly turning away the suitors. But meanwhile, the suitors were eating Odysseus' family out of house and home. To add insult to injury, the suitors mocked and mistreated the disguised Odysseus.

Odysseus revealed his identity to his son, Telemachus; his swineherd, Eumaeus; and his goatherd, Melanthius. Together, they slaughtered all the suitors, and Odysseus regained his wife and kingdom.

OEDIPUS THE KING (e′ duh pus)

Oedipus was a prince of Corinth. He learned from a prophecy that he would someday marry his mother and murder his father. Not knowing that he was only the adopted son of the king and queen, Oedipus fled Corinth.

Eventually, he became the king of Thebes (*see* OEDIPUS AND THE SPHINX) and married Queen Jocasta, whose husband Laius had recently been murdered. Years later, a plague struck Thebes. An oracle said that Oedipus must find Laius' murderer in order to end the plague.

Oedipus set to work solving the mystery, but was horrified by what he learned. He himself had unknowingly killed Laius before he became king. Moreover, Laius and Jocasta were his real parents; they had abandoned him as a baby. So Oedipus had failed to escape the prophecy. He had, indeed, married his mother and murdered his father.

Oedipus put out his own eyes in self-punishment. Then he fled Thebes and wandered through Greece for the rest of his life as a beggar.

This story was the basis of Sophocles' tragedy *Oedipus the King*.

Sigmund Freud, the founder of psychoanalysis, believed that young boys pass through a stage of feeling sexual desire for their mothers and aggression toward their fathers. Freud called this stage the *Oedipus complex*.

OEDIPUS AND THE SPHINX (e′ duh pus *and the* sfinks)

The citizens of Thebes were afraid to set foot outside their city because the Sphinx was terrorizing the countryside. The Sphinx had the body of a winged lion and the head of a woman. Whenever she met a person on the road, she asked a riddle, and she killed anyone who answered it incorrectly. For quite some time, no one guessed its answer, and many people died.

One day, a young traveler named Oedipus encountered the Sphinx, and she asked him her riddle.

"What goes on four legs by morning, two legs at noon, and three at night?"

"Man," replied Oedipus quickly. "He crawls on all fours as a baby, walks upright when full-grown, and needs a cane when he's old."

Oedipus' answer killed the Sphinx. In gratitude, the citizens of Thebes made him their king.

Today, a mysterious, puzzling person is sometimes described as a *sphinx*.

PEGASUS (pe′ guh sus)

Pegasus was a winged, flying horse that sprang up from Medusa's blood when she was slain by Perseus (*see* MEDUSA). For a time, Pegasus belonged to the young hero Bellerophon, who rode the horse on many adventures. Upon Pegasus' back, Bellerophon slew the dreaded Chimaera, a fire-breathing monster with the tail of a snake, the body of a goat, and the head of a lion. Pegasus threw Bellerophon when the youth tried to ride him to the heights of Olympus. After that, Pegasus was kept in the Olympian stables.

Today, an imaginary monster with strange parts is called a *chimaera*.

PYGMALION AND GALATEA (pig māl′ yun *and* ga luh tē′ uh)

Pygmalion was a sculptor who despised women and decided never to marry. However, he eventually made a statue of a woman so beautiful that he fell in love with it. He prayed to Aphrodite for a woman just like his statue, and Aphrodite obliged by bringing the statue to life. Pygmalion called the living woman Galatea. They were married happily and had a son named Paphos.

Bernard Shaw wrote a famous play called *Pygmalion* about a professor who teaches a London flower girl to behave like a lady. Shaw's play was adapted into the musical *My Fair Lady*.

PYRAMUS AND THISBE (pir' a mus *and* thiz' bē)

Pyramus and Thisbe were in love, but their parents forbade them to marry. They often spoke to each other through a crack in the wall between their two homes. Finally, they decided to meet at a nearby tomb. Thisbe arrived there first, but was chased away by a lion. She dropped her scarf, which the lion seized and tore. When Pyramus arrived and found the scarf, he believed that Thisbe had been eaten by the lion, so he killed himself. Thisbe returned and found Pyramus' body, then killed herself as well.

This tragic story is hilariously parodied by William Shakespeare in *A Midsummer Night's Dream*.

ROMULUS AND REMUS (räm' yuh lus *and* rē' mus)

According to Roman legend, Romulus and Remus were twin brothers, descendants of the hero Aeneas (*see* DIDO AND AENEAS). Romulus and Remus were abandoned as children and set afloat on the river Tiber until they came to rest under a fig tree. There they were found by a she-wolf and a woodpecker, who nursed and fed them. Later, they were adopted and raised by a herdsman. When the brothers grew up, they founded a city where the fig tree grew. Romulus killed Remus, and the city was named Rome after him. Romulus eventually became a god.

SISYPHUS (si' suh fus)

Sisyphus was the founder of Corinth and the most cunning mortal who ever lived. One day, he happened to observe Zeus abducting the daughter of his friend Asopus. Sisyphus told Asopus who had taken his daughter, provoking Zeus' anger. Zeus sent Thanatos, the god of death, to claim Sisyphus. But Sisyphus captured Thanatos and held him prisoner, making it impossible for anyone to die. Zeus forced Sisyphus to free Thanatos, and Sisyphus died and went to the Underworld. But Sisyphus tricked Hades into allowing him to return to earth again.

THUMBNAIL MYTHS

When Sisyphus finally died of old age and returned to the Underworld, he was sentenced to spend eternity at a tedious and futile task. He was to roll a huge boulder up a hill. Whenever he reached the top of the hill, the boulder would roll back down, and Sisyphus would have to roll it back up again.

Albert Camus wrote a philosophical essay called *The Myth of Sisyphus*. In it, he used Sisyphus' task as a symbol of the absurdity of human existence.

TANTALUS (tan' tul us)

Tantalus was much loved by the gods and was even invited to dine with them on Olympus. But he offended the Olympians by giving ambrosia and nectar—the food and drink of the gods—to mortals. He committed a far worse crime by killing his son, Pelops, and serving him as a dish to the gods. In the Underworld, he was sentenced to eternal thirst and hunger, surrounded by water he could not drink and fruit he could not eat. Moreover, a huge stone hung over his head, always ready to fall.

From Tantalus' name comes the word *tantalize*, which means to tease or torment with something just out of reach.

THESEUS AND THE MINOTAUR
(thē' sē us *and the* mi' nuh tor)

Theseus was a heroic prince of Athens. For many years, Athens was tyrannized by King Minos of Crete, who demanded that Athens send 14 youths—seven girls and seven boys—to Crete once every nine years. There, the young people were fed to the Minotaur, a half-man, half-bull monster who lived in a vast maze called the Labyrinth.

Theseus went to Crete, hoping to end this cruel custom. Minos' daughter, Ariadne, fell in love with Theseus, and decided to help him kill the Minotaur. She asked the maze's designer, Daedalus [*see* DAEDALUS

Theseus and the Minotaur, 1st-century-A.D. mosaic

249

AND ICARUS], how to get in and out of the Labyrinth. On Daedalus' advice, she gave Theseus a huge ball of thread. Theseus unrolled the thread as he went inside the Labyrinth. He met the Minotaur and killed it with his bare hands. Then he followed the thread out of the Labyrinth again.

Today, a complicated maze is often called a *labyrinth*.

Mary Renault wrote a novel based on the story of Theseus and the Minotaur called *The King Must Die*.

THE TROJAN HORSE (trō′ jun)

The Trojan War dragged on for almost 10 years, with no victor. At last, the wily Greek chieftain Odysseus [see the play ODYSSEUS AND THE SIRENS] came up with a plan to seize the city of Troy by trickery.

First, the Greeks built a huge, hollow wooden horse. Then they boarded their ships and sailed a short distance from Troy, leading the Trojans to think they had given up and gone home. A Greek soldier named Sinon presented himself to the Trojans, pretending to have deserted the Greeks. He said that the horse was a sacred offering to the goddess Athena, and that it would bring great luck to the Trojans if they brought it inside their gates. The Trojans did so, not knowing that several Greek chieftains were hiding inside its belly.

Night came, and the Greek chieftains climbed out of the horse. They opened the gates of Troy and let in the Greek army, which had returned in the ships. Troy was then easily defeated.

Today, a gift which conceals some sort of danger is called a *Trojan horse*. The term has even been used to describe a type of computer virus.

GLOSSARY

Ajax (a′ jăks): the name of two Greek warriors who fought in the Trojan War. They had the same name but were of different statures. Greater Ajax, one of the bravest Greek warriors, killed himself during the war; Lesser Ajax died on the way home from the war.

Alecto (a lek′ tō): one of the three FURIES

ambrosia (am brō′ zha): the food of the Olympian gods. Along with the drink called NECTAR, it kept the gods immortal. Today, a delicious food is sometimes called *ambrosia*. Specifically, it is the name of a dessert made from oranges and coconut.

Aphrodite (ăf ro dī′ tē): the Greek name for the goddess of love; her Roman name is VENUS. The word *aphrodisiac*, meaning a love potion, comes from her name.

Apollo (a pol′ ō): in Greek and Roman mythology, the god of sunlight, prophecy, medicine, archery, poetry, and music. The word *Apollonian* means balanced, harmonious, well-ordered, or rational—the opposite of *Dionysian* [see DIONYSUS].

Ares (a′ rēs): the Greek name for the god of war and violence; his Roman name is MARS.

Artemis (ar′ te mis): the Greek name for the goddess of the moon and the hunt; her Roman name is DIANA.

Athena (a thē′ na): in Greek mythology, the goddess of wisdom, war, and crafts. She is also called Pallas or Pallas Athena; her Roman name is MINERVA. She was the patron of the Greek city of Athens.

Atlas (ăt′ las): a TITAN, the brother of PROMETHEUS and EPIMETHEUS. Atlas was sentenced by the Olympian gods to hold up the sky on his shoulders; according to some sources, he held up the world as well. Today, a book of maps is called an *atlas*.

Bacchus (ba′ kus): the Roman name for DIONYSUS

Calliope (ka lī′ o pē): the MUSE of epic poetry. Today, there is a steam-powered musical instrument called a *calliope*.

Cancer (kan′ sar): a CONSTELLATION that represents a crab [*see the play* PHAETON AND THE SUN CHARIOT]

centaurs (sen′ tors): mythical creatures with the heads, arms, and torsos of humans and the bodies of horses. Centaurs were considered savage and ill-behaved, except for the wise centaur CHIRON.

Cerberus (ser′ ber us): the three-headed dog that guarded the UNDERWORLD [*see the play* EROS AND PSYCHE]

Ceres (sir′ ēz): the Roman name for DEMETER. The word *cereal* comes from her name.

Chaos (kā′ äs): a huge shapeless mass that existed before anything else in the universe [*see the introductory essay* FROM CHAOS TO OLYMPUS]. Today, a great state of confusion is called *chaos*. There is also a branch of science called *chaos theory* that deals with unpredictable systems ranging from city traffic to weather patterns.

Charon (ker′ an): the ferryman who carried the dead across the river STYX to the UNDERWORLD [*see the plays* PHAETON AND THE SUN CHARIOT *and* ORPHEUS AND EURYDICE]

Charybdis (ka rib′ dis): a monster that lived beneath the sea. She would swallow huge amounts of water, creating whirlpools; then she would belch up the water, creating terrible waves. She caused many shipwrecks [*see the play* ODYSSEUS AND THE SIRENS; *see also* SCYLLA].

Chiron (kī′ rän): a wise CENTAUR. He was the teacher of many gods and heroes, including APOLLO [*see the play* PROMETHEUS UNBOUND; *see also* ASCLEPIUS *in* THUMBNAIL MYTHS].

Clio (klī′ ō): the MUSE of history [*see the play* PANDORA]

Clymene (klī mē′ nē): the mother of PHAETON [*see the play* PHAETON AND THE SUN CHARIOT]

Clytemnestra (klī tem nes′ tra): sister of HELEN and sister-in-law of MENELAUS. She and her lover, Aegisthus, murdered her husband, the Greek chieftain Agamemnon, when he came home from the Trojan War.

constellation (kon sta lā shun): a formation of stars in the sky, thought by ancient people to represent mythical figures [*see* CANCER, LEO, SCORPIO, *and* TAURUS; *see also the play* PHAETON AND THE SUN CHARIOT]

Crete (krēt): a large island in the eastern Mediterranean, to the south of Greece [*see* THESEUS AND THE MINOTAUR *in* THUMBNAIL MYTHS]

Cronus (krō′ nus): a TITAN, the father of the gods of OLYMPUS [*see the introductory essay* FROM CHAOS TO OLYMPUS]. His name is sometimes spelled Cronos, which means *time*. The word *chronology*, meaning an order of events, comes from this name; so does *chronic*, which describes something that happens again and again.

Cupid (kyū′ pud): the Roman name for EROS. Although the Greeks and Romans originally saw him as a handsome young man with wings, the Romans eventually portrayed him as an angelic baby.

Cyclopes (sī klō′ pēz; singular *Cyclops* is pronounced sī′ klops): a race of one-eyed, cannibalistic giants [*see* ODYSSEUS AND THE CYCLOPES *in* THUMBNAIL MYTHS]

Delphi (del′ fē): a town in ancient Greece, the site of an ORACLE of APOLLO. The ancient Greeks believed Delphi to be the center of the world.

Demeter (de mē′ ter): the Greek name for the goddess of the earth, agriculture, and fertility; the mother of PERSEPHONE [*see the play* DEMETER AND PERSEPHONE]. Her Roman name is CERES.

Diana (dī a′ na): the Roman name for ARTEMIS

Dionysus (dī uh nī′ sus): the Greek name for the god of wine, revelry, and drama; his Roman name is BACCHUS [*see* DIONYSUS AND THE PIRATES *and* THE DEATH OF ORPHEUS *in* THUMBNAIL MYTHS]. The word *Dionysian* means ecstatic, frenzied, or uncontrolled—the opposite of *Apollonian* [*see* APOLLO].

Eleusinian Mysteries (el yu si′ ne un): religious rites sacred to DEMETER, celebrated in the town of Eleusis. What they consisted of remains unknown [*see the play* DEMETER AND PERSEPHONE].

Eleusis (e lū′ sis): a town in ancient Greece where the ELEUSINIAN MYSTERIES were celebrated [*see the play* DEMETER AND PERSEPHONE]

Epimetheus (ep i mē′ thē us): a TITAN, the less intelligent brother of PROMETHEUS. His name means *afterthought* [*see the play* PANDORA].

Erato (er′ a tō): the MUSE of love poetry [*see the play* EROS AND PSYCHE]

Erebus (er′ e bus): the bottomless depths. According to classical creation stories, Erebus and Night gave birth to Love [*see the introductory essay* FROM CHAOS TO OLYMPUS].

Eridanus (e rid′ a nus): ancient name for what is now the Po River in Italy. PHAETON fell to its banks from the sun chariot. And it was there where his mourning sisters turned into poplar trees [*see the play* PHAETON AND THE SUN CHARIOT].

Eris (er′ is): the goddess of discord and strife [*see the play* THE APPLE OF DISCORD]

Eros (er′ ōs): the god of love, the son of APHRODITE [*see the plays* DEMETER AND PERSEPHONE *and* EROS AND PSYCHE]. The word *erotic*, having to do with romantic love, comes from his name.

Eurydice (ū rid′ i sē): the wife of ORPHEUS, lost by him in the UNDERWORLD [*see the play* ORPHEUS AND EURYDICE]

Eurylochus (ū ril′ o kus): ODYSSEUS' helmsman [*see the play* ODYSSEUS AND THE SIRENS]

Euterpe (ū ter′ pē): the MUSE of lyric poetry [*see the play* ORPHEUS AND EURYDICE]

Fates (fāts): three sister goddesses—Clotho, Lachesis, and Atropos—who decided the destinies of both mortals and gods. Clotho spun the thread of life, Lachesis measured the thread's length, and Atropos cut it with her shears.

Furies (fyur′ ēz): three sister goddesses of vengeance and punishment. Their names were TISIPHONE, MEGAERA, and ALECTO. They lived in the depths of the UNDERWORLD and visited the living to pursue wrongdoers [*see the play* ORPHEUS AND EURYDICE]. The Greeks called them *Erinyes*, which meant "angry ones." But to calm their wrath, people sometimes called them *Eumenides*, which meant "kindly ones." Indeed, according to the playwright Aeschylus in his *Oresteia* trilogy, they were eventually turned into kindly goddesses.

Gaia (jē′ uh): in classical creation stories, the original Earth goddess [*see the introductory essay* FROM CHAOS TO OLYMPUS]. She and URANUS gave birth to a number of children, including the TITANS. In today's science, the *Gaia hypothesis* suggests that all life on Earth might be a single system.

Hades (hā′ dēz): the god of the UNDERWORLD and the dead; his Roman name is PLUTO. The UNDERWORLD itself is sometimes called *Hades* [*see the plays* DEMETER AND PERSEPHONE *and* ORPHEUS AND EURYDICE].

Hecate (hek′ a tē): a goddess of magic and sorcery [*see the play* DEMETER AND PERSEPHONE]

Hecuba (hek′ u ba): the queen of TROY, wife of PRIAM, and mother of PARIS [*see the play* THE APPLE OF DISCORD]

Helen (he′ lun): the queen of SPARTA and the wife of MENELAUS. She was kidnapped by the Trojan prince PARIS and taken to TROY. The Trojan War was fought to get her back [*see the plays* THE APPLE OF DISCORD *and* PROTEUS].

Helios (hē′ lē ōs): in Greek mythology, the god who drove the chariot of the sun across the sky [*see the plays* DEMETER AND PERSEPHONE *and* PHAETON AND THE SUN CHARIOT]. The Romans assigned this task to APOLLO.

Hephaestus (he fes′ tus): the Greek name for god of fire, artisans, and metalworkers; his Roman name is VULCAN [*see the play* PANDORA].

Hera (hir′ a): the Greek name for the queen of the Olympian gods and the sister-wife of ZEUS; her Roman name is JUNO [*see the plays* PANDORA, PHAETON AND THE SUN CHARIOT, *and* THE APPLE OF DISCORD]. She was also the goddess of marriage and childbirth.

Heracles (her′ a klēz): the Greek name for a hero of superhuman strength and courage; he is commonly known by his Roman name HERCULES. He was the son of the god ZEUS and the mortal woman Alcmena [*see the play* PROMETHEUS UNBOUND; *see also* THE LABORS OF HERACLES *in* THUMBNAIL MYTHS].

Hercules (hur′ kyu lēz): the Roman name for HERACLES. Today, a feat of enormous strength or determination is described as *Herculean*.

Hermes (hur′ mēz): the Greek name for the messenger of the Olympian gods; his Roman name is MERCURY. He was also a god of trade, travel, and theft [*see the plays* DEMETER AND PERSEPHONE *and* THE APPLE OF DISCORD].

Hesiod (hē′ si od): a Greek poet of the 8th century B.C. He was the author of the *Theogony* and *Works and Days* [*see the play* PANDORA].

Hestia (hes′ ti a): the Greek name for the goddess of the hearth; her Roman name was VESTA. She protected beggars and invented house-building.

Hippocrene (hip′ ō krēn): a fountain on the slope of MT. HELICON. It appeared when the winged horse Pegasus kicked the slope with his hooves [*see* PEGASUS *in* THUMBNAIL MYTHS]. Its waters were sacred to the MUSES and gave inspiration to poets [*see the play* PANDORA].

Homer (hō′ mur): a Greek epic poet. Whether he actually lived or not is uncertain, but he is said to be the author of the *Iliad* and the *Odyssey*, both written around the 9th century B.C. Homer is also traditionally believed to have been blind.

Iapetus (ī ăp′ ē tus): a TITAN, the father of ATLAS, PROMETHEUS, and EPIMETHEUS

Idothea (ī do′ thē a): daughter of the sea-god PROTEUS. She helped MENELAUS to catch Proteus and force him to prophesy [*see the play* PROTEUS].

Iris (ī′ ris): the Olympian messenger goddess

Ithaca (ith′ a ka): an island off the eastern coast of Greece, home of the hero ODYSSEUS

Jove (jōv): a Roman name for ZEUS. The word *jovial*, meaning "hearty and friendly," comes from his name.

Juno (jū′ nō): the Roman name for HERA. The month of June is named after her.

Jupiter (jū′ pu tur): a Roman name for ZEUS. It is also the name of the fifth planet from the sun.

Kore (kō′ rē): the name of PERSEPHONE before she went to the UNDERWORLD [*see the play* DEMETER AND PERSEPHONE]

Leo (lē′ ō): a CONSTELLATION that represents a lion [*see the play* PHAETON AND THE SUN CHARIOT]

Leto (lē′ tō): a TITAN, the mother of APOLLO and ARTEMIS

Maenads (mē′ nădz): female followers of DIONYSUS, known for their wild and frenzied behavior. They were also called *Bacchantes* or *Bacchae* [*see* THE DEATH OF ORPHEUS *in* THUMBNAIL MYTHS].

Mars (märz): the Roman name for ARES. The word *martial*, meaning "warlike," comes from his name. Mars is also the name of the fourth planet from the sun.

Megaera (me jē′ ra): one of the three FURIES

Melpomene (mel pom′ e nē): the MUSE of tragedy [*see the play* DEMETER AND PERSEPHONE]

Menelaus (men e lā′ us): the king of SPARTA and the husband of HELEN. When Helen was stolen by the Trojan prince PARIS, Menelaus summoned the chieftains of Greece to fight the Trojan War [*see the plays* THE APPLE OF DISCORD *and* PROTEUS].

Mentor (men′ tōr): a loyal friend of ODYSSEUS. ATHENA disguised herself as Mentor in order to persuade Odysseus' son, TELEMACHUS, to go searching for his father. Today, a respected teacher or guide is called a *mentor*.

Mercury (mur′ kyu rē): the Roman name for HERMES. It is the name of the first planet from the sun and also of a silver-white metal that is liquid at normal temperatures. The word *mercurial*, meaning "unpredictable" or "moody," comes from this name.

Milky Way: the galaxy that includes our own solar system. The stars in the Milky Way stretch across the night sky in a wide band [*see the play* PHAETON AND THE SUN CHARIOT].

Minerva (mu nur′ vuh): the Roman name for ATHENA

Mt. Caucasus (kä′ kuh sus): a legendary peak in the Caucasus Mountains, which lie between the Black Sea and the Caspian Sea in Eurasia. PROMETHEUS was chained to this peak as punishment for stealing fire from the gods [*see the plays* PANDORA *and* PROMETHEUS UNBOUND].

Mt. Etna (et′ nuh): a volcano in SICILY, the highest in Europe [*see the play* DEMETER AND PERSEPHONE]

Mt. Helicon (hel′ i kon): a mountain in Greece and the home of the MUSES. The poet HESIOD lived near Mt. Helicon [*see the play* PANDORA].

Mt. Ida (ī′ duh): a mountain in Asia Minor, near TROY. The Trojan prince PARIS grew to manhood there [*see the play* THE APPLE OF DISCORD].

Mt. Olympus (uh lim′ pus): a mountain in Greece and the home of the gods. The word *Olympian*, meaning "grand" or "lofty," comes from this name. In ancient Greece, athletic games were played at a place called Olympia. The Olympic Games of today continue this tradition.

Muses (myūz′ uz): nine goddesses of artistic inspiration who made their home on MT. HELICON. Ancient Greek and Roman authors often began their poems with appeals for their aid. Their names were CALLIOPE, CLIO, ERATO, EUTERPE, MELPOMENE,

GLOSSARY

POLYHYMNIA, TERPSICHORE, THALIA, and URANIA. Today, to *muse* means to become lost in thought. Also, a person who offers creative help and inspiration is sometimes called a *muse*.

nectar (nek′ tur): the drink of the Olympian gods. Along with the food called AMBROSIA, it kept the gods immortal. Today, a sweet drink is sometimes called *nectar*. It is also the name of the liquid from a flower used by bees in making honey.

Neptune (nep′ tūn): the Roman name for POSEIDON. It is also the name of the eighth planet from the sun.

nymphs (nimfs): minor nature goddesses. There were many kinds of nymphs connected with various aspects of nature, including the sea, streams, and trees [*see the plays* ORPHEUS AND EURYDICE, THE APPLE OF DISCORD, PROTEUS, *and* PROMETHEUS UNBOUND; *see also* DAPHNE AND APOLLO *and* ECHO AND NARCISSUS *in* THUMBNAIL MYTHS].

Odysseus (ō dis′ ē us): the king of ITHACA and Greek hero of the Trojan War; the husband of PENELOPE and the father of TELEMACHUS. After the Greek victory over Troy, Odysseus was forced to wander the world for many years before returning home [*see the play* ODYSSEUS AND THE SIRENS; *see also* ODYSSEUS AND THE CYCLOPES, ODYSSEUS' HOMECOMING, *and* THE TROJAN HORSE *in* THUMBNAIL MYTHS].

Oenone (ē nō′ nē): a NYMPH who was loved but abandoned by PARIS. Years later, when Paris was mortally wounded in the Trojan War, Oenone refused to heal him [*see the play* THE APPLE OF DISCORD].

oracle (or′ a kul): a person who makes prophecies, or a shrine where prophecies are made [*see the play* EROS AND PSYCHE; *see also* ANDROMEDA, THE DEATH OF ORPHEUS, *and* OEDIPUS THE KING *in* THUMBNAIL MYTHS]. The most famous oracle in ancient Greece was at DELPHI. Today, the word *oracular* means "prophetic" or "high-sounding."

Orpheus (or′ fē us): a great singer and poet in classical stories. He made a famous journey to the UNDERWORLD in a failed attempt to bring his wife, EURYDICE, back from the dead [*see the play* ORPHEUS AND EURYDICE; *see also* THE DEATH OF ORPHEUS *in* THUMBNAIL MYTHS].

Ovid (ä′ vid): a Roman poet, 43 B.C.–17 A.D. His epic poem *Metamorphoses* retells many classical myths, including those of PHAETON AND THE SUN CHARIOT and DEMETER AND PERSEPHONE.

Pandora (pan dō′ ra): in classical creation stories, the first mortal woman. She opened the jar (often said to be a box) that contained all the troubles that plague humankind [*see the play* PANDORA]. Her name means *allgiving*. Today, something that might produce unexpected troubles is often described as a *Pandora's box*.

GLOSSARY

Paris (par' is): a prince of TROY, the son of PRIAM and HECUBA. He started the Trojan War by abducting HELEN, the wife of the Greek chieftain MENELAUS [*see* OENONE; *see also the play* THE APPLE OF DISCORD].

Penelope (pē nel' ō pē): the wife of ODYSSEUS. For many years, she waited patiently for her husband's return from his travels [*see the play* ODYSSEUS AND THE SIRENS; *see also* ODYSSEUS' HOMECOMING *in* THUMBNAIL MYTHS].

Persephone (per sef' ō nē): the Greek name for DEMETER's daughter; her Roman name is PROSERPINE [*see also* KORE]. She was married to HADES and lived part of the year in the UNDERWORLD [*see the plays* DEMETER AND PERSEPHONE, ORPHEUS AND EURYDICE, *and* EROS AND PSYCHE].

Phaeton (fā' a ton): the son of CLYMENE and the sun god HELIOS. Phaeton caused terrible destruction when he tried to drive his father's chariot across the sky [*see the play* PHAETON AND THE SUN CHARIOT].

Pharos (fā' räs): an island off the coast of Egypt. MENELAUS struggled there with the shape-shifting god PROTEUS [*see the play* PROTEUS].

Pluto (plū' tō): the Roman name for HADES. The word *plutocrat*, meaning a person of wealth and power, comes from this name.

Polyhymnia (pol i him' ni a): the MUSE of songs to the gods [*see the play* PROMETHEUS UNBOUND]

Poseidon (pō sī' don): the Greek name for the ruler of the sea and maker of earthquakes. His Roman name is NEPTUNE.

Priam (prī' am): the king of TROY, husband of HECUBA, and father of PARIS [*see the play* THE APPLE OF DISCORD]

Prometheus (prō mē' thē us): a TITAN celebrated for his wisdom and his love for humankind, the brother of ATLAS and EPIMETHEUS. His name means *forethought* [*see the plays* PANDORA *and* PROMETHEUS UNBOUND].

Proserpine (prä' sur pīn): the Roman name for PERSEPHONE

Proteus (prō' tē us): a shape-shifting god who lived on the island of PHAROS [*see the play* PROTEUS]. The word *protean*, which means "changeable," comes from this name.

Psyche (sī' kē): a beautiful young woman loved by EROS [*see the play* EROS AND PSYCHE]. Her name originally meant *soul* or *butterfly*. Today, the word *psyche* refers to the human mind. Many words come from it, including *psychiatry* and *psychology*.

Rhea (rē' uh): a TITAN, the mother of the Olympian gods [*see the introductory essay* FROM CHAOS TO OLYMPUS]

Saturn (sa′ turn): the Roman name for CRONUS. The Romans believed that Saturn ruled over the Golden Age, a time when humankind lived in perfect happiness and equality. A *Saturnalia* is a celebration in which social ranks are ignored. The day Saturday is named after him. Saturn is also the name of the sixth planet from the sun.

satyrs (sā′ turz): minor nature gods, followers of DIONYSUS. Although they looked somewhat like men, they were covered with fur and had the legs, feet, and horns of goats. They were given to wild partying and lewdness.

Scorpio (skor′ pē ō): a CONSTELLATION that represents a scorpion [*see the play* PHAETON AND THE SUN CHARIOT]

Scylla (sī′ luh): a six-headed monster with long necks to support her heads. She lived in a cave on a cliff, high above the sea. Whenever a ship sailed by, her heads reached down, snatched up some of the sailors, and ate them. She lived close to the whirlpool-monster CHARYBDIS, and sailors found it impossible to sail between CHARYBDIS and SCYLLA safely [*see the play* ODYSSEUS AND THE SIRENS]. Today, when people talk about being "between Scylla and Charybdis," they mean that they are caught between two equally difficult situations.

Semele (sem′ e lē): the mortal mother of DIONYSUS

Sicily (si′ si lē): a large island in the central Mediterranean, off the coast of Italy

Sirens (sī′ runz): birdlike creatures with the heads of women. They lived on an island in the Mediterranean, where they lured sailors to their deaths with their singing [*see the plays* DEMETER AND PERSEPHONE *and* ODYSSEUS AND THE SIRENS]. Sources differ as to how many of them there were. Today, a loud, shrill alarm is called a *siren*.

Sparta (spar′ ta): a city in Greece (*see* MENELAUS *and* HELEN). During the 5th century B.C., Sparta rivaled and eventually defeated Athens as a military power. The soldiers of Sparta were known for their skill, discipline, and courage. The word *Spartan*, meaning "strict and severe," comes from this name.

Styx (stiks): the river that lies between the worlds of the living and the dead. The ferryman CHARON carries the dead across it to the UNDERWORLD [*see the plays* PHAETON AND THE SUN CHARIOT *and* ORPHEUS AND EURYDICE].

Taurus (tor′ us): a CONSTELLATION that represents a bull [*see the play* PHAETON AND THE SUN CHARIOT]

Telemachus (tē lem′ a kus): the son of ODYSSEUS. He set out on a voyage in search of his lost father [*see* MENTOR]. When Odysseus at last reached home, Telemachus helped him slay PENELOPE's suitors [*see* ODYSSEUS' HOMECOMING *in* THUMBNAIL MYTHS].

Terpsichore (turp sik′ ō rē): the MUSE of choral dance and song, mother of the SIRENS [*see the play* ODYSSEUS AND THE SIRENS]. The word *Terpsichorean*, referring to things having to do with dance, comes from this name.

Thalia (tha lī′ a): the MUSE of comedy [*see the play* PROTEUS]

Thanatos (than′ a tos): the god of death [*see* SISYPHUS *in* THUMBNAIL MYTHS]

Thrace (thrās): a region of northeastern Greece. ORPHEUS married EURYDICE there [*see the play* ORPHEUS AND EURYDICE].

Tisiphone (ti sif′ ō nē): one of the three FURIES

Titans (tī′ tunz): the gods who ruled the universe before ZEUS and the gods of MT. OLYMPUS came to power [*see the introductory essay* FROM CHAOS TO OLYMPUS]. The word *titanic* has come to mean "huge and impressive;" it was also the name of a famous ship that sank in 1912.

Troy (troi): a city in Asia Minor on the coast of the Aegean Sea; the site of the ten-year Trojan War, which Troy lost to Greece [*see the play* THE APPLE OF DISCORD]. Although Troy was once thought to be purely legendary, archeology has proven that it really existed.

Typhon (tī′ fon): a hundred-headed giant who warred against the Olympian gods. Zeus buried him beneath MT. ETNA [*see the introductory essay* FROM CHAOS TO OLYMPUS; *see also the play* DEMETER AND PERSEPHONE]. The word *typhoon*, meaning a tropical storm, comes from this name.

Underworld (un′ dur wurld): the world of the dead; it is sometimes called HADES after its ruler [*see the plays* DEMETER AND PERSEPHONE, ORPHEUS AND EURYDICE, *and* EROS AND PSYCHE]. Many cultures all over the world tell stories of an Underworld.

Urania (yü rā′ ne a): the MUSE of astronomy [*see the play* PHAETON AND THE SUN CHARIOT]

Uranus (yur′ uh nus): the father of the TITANS [*see the introductory essay* FROM CHAOS TO OLYMPUS]. It is also the name of the seventh planet from the sun.

Venus (vē′ nus): the Roman name of APHRODITE. It is also the name of the second planet from the sun.

Vesta (ves′ tuh): the Roman name for HESTIA. The word *vestal*, meaning "pure," comes from this name.

Vulcan (vul′ kun): the Roman name for HEPHAESTUS. The word *volcano* comes from this name.

GLOSSARY

Zephyr (zef′ er): the west wind [*see the play* EROS AND PSYCHE]. Today, a gentle breeze is sometimes called a *zephyr*.

Zeus (züs): the Greek name for the ruler of the Olympian gods and the brother-husband of Hera; his Roman names were JOVE and JUPITER [*see the introductory essay* FROM CHAOS TO OLYMPUS; *see also the plays* PANDORA, PHAETON AND THE SUN CHARIOT, THE APPLE OF DISCORD, *and* PROMETHEUS UNBOUND]. He was famous for wielding the thunderbolt.

FOR FURTHER READING

Asimov, Isaac. *Words from the Myths.* New York: Signet, 1969.

Bulfinch, Thomas. *Bulfinch's Greek and Roman Mythology: The Age of Fable.* New York: Dover, 2000.

Echoes from Mt. Olympus. Perfection Learning Editors. Logan: Perfection Learning Corporation, 2001.

Eliot, Alexander. *The Universal Myths: Heroes, Gods, Tricksters and Others.* Lincolnwood: New American Library, 1990.

Evslin, Bernard. *The Adventures of Ulysses.* New York: Scholastic, 1989.

Evslin, Bernard, Dorothy Evslin, and Ned Hoopes. *The Greek Gods.* New York: Scholastic, 1995.

Evslin, Bernard, Dorothy Evslin, and Ned Hoopes. *Heroes & Monsters of Greek Myth.* New York: Scholastic, 1999.

Evslin, Bernard. *Heroes, Gods and Monsters of the Greek Myths.* New York: Bantam, 1989.

Gates, Doris. *Lord of the Sky: Zeus.* New York: Penguin, 1982.

Graves, Robert. *Greek Gods and Heroes.* New York: Laurel-Leaf, 1995.

Graves, Robert. *The Greek Myths.* 2 vols. New York: Penguin, 1990.

Hadas, Moses, ed. *Greek Drama.* New York: Bantam, 1982.

Hamilton, Edith. *Mythology: Timeless Tales of Gods and Heroes.* New York: Warner, 1999.

Lies, Betty Bonham. *Earth's Daughters: Stories of Women in Classical Mythology.* Golden: Fulcrum, 1999.

Morford, Mark P.O. and Robert J. Lenardon. *Classical Mythology.* 6th ed. Oxford: Oxford U. Press, 1998.

Orgel, Doris. *We Goddesses: Athena, Aphrodite, Hera.* New York: DK, 1999.

Osborne, Mary Pope. *Favorite Greek Myths.* New York: Scholastic, 1989.

FOR FURTHER READING

Owens, L.L. *Tales of Greek Mythology.* Logan: Perfection Learning Corporation, 1999.

PLC Editors. *Retold Classic Myths.* Vol. 3. Logan: Perfection Learning Corporation, 1990.

Price, Michele and William S.E. Coleman, Jr. *Retold Classic Myths.* Vol. 1. Logan: Perfection Learning Corporation, 1990.

Rouse, H.D. *Gods, Heroes, and Men of Ancient Greece.* New York: Signet, 1957.

Russell, William F. *Classic Myths to Read Aloud.* New York: Crown, 1992.

Suter, Joanne. *World Myths and Legends: Greek & Roman.* Belmont: Fearon/Janus, 1992.

Switzer, Ellen and Costas. *Gods, Heroes and Monsters.* New York: Atheneum, an imprint of Simon and Schuster, 1988.

Uhls, Jim. *Retold Classic Myths.* Vol. 2. Logan: Perfection Learning Corporation, 1990.

Woff, Richard. *Bright-Eyed Athena: Stories from Ancient Greece.* Los Angeles: J. Paul Getty Museum, 1999.